science subjects made easy

books by henry thomas

SCIENCE SUBJECTS MADE EASY

THE LIVING WORLD OF PHILOSOPHY

THE STORY OF THE HUMAN RACE

MATHEMATICS MADE EASY

HENRY THOMAS, Ph.D.

science subjects
made easy

A GUIDE TO THE 10 BASIC SCIENCES

ILLUSTRATED WITH LINE DRAWINGS

DOUBLEDAY & COMPANY, INC., GARDEN CITY, NEW YORK, 1953

46997

contents

EIGHT   ANTHROPOLOGY—MAN'S PLACE IN NATURE

introduction

This book is designed for three classes of readers: (1) those who desire to familiarize themselves with the fascinating mysteries of nature; (2) those who seek to broaden their cultural background through a more complete understanding of the various sciences; and (3) those who plan to select one or more of the sciences as a basis for their life's work.

In a more general sense, however, the book is intended for all those interested in the world around us. We are a race of inquisitive animals. We begin to ask questions as soon as we learn to talk. From our very infancy we want to know the *why*, the *what*, and the *how* of things. Why does this world of ours exist? What sort of world is it? And how can we best adapt it to our everyday needs and comforts?

The *why* of the world is the province of philosophy. Science examines the *what* and the *how*. The philosopher blazes the trail, and the scientist charts the way. The philosopher leaps into the dark, and the scientist follows with a lighted lantern to determine the direction of the journey, to point out the pitfalls, and to set the limits of safety and common sense.

It is the business of the scientist, in other words, to discover the substantial island of fact in the infinite ocean of mystery. Science is the attempt to obtain a clear-eyed vision of the world and to ascertain our proper place in the scheme of things. It deals, in its totality, with the *intellectual interpretation and the practical application of the laws of nature.*

The interest in science is universal. Every one of us is a born scientist. Watch the baby in the cradle turning its eyes toward the light and clutching the world with its fingers—observing, selecting, rejecting—patiently and painfully collecting its impressions in the laboratory of its senses. And now watch the scientist in his study. He, too, is examining and verifying his impressions through the apparatus of his senses; for our scientific instruments—the telescope, the microscope, the chronometer, the amplifier, the acousticon—are but the mechanical extensions of our eyes and our ears and our hands. All of us alike are constantly trying to discover the nature of the world we live in, and the manner in which we can utilize it to our greatest advantage.

The purpose of science, therefore, is to understand nature in order that we may widen our horizons, and to harness it in order that we may enrich our lives. We are so constituted that we crave knowledge for its own sake, and need it for humanity's sake.

Our scientific knowledge to date, however, is but fragmentary at best. Our picture of the world is that of a jigsaw puzzle. Many of the pieces are still missing; and of the pieces that we have, only a few can be fitted into their proper places. If we had all the missing pieces—that is, if we thoroughly understood the constitution of matter, the meaning of mind, the nature of electricity, and the origin of life—we might then be able to put together a logical picture of the world. But as it is, we have only bits of disconnected landscape, hints of possible patterns, guesses, hypotheses, intuitions, and doubts. "We may well admit," writes Sir James Jeans, "that science cannot at present hope to say anything final on the questions of human existence and human destiny."

Yet every day the light of our knowledge grows clearer and the features of the landscape become more distinct. The pioneers of science are beginning to recognize in the world something of the nature of a definite design. And it will be our privilege in this book to share in the adventures of the scientific pioneers, to join them in their discoveries, to trace out with them their newest victories and vistas, and to stand in their eager company poised upon the horizon of still greater regions to be explored. Today we have advanced thus far. But tomorrow is another day!

And how does the world appear in the light of today? It is a world that never for a moment stands still. Our so-called scientific observations are not the recordings of permanent facts. They are merely the snapshots of a changing universe caught at a given instant—arrested bits of a restless panorama that at every instant present an entirely different view. Look at a piece of burning paper. Just exactly what is it? The day before yesterday—I am telescoping the time element for the purpose of this illustration— it was a seed; yesterday it was a solid tree; today it is a soft white sheet on fire; tomorrow it will be a heap of ashes; the day after tomorrow, a scattering of dust carried away by the wind. What is true of the sheet of paper is true of every object in the universe —of the universe itself.

The world as seen through the eyes of modern science, therefore, is not a static thing but a fluid process. On the whole, it would appear, a *regular* process—a continuous evolution rather than a welter of haphazard revolutions. *A unit of integration.* Every portion of the universe, as Professor Whitehead has observed, "would seem to be in mutual interaction with every other." You, the chair you sit on, the room containing the chair, the building enclosing the room, the street, the city, the state, the country, the earth, the solar system, the universe—all are united into a single interrelationship of motion. Dust into atoms, into bodies and bricks, into animals and buildings and men, into rubble and decay, and back into atoms and dust.

And the aim of science is to discover the *constant relations* in the everlasting changes of our world—the patterns, if there be any, in this welter of commotion.

But, in our effort to arrive at a practical method for measuring the world's motions and ascertaining its patterns, we must remember that we, the measurers, as well as our measuring instruments, are parts of this changing world. There are no stationary observers, no fixed points of observation, and no absolute facts. Every finding is tentative and subject to further experimentation and correction. The tendency of modern science, therefore, is to correlate the findings of as many investigators as possible, each of them afloat upon his own moving platform and examining the world from his own point of view. In this way alone can we hope to discover the approximate truth and to elaborate an expedient formula for the steering of our separate vessels in the irresistible current of life.

Today science is co-operative. The most important discoveries —such as the splitting of the atom, for example—are made through the pooled collaboration of the greatest minds. Learning, in the happy phrase of Lancelot Hogben, has become a "social business."

The social business of modern scientific learning is not only more *co-operative* than the individual gropings of the past; it is also more *comprehensive*. The various sciences are now regarded as an *organic unit*. The discoveries in any one field are brought to bear upon the investigations of all the other fields. An increase of knowledge in astronomy means an increase of knowledge in astrophysics, in chemistry, in geology, in mathematics, in the entire scope of the human endeavor to decipher the cosmic scene. Modern science is a "united war against ignorance."

And it is gradually acquiring a united language. In the past every branch of science had its own obscure vocabulary that was unintelligible even to the advanced workers in the various other branches. The result was a lack of co-ordination and a consequent barrier against widespread and rapid scientific progress. But today, with the acquisition of a general scientific vocabulary, *it is possible to translate the entire picture of accumulated knowledge into the lucid language of everyday speech.*

This, in brief, is the main purpose of our book. In order to review the entire panorama as it appears today, we first examine the background—that is, the nature of the universe. We then fill in the details—the stars, the meteors, the comets, and the planets—until we come to the object of greatest interest to us: the earth. Here we examine the stage for the human drama, with its setting and its prologue—the geology and the geography and the chemistry and the physics of the earth, the mathematical relationships of the earth and the heavens, and the various aspects of plant and animal life—until we come to the entrance of the leading actor, Man. From this point on we observe the human essence of the drama, with an effort to understand its continuity—

the anthropology of the race and the physiology and the psychology of the individual.

And in the treatment of the various sciences we emphasize not only their *theoretical* but their *practical* value. We point out the links which unite them into a chain of universal principles, the logical continuity of this chain which enables us to see how every one of the sciences merges into all the other sciences, and the useful application of our scientific knowledge in our everyday life. At the end of every chapter we append four special sections, as follows:

1. A set of review questions and answers. (See below.)

2. Biographical sketches of the men who have made the greatest contributions to that science.

3. A job analysis as an aid to the selection of a career in that scientific field.

4. A carefully selected bibliography as a guide to the further study of that science.

As an additional aid to the better understanding of the sciences, we include a number of illustrations for the various chapters and a comprehensive index at the end of the book.

And, above all, we present the material in a simple and picturesque style. Our aim throughout the book is to show that the acquisition of knowledge can be made as exciting as the reading of a novel.

REVIEW QUESTIONS

At the end of each chapter we have included a set of fifty review questions on the subject matter taken up in the chapter. We suggest here a plan for using these questions which will enable you to get the most benefit from them. Write your answers to these questions, as well as to the questions printed at the end of the other chapters, on a sheet of paper. You can then correct your own answers by comparing them with those printed after the various lists of questions.

In order to grade your knowledge of the various subjects, credit yourself with two points for each correct answer. Since there are fifty questions for each of the subjects, you will get a perfect grade of 100 if you answer all the questions correctly. A grade ranging from 90 to 100 is excellent; from 80 to 89, good; from 70 to 79, fair; 60 is a "passing" grade; anything below 60 is poor.

If your grade is too low to satisfy you—and in our quest for knowledge anything below perfection should be regarded as too low—reread the chapter, again and again if necessary, until you have become thoroughly familiar with the field.

science subjects made easy

astronomy—a journey through the heavens

THE HISTORY OF ASTRONOMY

The age of the human race is about three hundred thousand years; the age of scientific astronomy, three thousand years; and the age of the telescope, a matter of only three hundred years. We have just begun our survey of the heavens. We are still in the kindergarten stage of our education in astronomy.

As to the future of this education, we shall probably continue to live and to learn for another two billion years. This means that no less than sixty-seven million generations of scholars will come after us. If today we are in the infancy of our knowledge, we are embarked upon a curriculum that may make the coming generations as familiar with the heavens as we are now familiar with our own back yards. Greater telescopes, increased mental capacities, instruments of computation and of locomotion that may carry us, physically as well as mentally, from star to star—all these possibilities may open up horizons that cannot even be imagined at the present time.

Yet even with our inadequate apparatus and our limited minds we have reached a point from which we can take a majestic view of the celestial scene. Let us briefly trace the road that has brought us to this vantage point for our observation of the universe.

One of the earliest attempts to explain the universe is to be found in the Old Testament. Here the earth is pictured as the central garden of creation, illuminated by the torches of the sun and the moon, and by the lesser candles of the stars.

The universe as conceived by the ancient astronomer Ptolemy, with the Earth at the center and the other heavenly bodies revolving around it.

Before long, however, the more observant among the scientists began to question the accuracy of this picture. The sun, they said, is more than a lamp in the heavens. It appears so small because it is so far away. In reality it is considerably larger than the earth. One of the Greek scientists, Aristarchus of Samos (about 280 B.C.), went so far as to conjecture—although he had no instruments to *prove* his conjecture—that the earth is not the center of the universe. "It is merely one of several planets which revolve in circles around the sun." Moreover, he declared—together with Pythagoras—that the earth "rotates upon its own axis." All this, he said, is proved by the regular succession of day and night and by the cyclical variations of the seasons.

But the ancient world found it difficult to accept such views. "It is the duty of the Greeks," said the philosopher Cleanthes, "to indict Aristarchus of Samos on the charge of impiety for putting the Hearth of the Universe—that is, the Earth—into motion."

And so the world rejected the "impious" theory of Aristarchus and adopted the more "orthodox" picture of the universe as presented in the astronomical system of Ptolemy (about A.D. 140). According to this system, man is the monarch of the Earth, and the Earth is the center of the universe. The Moon, Mercury, Venus, the Sun, Mars, Jupiter, and Saturn are planets, said Ptolemy, which move in circular paths around celestial points. And these points themselves move in circles around the motionless Earth. All this complicated rotation of the satellites of the Earth promoted no other purpose than to emphasize the dignity of man.

Such was the view of the heavens as accepted in the Middle Ages. Now and then, to be sure, there were some who questioned this view. "I have long considered," wrote Cardinal Nicholas of Cusa (1440), "that this earth is not fixed, but moves as do the other stars. To my mind the earth turns upon its axis once every day and night." But such skeptics were either howled down or treated with silent disdain. Occasionally, when a doubter expressed his ideas too strenuously—as in the case of Giordano Bruno—he was burned at the stake.

Yet in spite of all this opposition the pioneers of science continued to explore the heavens, until finally Copernicus disproved the Ptolemaic theory of "cycles and epicycles." In his famous book, *On the Revolutions of the Celestial Spheres* (1543), he showed that the complications of the Ptolemaic system were not only illogical but unnecessary. The cycle of the seasons, the succession of day and night, and the varying positions of the heavenly bodies could be simply explained, he said, on the theory that the Sun is the fixed center of our universe and that all the planets, *including the Earth,* rotate around the Sun.

And thus Copernicus returned to the idea of Aristarchus—an idea that had been abandoned for almost two thousand years.

And then came the telescope, to demonstrate the soundness of this idea. In 1608 the Flemish optician, Hans Lippershey, was making a pair of eyeglasses when he hit upon a remarkable discovery. He noticed that he could "bring distant objects near" by placing a convex and a concave glass together. This accidental discovery interested Galileo, who began to experiment with the idea and who, the following year, produced the first "magic eye" to "gaze into the distant stars."

It was on August 21, 1609, that Galileo made his public demonstration of the first scientifically constructed telescope in history. Inviting the doge and the senators of Venice to climb with him to the bell tower of the Campanile, he allowed them to look through his "wonderglass." And, to their amazement, they beheld "sails and shipping . . . so far off that it was two hours before they could be seen with the naked eye." They beheld "the traffic in a dozen harbors, the cattle grazing on the distant hillsides, and the worshipers going in and out of their churches in the faraway towns and villages." And then at night, turning their gaze to the heavens, they beheld the stars "almost near enough to touch with their fingers."

The invention of Galileo's telescope marked a turning point in human thought, for with the help of this telescope "the veil of the universe was thrust aside" and the heavens began to yield up their secrets. "I give thanks to God," wrote Galileo, "who (by means of my spyglass) has been pleased to make me the first observer of marvellous things unrevealed to bygone ages. . . . I have ascertained that the moon is a body similar to the earth. . . . I have beheld a multitude of fixed stars never before seen. . . . I have discovered . . . the nature of the Milky Way. . . . But the greatest marvel of all is the discovery of four new planets. . . . *I have observed that they move around the sun.*"

And thus the astronomical theory of Copernicus had become a scientific fact. Man had been removed from the center of the universe and put into his proper place—a speck of dust revolving around a huge central sun.

But if man had lost his old pomposity, he had gained a new vision. "What would you rather have," asked an oriental poet, "the arrogance of an imprisoned king, or the humility of a philosopher on the wing?" Our winged adventure into the heavens has carried us from the crude little "spyglass" of Galileo to the gigantic 200-inch telescope at the California Institute of Technology. Every year we are extending the horizons of our astronomical knowledge. Little by little we are becoming aware of the grandeur of the scale upon which the universe is built—nebulae a million times more tenuous, and stars a million times more solid, than anything we know on earth; celestial bodies so distant that their light, traveling at the rate of 186,000 miles a second, takes hundreds of thousands of years to reach us; "campfires and watchers of the night" extinguished before the human race was born yet visible even now within the range of the telescopic eye; a concourse of blazing suns as innumerable as the grains of dust in the city of New York, each of them treading its allotted path in the revolving pattern of the heavens; and centuries ticking off as seconds on the face of the astronomical time clock.

The astronomers have removed us from the center. But they are bringing us closer to heaven every day.

THE FORMATION OF THE UNIVERSE

We are so close to heaven, and yet we understand so little about it. At present there are a number of theories about the beginnings of the universe. Of these theories the following, known as the "tidal evolution hypothesis," has received perhaps the most serious consideration in advanced scientific circles:

About two hundred million million years ago—beyond that point it is impossible for the imagination to travel—matter came into being. How it came into being, whether spontaneously or through some "external" design, the scientists do not pretend to know. The philosophers and the theologians may talk about "the agitation of the ether by the finger of God." But the scientists make it their business not to profess faiths but to ascertain facts.

And they have ascertained, through their correlated observations, that energy became crystallized into matter at some such period as mentioned above. That period marked the beginning not only of matter, but also of time and of space. It was, so to speak, a triple birth.

The original form of this space-time-and-matter phenomenon was that of a single nebula—or cloudlike accumulation of gases—enormous beyond human computation.

This nebula, impelled by the energy that had brought it into being, began to rotate in a spiral. The rapidity of the rotation broke up the nebula into various masses, or smaller nebulae—each of them a whirlpool of boiling gases. As time went on these nebulae in turn broke up into stars—enormous vessels "sailing" through the heavens at an average speed of more than sixty thousand miles an hour. Some of these stars became separated into two or more stars, each of them whirling away upon its individual course in the universal pattern of the heavens.

And then, at a given point in time—about five thousand million years ago, the astronomers believe—one of the greater stars came too close to one of the lesser stars, known to us as the Sun. The attraction of the greater star produced a tidal wave upon the Sun. The spray of boiling gases flew off into space, and then began to whirl in elliptical paths around the Sun.

These whirling "conglomerations of gases" were the newly formed planets in our own little corner of the heavens—Mercury, Venus, the Earth, Mars, Jupiter, Saturn, Uranus, Neptune, and Pluto. All these planets were born at the same time, in a single eruption of the Sun. As time went on, their paths around the Sun became more circular and the gases became liquefied into water and solidified into metals and rocks and, ultimately, into plants and animals and the human race. You and I, the Earth, the Sun, and the most distant constellations belong to a single cosmic family. We are all compounded of the selfsame "frozen fire" that went into the creation of the star dust and the earth dust and the living dust of man.

But let us look a little more closely into this interstellar relationship.

THE STARS AND THEIR FAMILY GROUPS

When the nebulae became divided into family groups, the stars formed themselves into constellations and began their restless journey across the heavens.

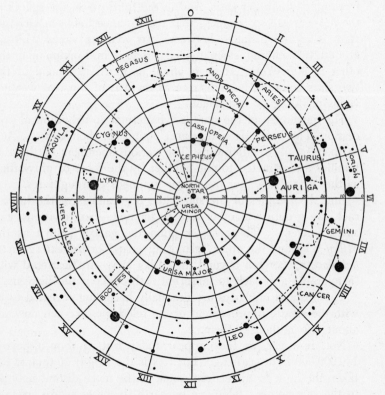

The sky of the Northern Hemisphere, showing stars and constellations.

These constellations tear along through the heavens in different directions and at different speeds. Yet there is no chaos in their motion, and very little danger of collision. In the first place, the various stars of any one constellation—as, for example, the five central members of the Big Dipper—move together in the same direction, like a military formation of airplanes bent upon a single mission. In the second place, all the stars have a tendency to move in a direction parallel rather than perpendicular to one another. Whether singly or in clusters, the stars keep to their appointed lanes of traffic, without any violation of the speed laws and without any "cutting in" to interfere against the freedom of the other stars. And in the third place, the spaces in the heavens are so immense that the distance between any two stars is as the distance between two weather vanes whirling around two church steeples—one situated in London and the other in New York. There is about as much likelihood of the two stars colliding in mid-space as there is of the two weather vanes colliding in mid-ocean.

The movement of the stars is a patterned and rhythmical procession. The heavenly bodies are "bound" to their courses. And to their family relationships. The various members of the star families are attracted to one another by the force of gravitation as they travel together over their luminous thoroughfares.

And the families of the stars, like the families of the human race, are grouped together into larger units—constellations, galaxies, universes. These larger units—the galaxy known as the *Milky Way* and the other "island universes," or the *extragalactic nebulae* that stretch beyond the Milky Way—are scattered with "a tolerable approach to uniformity" throughout the heavens.

These island universes are gradually becoming revealed to us with the steady improvement of the telescope. We can now see about two million of them.

Not, however, as they appear today but as they appeared 140,000,000 light-years ago. For this is the length of time it has taken the light to travel from some of the more distant nebulae to the astronomer's telescope on earth. In other words, we see today the cosmic drama that was enacted in the heavens millions of years before man appeared upon the scene.

But if these distances of time and space are too difficult to grasp, the general idea of the cosmic pattern falls easily within our human ken. For it is similar in design to the familiar little patterns of our daily existence. Just as the days and the seasons and the rivers and the races of men are united in one rhythmic motion of the Earth around the Sun, so are all the spirals and nebulae and galaxies and agglomerations of stars united in one rhythmic motion of the universe across the heavens. Motion within motion, rotation within rotation, and—it would seem—a single inflexible law sustaining their courses and safeguarding them all from falling apart.

THE MILKY WAY

The two million island universes that float over the tremendous ocean of space compose but a small fraction of the total number of galaxies in existence. Before long, the leading astronomers believe, there will be telescopes powerful enough to disclose about sixteen million of these universes. And even this will be little more than a beginning.

Now every one of these galaxies, as we have seen, is an aggregation of many families of stars. Some of these family groups are small. A few stars, like the Sun, travel alone—in stellar bachelorhood, so to speak—although the Sun has a number of planets revolving around it. But most of the stars are gregarious. They travel in clusters ranging all the way from two or three to several thousand. One of these groups, the so-called *globular cluster of Hercules*, is a gigantic "ball of light" containing about thirty-five thousand visible and probably close to a million invisible stars.

Yet even in this "closely packed" family, if we could station ourselves on an imaginary planet rotating around the central star, all the other stars would appear only as pin points of light.

So much, then, for our swift and breathless glimpse into the millions of universes of which we are privileged to be an infinitesimal part. And now we can turn our attention to our own celestial province, the Milky Way. For this is the region in which our terrestrial tenement is located.

The Milky Way is a necklace of light that encircles a sector of the heavens. Though almost invisible under the full moon, it glitters on moonless nights like an arabesque of innumerable jewels. It can best be observed about thirty degrees below the equator. From a mountain in that part of the hemisphere—say in South America or in South Africa—it appears like a blaze of golden sparks sweeping from horizon to horizon across the sky. Some of its brighter constellations as observed from the Southern Hemisphere can throw a faint reflection upon the Earth, like the shadow cast by the rising Moon.

The ancients looked upon the Milky Way as the star-paved highway of the gods, and upon the constellations as their palaces. Here they entertained one another on their journeys to their celestial councils, discussed their divine problems, and enjoyed, in their idle moments, the spectacle of man's stupidity to man.

Somewhat later the more imaginative among the ancients beheld in the heavens the figures of animals and men. And so they classified and named the constellations in accordance with their appearance—*the Great Bear, the Winged Horse, the Lion, the Bull, the Crab, the Goat, the Scorpion, the Archer, the Maiden, the Ram.*

The astronomers of the present day have retained the ancient (Latin) names of the constellations—*Ursa Major, Pegasus, Leo, Taurus, Cancer, Capricorn, Scorpius, Sagittarius, Virgo, Aries.* But they have traveled far from the ancients in their knowledge of the nature and the configuration of the stars. They now recognize the Milky Way as a luminous shell, of a whitish hue and with irregular edges, that divides the celestial sphere into two nearly equal parts. It is the universe in which we live. In shape it resembles the edge of a thick watch, jeweled with about forty billion stars. The "milky" color is due to the blending of the lights in this enormous stellar congregation; and the faintness of the shimmer is due to the tremendous distances of these stars.

And one of the smallest of these stars, yet to us the brightest because it is the nearest, is the Sun.

HIS MAJESTY, THE SUN

The Sun, though a dwarf among the stars, is a giant as compared to the Earth. Its volume is over a million times the volume of the Earth. It is the sole ruler of the celestial colony tucked away in our own little corner of the universe—the dispenser of our warmth, our light, and our life. A mere sparkle in the blaze of the astronomical furnace, it is to us the most important of the heavenly bodies. Without the Sun, our Earth would become a pellet of ice adrift upon a sea of eternal darkness.

Yet the Sun is about ninety-three million miles away from us. It exerts its influence by remote control, and it sheds upon us but a fraction of its energy. And it is a fortunate thing for us that we are so far away from the total power of its radiation. For if ever we came too close to the Sun, the entire Earth would be shriveled immediately into a cinder. The Earth revolves around the Sun like a moth around a lamp. But, unlike the moth, the Earth is kept always at a safe distance away from the flame.

The central flame of the Sun is a rotating sphere of incandescent matter surrounded by an envelope of gases that are being stirred incessantly into geysers of fire. These explosive eruptions —called *prominences*—shoot out from the Sun at incredible speeds, and sometimes leap into space for hundreds of thousands of miles.

In addition to the prominences, we can observe another sort of disturbance upon the Sun's surface. This disturbance consists of a succession of tornadoes familiarly known as *sunspots*. The difference between a solar eruption and a solar tornado is that the eruption shoots outward into space, while the tornado spins over the surface in a "sandstorm" of flaming gases. What we see as a dark spot is the flat top of the mushroom-shaped vortex occasioned by the spin. While still very hot and bright, the spot has become in the expansion of the storm somewhat cooler and less luminous than the rest of the surface. Hence the dark appearance.

These tornadoes of the Sun can travel at a velocity of about 360,000 miles an hour—about three thousand times the average speed of a tornado on earth. The Sun's wind, if it struck the United States, would uproot Mount Washington and whirl it like a feather into the air.

The violence of these sunspots appears to increase and to decrease in a regular cycle, reaching a maximum about every eleven years. It is, as it were, a rhythmical breathing of the Sun. And—although it has not as yet been established as a scientific fact—it would seem that the maximum of intensity in the sun storms is accompanied by an increased intensity in the storms of the Earth. At such periods the magnetic needle is subject to capricious gyrations, communication by wire and radio becomes difficult, and the Northern Lights appear more frequently and shine more brilliantly in the sky.

But to return to our more exact knowledge as to the nature of the Sun. It is, as we have noted, a sphere of incandescent matter in continuous rotation. Like the Earth, it revolves about an axis. The astronomers know this fact through their observation of the sunspots. By following the various positions of the sunspots, they have estimated that the surface of the Sun makes a complete revolution around its axis in about twenty-six days. All the celestial bodies rotate at various speeds, and make their cyclical revolutions in various units of time, depending upon their size. The Great Nebula in Andromeda, for example, rotating at a speed of hundreds of miles a second, makes a complete revolution around its axis in nineteen million years. This is but a hint as to the comparative *littleness* of the Sun.

As the Sun rotates around the axis, it pours out a radiation of light and heat into every direction. And, as it radiates, it keeps on decreasing its energy—that is, losing its weight—at the rate of a billion tons every four minutes. Should this loss of weight continue at the same speeds in the future, it would take the Sun no less than fifteen million million years to pour itself out completely into space. And this is a hint as to the comparative *greatness* of the Sun.

And now a word as to the structure of the Sun's interior. The outer surface, as we have seen, is an envelope of luminous gases punctuated by explosive eruptions and whirling tornadoes. The inner substance, however, is not gaseous but solid. So solid, indeed, that a cubic foot of matter at the Sun's center weighs about thirteen times as much as a cubic foot of lead. And the temperature of the Sun's center has been estimated at about 50,000,000° Centigrade. A fragment of the Sun about the size of a pinhead, were it existent on the Earth, would pour out enough heat to kill every single living creature within a radius of a thousand miles.

THE PLANETS AND THEIR SATELLITES

The attraction of the Sun keeps the planets, as by invisible strings, whirling in circles around it. This family of planets revolving around their parent, the Sun, may be divided into two groups: four minor "children"—Mercury, Venus, the Earth, and Mars; and five major "children"—Jupiter, Saturn, Uranus, Neptune, and Pluto. The minor planets are comparatively close to the Sun, and the major planets are very far away from it.

Diameter of the Sun

The Sun and the nine planets, showing their relative sizes.

Closest of all to the Sun comes Mercury. Venus is next. The orbits of these two planets fall within the orbit of the Earth, which follows next. And off into space, beyond the Earth's pathway, comes the orbit of Mars, the outermost of the minor planets.

And now there is a wide interval in the procession of the planets around the Sun. But this interval is not empty; on the contrary, it is filled with thousands of marching planets called *asteroids.* These asteroids are considerably smaller than the Earth, the largest of them, Ceres, having a circumference of only fifteen hundred miles.

Next beyond the asteroids come the orbits of the five major planets. Of these major planets, Jupiter follows the innermost course and Pluto the outermost.

This procession of the planets, though it is confined to but a tiny parish of the universe, covers a tremendous area from our terrestrial point of view. The outermost planet, Pluto, is almost four thousand million miles away from the Sun. This figure can be mathematically stated, but it can barely be visualized by the human mind.

As regards the distances and sizes of the planets within the solar system, the astronomer Sir John Herschel (1792–1871) devised a comparative simile which may be roughly reproduced as follows:

Imagine the Sun to be a ball, about two feet in diameter, lying in the center of a level field. The arrangement of the planets, brought down to the same scale, would make some such pattern as this:

	DISTANCE FROM THE SUN	COMPARATIVE SIZE
Mercury	82 feet	a mustard seed
Venus	142 feet	a pea
Earth	215 feet	a pea
Mars	327 feet	a small peppercorn
Jupiter	¼ of a mile	an orange
Saturn	⅖ of a mile	a small orange
Uranus	¾ of a mile	a cherry
Neptune	1¼ miles	a plum

(Pluto is not included in this comparison, because its existence was not discovered until 1930, fifty-nine years after Sir John Herschel's death. The size of Pluto, however, has been estimated at about one tenth the size of the Earth, and it is 3,680,000,000 miles from the Sun.)

Such, in brief, is the assemblage of the planetary pageant around the Sun. And the orbit of the planets is not exactly circular but elliptical. When we talk about the distance between a planet and the Sun, we mean the *average* distance from the Sun at the center to the curvature of the orbit. Thus the distance of Mercury from the Sun varies from 28,500,000 miles to 43,500,000 miles. Hence we say that the average distance of Mercury from the Sun—or the average radius of its orbit—is 36,000,000 miles.

And thus the entire distance *across* the orbit of Mercury, the "innermost" of the solar planets, is 72,000,000 miles. And the entire distance *around* this orbit is about 226,000,000 miles.

But the distance across the orbit of Pluto, the "outermost" of the solar planets, is over a hundred times the distance across the orbit of Mercury. And the total circumference of this outermost of the planetary orbits is about 25,000,000,000 miles.

Try to catch your breath for a moment at the spectacle of the stupendous area comprehended in the revolutions of the solar planets—our little flotilla of vessels cruising around their lighthouse in the vastitudes of space. And then take a leap into the darkness beyond the remotest border of this planetary group of ours. *You will have to travel twenty-five millions of millions of miles—over six thousand times the distance between the Sun and its outermost planet—before you can come to the nearest of the stars.*

This is how far our own little family of planets is removed from the rest of the celestial host.

And now let us return to our own solar system, and let us examine our planets one by one.

mercury

Of all the nine planets, Mercury is not only the nearest to the Sun but the smallest. Its diameter is about three eighths the diameter of the Earth. The length of its year—that is, its complete revolution around the Sun—is eighty-eight days, or about three months.

Since Mercury travels so close to the Sun, it can be seen only as an evening star, setting just after the Sun, or as a morning star, rising just before the Sun.

To the ancient Greeks, who saw it sometimes in the evening and sometimes in the morning, it appeared as two stars—called respectively *Mercury* and *Apollo*.

venus

Venus, whose orbit lies next to the orbit of Mercury, has a diameter just a trifle less than the diameter of the Earth. It revolves around the Sun in 225 days, at an average distance of sixty-seven million miles. Owing to its comparative size and nearness to the Earth—twenty-six million miles—it appears to us as the brightest of the heavenly bodies after the Sun and the Moon. Like Mercury, Venus appears both as an evening and as a morning star. And therefore Venus, too, was regarded by the ancients as two stars—*Hesperus* in the evening, and *Phosphorus* in the morning.

Of all the nine planets, Mercury and Venus alone are unattended by moons.

the earth and the moon

Imagine yourself transported to Venus and gazing through a telescope at the sky. Away out in space shines a brilliant star—and not far from it another, smaller star that keeps changing its position and is therefore (you will conclude) revolving around the bigger star.

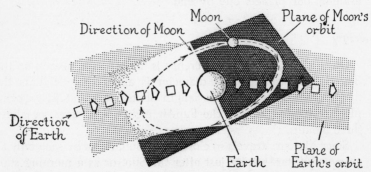

The Earth and the Moon revolve in orbits which are on different planes. This explains why the Moon can pass between the Sun and the Earth once every twenty-eight days without bringing about an eclipse of the Sun.

And now, examining the bigger star more closely through your telescope, you will notice here and there upon its surface irregular spots. What are these spots—Oceans? Continents? Valleys? Mountains? Glaciers? Woods? Some of these spots seem to be in motion. Living little creatures, perhaps, in battle array? Or merely scudding clouds?

Observe now the smaller star revolving around the larger star. If you have chosen the proper moment for your observation, you will see a dark round shadow moving across the face of the larger star and blotting it slowly out of sight.

A strange and beautiful phenomenon. What are the names of these stars? And what is the meaning of the shadow?

Whatever their names in the mysterious Directory of the Heavens—if indeed they have been dignified by any names at all —you have just witnessed what the human race knows as the Earth, the Moon, and the eclipse of the Sun.

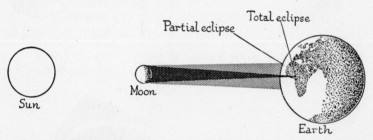

Diagram of the eclipse of the Sun. It can be seen that a total eclipse occurs when the Moon and Sun are in a direct line with a particular area on the Earth. A partial eclipse occurs when the Moon is in such a position as to block out only a portion of the Sun.

In this section we shall consider the relation of the Earth to the other heavenly bodies. Its geology and its geography will be examined later on.

What, then, is this planet known to us as the Earth? It is a globular body of matter, about eight thousand miles in diameter, held together by the mutual attraction of its parts. It makes a daily rotation about its axis and a yearly revolution around the Sun. The average distance between the Earth and the Sun is about ninety-three million miles.

The Earth is not a perfect sphere, since it bulges somewhat at the equator and is flattened slightly at the poles. Its surface is relatively smooth; the highest mountains upon it, as compared to its total area, are but specks of insignificant anthills.

The axis of the Earth, as it travels around the Sun, is not perpendicular to the orbit, but is tipped from the perpendicular at an oblique angle of 23½ degrees. As a result of this obliquity, the Northern Hemisphere is inclined *toward* the Sun, and the

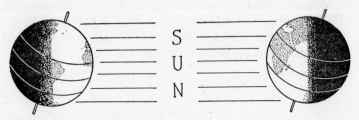

This diagram shows how changes in seasons on the Earth come about. The axis of the Earth is tilted so that at various times of the year more sunlight will fall on certain portions of the Earth than at other times.

Southern Hemisphere *away from* the Sun, in June, July, and August. In December, January, and February the exact opposite holds true. In those months the Northern Hemisphere is inclined *away from* the Sun, and the Southern Hemisphere *toward* the Sun.

This explains the variations of the seasons. When it is summer north of the equator, it is winter south of the equator. When the days are the longest and the Sun is the warmest in the United States, the days are the shortest and the Sun is the coldest in Argentina. And vice versa.

As the Earth, with its changing seasons, keeps revolving around the Sun, it is accompanied by its satellite, the Moon, which in turn keeps revolving around the Earth. The orbit of the Moon, like the orbit of the Earth, is elliptical; and the average distance from the Earth to the Moon is 239,000 miles—a mere trifle on the astronomical scale. Trips to the Moon are almost within the range of scientific possibility.

There are various theories as to the origin of the Moon just as there are various theories as to the origin of the Earth. Perhaps the most plausible of all is the so-called "tidal theory." Just as the Earth was torn away in a tidal wave from the Sun when the Sun came too close to another star, just so the Moon was torn away in a tidal wave from the Earth when the Earth—in its infancy, before its orbit had become fixed—came too close to the Sun. The Moon, therefore, is a part of the Earth, just as the Earth is a part of the Sun.

But whatever its origin, the Moon today is the constant attendant of the Earth in its journey around the Sun. And, like the Earth, it rotates about its axis as it circles over its orbit. But, unlike the Earth, it makes a single rotation on its axis and a single

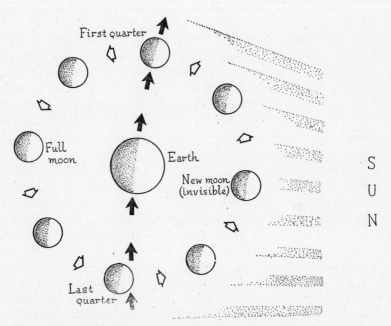

The phases of the Moon. The changing aspect of the Moon depends on the position from which we on Earth view the illuminated portion of the Moon. When the Moon stands directly between the Earth and the Sun, the Moon is completely in shadow and, hence, invisible. When the entire illuminated hemisphere of the Moon is turned towards us, we have a Full Moon.

revolution over its orbit in the same period of time—about twenty-eight days. Owing to this fact, the Moon "always presents the same face" to our view. We can see only one side of it. The other side is forever turned away from us.

And the side that we *do* see appears bright because it receives the light of the Sun and reflects it back to us. The Sun shines constantly upon one half of the Moon. Sometimes, depending upon the relative positions of the Sun, the Earth, and the Moon, we get a direct view of the Moon's illuminated surface—a phenomenon which we call the *Full Moon*. At other times, we get a side view of the illuminated portion—the so-called *Half-Moon*. At still other times we see but a thin sliver of the sun-lighted surface, and we call this the *Crescent Moon*.

At the Full Moon we can see its surface quite distinctly, since it is the nearest of all the heavenly bodies to us. As viewed through a telescope, the Moon presents an even more distinct picture. The most striking aspect of our satellite is the series of elevations or craterlike mountains which, to the naked eye, appear like the features of "the Man in the Moon." Some of these mountains have a circular wall many miles in diameter, "scooped out" to a fairly level floor on the inside. Their exact nature—whether a conglomeration of loose stone or a cohesion of solid rock—remains still a mystery.

Another of the striking lunar features is the presence of bright lines which radiate, like the spokes of a wheel, from several points on the surface. Apparently there was at some earlier period a great deal of volcanic activity upon the Moon.

At present, so far as we can tell, there is no motion on the Moon—no circulating air, no flowing water, no weather, no growth, no life.

And yet, though dead, it exerts a profound influence upon us. It "pulls" the ocean toward it and produces the tides. And here is an interesting point. The Moon attracts not only the ocean but the entire Earth. If this attraction were exerted always upon one side of the Earth, the Moon would be dragged back toward the Earth, from which it originally came. When within about 8000 miles of the Earth's surface, the moon would be shattered into fragments because of the pull caused by the Earth in the solid body of the Moon and these fragments would form a system of tiny satellites revolving around the Earth. But at present the Moon revolves around the Earth, the direction of the pull is always shifting, and thus the two bodies are kept perpetually apart and in their proper balance toward one another.

mars and its two moons

Though much smaller than the Earth, Mars is to us perhaps the most interesting of the planets.

Its average distance from the Sun is 141,500,000 miles. Its average distance from the Earth is about 50,000,000 miles.

The diameter of Mars is about half the diameter of the Earth, and its volume is about one eighth of the Earth's volume. In several respects, however, it is similar to the Earth. It rotates about its axis in about twenty-four hours, and it is "inclined" toward the Sun, like the Earth, at an angle of about 24 degrees. And thus it closely resembles the Earth in the length of its days and in the variation of its seasons. The Martian year—that is, the period of its rotation around the Sun—is about twice as long as our own year.

As viewed through the telescope, Mars seems to possess—like the Earth—air and water, for occasionally we can see cloudlike patches that obscure certain areas of the planet. And the presence of clouds would indicate an atmosphere and moisture—air and water. Furthermore, one of the most noticeable features on Mars is a zone of apparent snowcaps around the poles. These snowcaps diminish in the summer season—another indication of the presence of water on Mars.

The presence of air and water would lead us to the assumption that perhaps there is life on that planet. But the evidence pointing to a form of life similar to our own is rather negative.

In the first place, the distance of Mars from the Sun is so great that it receives less than half as much of the Sun's energy as the Earth. Though the surface near the equator is above freezing at noon, it is far below freezing all the rest of the time. Through the remainder of the planet, the sunlight is rarely strong enough to produce a temperature above the freezing point.

Furthermore, the atmospheric pressure on the Martian surface is only one half the atmospheric pressure on the highest of our terrestrial mountains. No plant or animal now living on Earth could exist in such a rare atmosphere.

This does not, of course, preclude the possibility of *some* form of life existing on Mars. But such life, if it does exist, is so different from our own that there is no basis for comparison or for communication. "The frequent suggestion that we might exchange signals with organisms on Mars," writes Professor Harlow Shapley, "is, I think, extremely preposterous. Those absurd people who try or recommend such experiments should first practice communicating with carrots and jellyfish."

Mars, therefore, is unlike the Earth with respect to its life—if, indeed, it has any life at all. But, like the Earth, it is a satellite-attended planet. It has two moons—considerably smaller but also considerably nearer than our own Moon. These two Martian satellites are probably from ten to eighteen miles in diameter. The first, Phobos, is about four thousand miles away from Mars and revolves around it in 7½ hours. The second, Deimos, is about fifteen thousand miles away from Mars and revolves around it in 30½ hours. To the inhabitants of Mars, should any such exist, the moons, owing to their nearness and the rapidity of their motion, would appear like the lights of two airplanes traveling through the night.

the asteroids

The gap in the solar system between the orbits of Mars and of Jupiter is filled, as we have observed, with thousands of little planets called *asteroids.*

If the larger planets may be likened to moths circling around the flame of the Sun, the asteroids may be compared to gnats. These tiny worlds vary in size from Ceres, which measures 480 miles across, to globules no larger than a balloon.

The orbits of the asteroids are very eccentric. Some of these "celestial Lilliputians" wander in an ellipse so elongated that it stretches inside the orbit of Mars and outside the orbit of Jupiter. Indeed, one of these erratic children of the solar procession has been known to approach to within three million miles of the Earth. The great majority of them, however, are kept well within their bounds—the interval of space between Mars, the last of the minor planets, and Jupiter, the first of the major planets.

jupiter and its nine satellites

Jupiter, which leads the procession of the five major planets around the Sun, is the Goliath of them all. Measuring in diameter almost ninety thousand miles, it is more than three times as large as all the other planets put together. It contains the volume of fourteen hundred Earths, with room to spare.

The length of its day—the period of its rotation around its axis —is ten hours; and the length of its year—the period of its revolution around the Sun—is about twelve of our terrestrial years.

Its distance from the Sun is 483,000,000 miles; from the Earth, about 390,000,000 miles.

Like the Earth, it contains an atmosphere. But unlike the Earth, it has practically no seasons, since its axis is almost perpendicular to its orbit, and therefore it faces the Sun at nearly the same angle throughout the year.

As observed through the telescope, this planet with its satellites —four of which are clearly visible—is one of the "show places" of the heavens. For these satellites of Jupiter, revolving around their "leader" much more rapidly than the Moon revolves around the Earth, perform a dance over the sky in a pattern which varies from hour to hour. Sometimes all four are seen on one side of Jupiter; at other times, three are on one side while the fourth has "pirouetted" around to the other side; and so on and on. Now and then we can see the shadows of these satellites as they roll like billiard balls across the face of their planet.

Altogether the revolution of the satellites of Jupiter—four of them visible and five invisible—around their revolving planet represents one of the most interesting phases in the procession of the entire planetary system around the Sun.

the rings of saturn

We have now traveled 483,000,000 miles from the Sun in our journey to survey the pageantry of the planets. And now, sailing off into space another 400,000,000 miles, we come to the next group in the pageant—Saturn, with its rings and its satellites.

This "jeweled" planet, though smaller than Jupiter, is by far the most beautiful member of the solar family. And the most unusual. Owing to the rings—at least three in number—which surround it, Saturn is unique among the planets, and perhaps among the entire congregation of the stars.

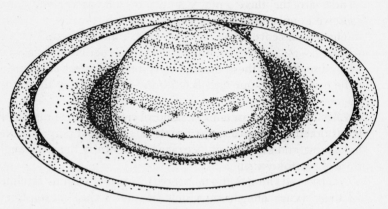

The planet Saturn and its rings.

The rings of Saturn are the orbits of innumerable particles—each of them probably no bigger than a grain of sand—which revolve perpetually around their planet. Perhaps they are the fragments of a former moon of Saturn exploded in collision with another heavenly body—Saturn itself, most likely. It is the belief of some of the leading astronomers that our own Moon is destined in time to come too close to the Earth. And then the Moon will break into fragments and the Earth, like Saturn, will have its jeweled rings.

But Saturn, in addition to the rings resulting from a shattered moon, possesses nine other satellites that are still intact. These, like the nine moons of Jupiter and our own Moon, are the off-spring of their planet—masses of matter torn away by the Sun and set in circular rotation around their parent. All the moons in the heavens are very small as compared to their planets. The largest of the Saturnian moons, known to us as Titan, is (relatively speaking) anything but titanic. Its diameter is only 3300 miles, while the diameter of Saturn is 75,000 miles.

But the diameter of the *orbit* of Saturn is 1,766,000,000 miles.

uranus, neptune, and pluto

These are the three outermost planets of the solar system. They were unknown to astronomers until very recent times. Uranus was discovered in 1781; Neptune, in 1846; and Pluto, in 1930.

The discovery of these three planets marks a decided advance in the expansion of our intellectual interests. For it brings three new members into our solar family and considerably widens the province to which we have been assigned for our living fraction of eternity. Uranus, Neptune, and Pluto are the outposts of what we may regard as the United Planets of the World. Uranus takes 84 years to make a single revolution around the Sun; Neptune, 165 years; and Pluto, 249 years. Yet these three remote planets, like their six traveling companions that are nearer to the Sun, owe their direction and their motion and their very existence to the selfsame source of energy to which we humans owe our light and our life.

And is this the total sum of our solar family? Time alone can give the answer.

COMETS

Thus far we have examined the more or less "solid" bodies in the heavens. We shall now consider those eccentric vagabonds of the universe known as *comets*.

A comet, said Oliver Wendell Holmes with more poetry than truth, is "ten million cubic miles of head, ten billion leagues of tail." Actually the tail of many a comet is very much shorter than the head, and there are quite a few comets which have no tails at all.

The so-called "tail" of a comet is a streamer sweeping along under the influence of the Sun. When the comet travels its erratic way over the heavens, matter is blown out from it like smoke from a locomotive. The pressure of the Sun's energy pushes away the tiny particles of matter that constitute the substance of the comet, so that the tail always points away from the Sun. And therefore, when the comet *approaches* the Sun, it carries its tail *behind* it; but when it *leaves* the Sun, it travels with its tail in *front*.

Sometimes a comet travels with two or three or even more tails spread out fanwise—an awe-inspiring sight.

But what is the nature of these spectacular vagrants that speed like flaming arrows across the sky? They are tenuous bodies compounded of gases, grains of sand, pebbles, and possibly larger blocks of metal and stone. The conglomeration is much more attenuated at the surface than at the center, and almost entirely gaseous at the tail.

The comets travel over the heavens in very long and narrow curves, so that sometimes they come far *within* the orbits of the solar planets, and at other times far *beyond* them. Some of the comets keep returning in their paths again and again, at regular intervals. Others whirl in from the depths of space to pay us a single visit, and then speed away forever.

Sometimes these speeding vagrants of the heavens come so close to the Earth that they actually brush us with their tails. What happens then? Nothing much, save a slight haze like the passage of a whiff of smoke. And even if a comet grazed us with its head—the chances against this occurrence are about fifteen million to one—we should get perhaps nothing worse than a dazzling shower of meteors.

And this brings us to our next subject.

METEORS, OR SHOOTING STARS

Often, on a clear night, you can see one or more stars shooting across the sky and then suddenly going out. These "shooting stars" are meteors—the tiniest of the solid bodies that travel over the sky.

To us, they are the best known of the heavenly bodies, for some of the meteors are solid enough to strike the Earth. Fortunately, we get only a small proportion of the celestial bombardment of the shooting stars. The vast majority—millions of them that come shooting toward us every hour—are consumed in the fire that flames up through the speed of their collision against our atmosphere. But those that reach the Earth may be looked upon as a consignment shipped from heaven for our scientific observations.

These meteors, when they fall upon the earth, are called *meteorites*. They are found to consist of stony substances, of metallic alloys such as iron and nickel, and of various other crystal and mineral combinations. Most of the meteors in our museums appear to have a "varnished" surface. This is due to the melting of the outside of the meteor as it darted earthward through the air.

Thus we have a direct acquaintance with at least *some* of the alien bodies in the vastness of the heavens. But as to the ancestry of these immigrants to the Earth, and as to the ports from which they have embarked, we are still almost completely in the dark. It has been suggested—but thus far it is nothing more than a theory—that the meteorites are the remainders of disintegrated comets. A comet is a flying congregation of meteors. When the comet reaches the end of its flight—that is, when it comes too close to a more powerful body in the heavens—it bursts into an explosion of celestial fireworks. One of these pyrotechnic displays was seen in 1799; another in 1833; still another in 1866, when "the entire heavens were filled with a downpour of metal and flame."

Most of the "metallic raindrops" from the exploding comets are probably absorbed by the stars. A few of them fall into our atmosphere—at a speed of about two thousand miles a minute—and are either consumed by the friction of the air or become imbedded in the Earth.

Such is one of the tentative conjectures on the still controversial subject of meteors. But their exact nature—their origin, their orbit (if any), and their place in the pattern of the universe—is still a mystery. In our exploration of the heavens we have reached but a stone's throw—astronomically speaking—from our terrestrial shores.

THE MEASURE OF SPACE

"Every increase of telescopic power," as Sir James Jeans reminds us, "has carried us deeper and deeper into space, and space has seemed to expand at an ever-increasing rate." And therefore, he continues, "we may well ask whether this expansion is destined to go on forever; are there any limits at all to the extent of space?"

In other words, is space infinite, or is it finite?

This is one of the most baffling questions in the entire field of science. For the human mind is unable to visualize the answer to this question. We can conceive neither an ending to space, nor an endless space. For, if space ends somewhere—that is, if it has a border—we want to know what is *beyond* that border. Is it nothingness? But we cannot imagine *nothingness*. The moment we imagine it, it becomes *something*. In other words, the mind can think only of space that continues without any final boundaries. There is no horizon in space where the mind can stop and say, "From here on I can no longer shoot out the arrows of my thought."

But, on the other hand, if space is endless, it becomes an object that cannot be encompassed by any stretch of the imagination. For the imagination is a yardstick of measurement. It cannot envision a thing without any dimensions. If we are told that space goes on to infinity, we want to know how far is infinity. That is, our minds can think of infinity only in finite terms. We cannot think of space in the abstract. It is, so far as our minds can go, a concrete thing. And a concrete thing must have a shape, a surface, a boundary, an end.

And thus we find ourselves mentally unable to understand space either with or without a limit. We can grasp neither the idea of *a beyond without space* nor of *space without a beyond*.

Yet there is a tendency in modern science to give a definite answer to the question as to whether space is finite or infinite. The tentative answer is that it is *finite,* but *unlimited.*

For space, like the Earth, is spherical. This is the theory of Einstein, accepted by many of the modern astronomers. According to this theory, a journey over space is like a journey over the Earth. Any traveler unaware of the curvature of the Earth's surface would imagine that if he started his journey from a given point and kept going in a straight line, he would travel forever into new fields. As a matter of fact, however, he would merely go around in a circle and return to the point from which he started. This would be true regardless of the direction in which he traveled. For the Earth's surface, though *unlimited* in the sense that it offers no barrier to our going on and on in every direction as far as we like, is nevertheless *finite* in extent. It has an area that can be definitely measured, computed, and fixed in the mind.

In like manner, if a traveler over the spherical surface of space started from any point and kept going in a straight line, he would finally return to his starting point. The surface of space, like the surface of the Earth, is unlimited in the endlessness of its curvature but finite in the extent of its area.

But the same question still arises to baffle us. Suppose space bends back upon itself and it is possible for us—at least in imagination—to circumnavigate its globular structure through every dimension and in every direction. What lies beyond that structure? Is it nothing? What do we mean by nothing? Empty space? What is it, and how far does it reach? Or is it something? What do we mean by something? Other globular bodies of space *beyond* space? How far do *these* reach?

So much, then, for the *theoretical* aspect of space—a perhaps insoluble problem which belongs to philosophy rather than to science. As regards the *practical* aspect of space, our measures are scientifically precise. But they are relative rather than absolute. Space has three co-ordinates—length, breadth, and thickness. In order to measure these three co-ordinates, the scientists have agreed upon a standard unit—the international meter which is carefully guarded in Paris.

But this unit, while effective in measuring small distances on Earth, is useless when we go out into space. We must therefore exchange our smaller for a larger unit—an *astronomical* unit—in our computation of the distances of the universe.

Let us glance at the manner in which we use the astronomical unit of measurement.

Suppose you want to ascertain the distance between a treetop and the ground. You can do this in three ways. Either you climb the tree with a tape measure in your hand; or you chop it down and then measure its length; or you avail yourself of the surveyor's telescope. This last method is to measure off a certain distance from the foot of the tree as a *base line,* and then to measure the *angle* subtended by the height of the tree. Given the base line and the subtended angle, it is merely a question of solving a simple triangle in order to compute the distance between the treetop and the ground.

This is the method the astronomers use in measuring the distances between the heavenly bodies and the Earth. There is, however, a slight difference. The surveyors of the heavens measure *two* angles instead of *one.* Moreover, they use considerably longer base lines.

For example, suppose the astronomers want to measure the distance from the Moon to the Earth. They take two points approximately a thousand miles apart—let us say, Massachusetts and Illinois—and then they make simultaneous observations of the Moon, determine the two angles, and with a thousand miles as their base line compute the necessary distance. Or else they can make two observations of the Moon from only one place but at intervals of about two hours. For in these two hours the point of observation will have traveled, through the Earth's rotation, a distance of about a thousand miles—thus giving them the necessary base line for their computation.

But in either case, the measurements have been taken *from* a moving object, the Earth, *to* a moving object, the Moon. And therefore they represent distances that are not absolute but relative. These measurements—*any* measurements taken in our world of incessant motion—are transitory relationships, and not permanent facts. Between a measurement of the heavens taken from the Earth today and another measurement taken six months from today, the Earth will have traveled in its orbit the considerable distance of almost two hundred million miles. In the universe, therefore, there is no such thing as an established interval between two fixed points.

And even these relative intervals, or distances, cover but a small horizon of space, in so far as our present-day scientific instruments are able to survey it. "The stars in the sky are so hopelessly numerous," writes Professor Harlow Shapley (and, he might have added, so hopelessly far away), "that we can never expect to find the distances of even one thousandth part of them."

And therefore, when we talk about space—that is, *scientifically understandable* space—we mean a finite group of moving island universes stretching out into tremendous but computable distances. In our terrestrial measurements we use the international meter as a standard. In our survey of the solar system, we use a different standard—the average distance of ninety-three million miles between the Earth and the Sun. But even this astronomical unit is inadequate in our approach toward the nearest of the stars. And so we must adopt a light-year as the standard "yardstick" for our stellar measurements. A light-year is the distance covered in one year by a ray of light traveling at the rate of 186,000 miles a second. Translated into ordinary arithmetic, a light year is about six million times a million miles.

And finally, when we travel beyond our own island universe to the other universes, we find ourselves obliged to use still larger units of measurement. Even a light-year now is as inadequate as an inch. And therefore we have extended the length of our measuring rod from *one* light-year to *several millions* of light-years.

Yet even our last measuring rod is insufficient to carry us to the outermost limits of the starry domain. But this, to date, is as far as we are able scientifically to explore into the depths of space. What lies beyond is anybody's guess.

THE MEANING OF TIME

Closely allied to space is time. Indeed, there are some scientists who maintain that time is but one of the dimensions of space. Thus, if we wanted to determine the volume of a mountain with scientific accuracy, we would have to take four separate lines for our measurement: length, width, height, and—to coin a word —*whenth*. This fourth dimension would denote the *time when* the measurement was taken. For, in this constantly changing world of ours, no object remains exactly the same at any two moments. A million years ago the mountain may have been much bulkier than it is today. A million years from now it may be only a heap of dust. Any *complete* picture of the mountain, or of any object whatsoever, must be built upon a structure of four lines—three of them spatial, depicting the object at rest, and one of them temporal, representing it in motion.

According to this theory, therefore, *time is the moving dimension of space.* Hence it is impossible to conceive of time without space, or of space without time. There is no such thing as a separate space composed of points, or of a separate time composed of instants, existing independently of the bodies and the events that exist within them. There is a continuity that may be called *space-time,* and this continuity includes both the bodies that occupy it and the events that move it. All distances are relative intervals which may be analyzed into space terms or time terms—inches, feet, yards, miles; minutes, hours, days, years. But all these measurements are *interrelated;* they are different dimensions of the selfsame body event—space-time, or the *moving universe.*

The theory which considers time as a dimension is the *theory of relativity.* Whether we accept this theory or prefer to consider space and time as separate entities, we must adopt new temporal as well as new spatial units of measurement in our study of the universe. From inches to light-years, from seconds to eons. Our conception of time has widened with the expansion of our scientific knowledge. We have discovered that the heavens are more than the star-lighted ceiling of the earth, and that creation is greater than a dramatic episode of six thousand years. We need new chronometers to register the life span of the universe—a geological hourglass to estimate the age of the earth, and an astronomical time clock to compute the generations of the stars.

The astronomical unit of measurement—the time that it takes the "hand" of the celestial time clock to circle once around the circumference of space—is, roughly speaking, several thousand million years.

And through all this perspective there is a continual whirlpool of stars revolving in every direction at a speed more than a thousand times the speed of an automobile. Yet this innumerable stellar congregation is so sparsely distributed that, comparatively speaking, space is as empty of stars as the earth would be of men if there were only a dozen of them roaming over its entire surface. The possibility of collision between two stars is about one in a million million million years.

THE BIOGRAPHY OF THE WORLD

In this section we shall consider the "life story" of our universe —its present tendency, its future course, its ultimate fate.

The body of the universe, of every object *within* the universe, is gradually wearing out. All tangible matter dissolves continually into intangible radiation. The world is losing weight every minute of every day. At this moment, the Sun weighs 360,000,000,000 tons less than it weighed twenty-four hours ago. Even the little tenement of our Earth is crumbling away at the rate of about ninety pounds a day.

And now an interesting question arises. Is this loss of substance permanent, like a log of wood consumed by flame? Or is it cyclical, like water in a river transformed into clouds that will change again into water to replenish the river?

The answer to this question is that the loss is permanent. The world is decomposing into final annihilation. The cause of all the world's motion, the activity of all material substance, is energy. Now there are two principles that govern the nature of energy. These two principles are called "the first and the second laws of thermodynamics." The first law of thermodynamics teaches us that energy is *indestructible;* it may change in form, but remains unchanged in amount. This would seem to point to a permanent existence of the universe, though under varying forms. Thus, the seed changes to a plant, the plant to a flower, the flower to a seed, and so on. But the second law of thermodynamics teaches us that energy, though permanent in *quantity*, varies in *quality*. And the variation is always in one direction. Thus, a million ergs of *light energy*—an erg is a quantity of measurement of energy in physics —can be changed into a million ergs of *heat energy*. But a million ergs of heat energy can never be changed back into a million ergs of light energy. Like water, energy always flows in one direction —"downward." In the mutation of energy, as in the current of a mountain brook or in the life course of a man, there is no turning back.

Thus the substance of the universe keeps on dissolving into radiation. But this amount of radiation can never be turned back into the same amount of energy. "When once the fall and breakage [of the quanta of energy] have taken place," writes Sir James Jeans, "it is as impossible to reconstitute the original large quanta as it was to put Humpty-Dumpty back on his wall." Energy keeps "running downhill" as it moves "the wheels of the world."

But it cannot keep going downhill forever. There must come a moment when it will touch bottom. And that moment will mark the end of the world. The energy will still be there, undiminished in quantity, but incapable of further change. It is as if a mountain brook had emptied itself completely into a stagnant pool at the bottom. The water is as abundant as ever, but it is no longer able to turn a single wheel or to push even a tiny feather across its waveless and lifeless surface. All the light will have become transformed into heat, but all the heat will never again succeed in producing light. So far as science can observe today, universal life, like human life, is an inevitable journey to the grave.

But let us not lose heart over this dismal prospect. The final dissolution of the world is a *long way off*. Indeed, it lies outside the boundaries of the human mind. The canvas of our ideas can be stretched from the creation of the world to its destruction; but it cannot go beyond the edges at either end. And so we must be content to keep our interests and our hopes centered upon the vast panorama of existence. From cosmic birth to cosmic death lies a vista wide enough and varied enough for all our individual dreams.

And for all our social aspirations as well. We have time enough to achieve every human desire this side of eternity. The ultimate realities are beyond our comprehension. It is sufficient for us to attend to the temporary realities of our cosmic scene—the moving picture of existence within the framework of space and time. This picture, so far as we can see, is bound to come to an end. But the end is beyond the widest horizon of the astronomer's calculation, the poet's fantasy, or the philosopher's thought.

And even in our own little corner of the picture the expectancy of human life is almost beyond computation. Whatever the origin of life, and however limited its range, we have been ushered into a play of which only the first few syllables have been spoken. And in the unfolding of the plot before the final curtain, we shall have learned perhaps to harmonize our human actions to the orbits of the stars. And then man will no longer collide against man, or nation against nation, or race against race.

And finally, when the Earth has become too cold for human habitation, mankind will have probably migrated en masse to another planet—a greater, brighter, and more comfortable theater for the further development of the play.

Is this a wild dream? On the contrary, it would seem to be the logical outcome of a scientific fact. The past history of man is but a moment as compared to the future. Or, to use another illustration, all the past centuries of human existence are as the thickness of a single sheet of tissue paper. Pile the future centuries like pieces of paper on top of one another—one sheet for every period to equal the duration of the past—and you will have a column higher than Mount Everest before you come to the last generation of man.

We shall have ample time, and an adequate stage, to play out the human drama to the full.

REVIEW QUESTIONS IN ASTRONOMY

1. How old is the human race?

2. How old is scientific astronomy?

3. How old is the telescope?

4. How long may the human race expect to live on this earth?

5. What, briefly, is the picture of the universe as presented in the Ptolemaic system?

6. Who finally disproved the Ptolemaic system?

7. What is the date of Galileo's first public demonstration of the telescope?

8. How fast does light travel?

9. According to the "tidal evolution hypothesis," about how old is the Earth?

10. What are the chances of collision in the traffic of the heavenly bodies?

11. About how many "island universes" has the telescope revealed to date?

12. What is the Milky Way?

13. How did the constellations get their names?

14. How big is the Sun, as compared with the other stars?

15. How far away from us is the Sun?

16. What are the "prominences" of the Sun?

17. What is a sunspot?

18. How rapidly is the Sun losing its weight?

19. How long, at this rate, would it take for the Sun to disappear?

20. What is the nature of the Sun?

21. How many planets are there in our solar system?

22. What are their positions, with reference to the Sun?

23. What are the asteroids?

24. Which is the smallest of the planets?

25. Which is the largest?

26. Which of the two planets have no moons?

27. What is the diameter of the Earth?

28. To what peculiarity of the Earth's axis are the various seasons due?

29. How far is the Earth from the Moon?

30. Has the Moon any air or water?

31. How are the tides of the Earth produced?

32. How big is Mars?

33. How long is the Martian year?

34. Has Mars any air or water?

35. Is there any life on Mars?

36. How big is Jupiter?

37. How long is the Jupiter day?

38. How long is the Jupiter year?

39. How many moons has Jupiter?

40. What are the rings of Saturn?

41. Will the Earth ever have such rings?

42. How many moons has Saturn?

43. When was Pluto discovered?

44. What is a comet?

45. What would happen if a comet were to collide with the Earth?

46. What is a meteor?

47. What is the standard astronomical unit for the measurement of space?

48. What, according to the theory of relativity, is time?

49. Are the distances between the heavenly bodies absolute or relative?

50. Will the world ever come to an end?

ANSWERS TO THE QUESTIONS IN ASTRONOMY

1. About three hundred thousand years.

2. About three thousand years.

3. About three hundred years.

4. About two billion years.

5. According to this theory, the Earth is the center of the universe, and all the planets and the stars and the Sun revolve around it.

6. Copernicus.

7. August 21, 1609.

8. 186,000 miles a second.

9. About five thousand million years.

10. The chance for collision between two stars is practically negligible—about one in a million million million years.

11. About two million.

12. A congregation of many stars, or "necklace of light," that encircles the sector of the heavens in which we live.

13. From the Latin names of the animals and men whose shapes resemble the outlines of the various constellations.

14. A mere "dwarf" among the stars.

15. About ninety-three million miles.

16. The geysers of fire that spurt out from the envelope of gases surrounding the Sun.

17. A tornado of flaming gases that whirl over the surface of the Sun but do not spurt out into space.

18. At the rate of a billion tons every four minutes.

19. About fifteen million million years.

20. An envelope of luminous gases on the outside, and an extremely solid core at the center.

21. Nine.

22. Their positions, in the order of their nearness to the Sun, are as follows: Mercury, Venus, the Earth, Mars, Jupiter, Saturn, Uranus, Neptune, Pluto.

23. A multitude of small celestial bodies, situated in the spaces between the orbit of Mars and that of Jupiter.

24. Mercury.

25. Jupiter.

26. Mercury and Venus.

27. About eight thousand miles.

28. To the fact that the axis is tipped from the perpendicular at an angle of 23½ degrees.

29. About 239,000 miles.

30. Most likely, no.

31. By the attraction of the Moon.

32. Its volume is about one eighth of the Earth's volume.

33. About twice as long as our own year.

34. Probably, yes.

35. Our scientific knowledge to date points to no life such as exists on the Earth.

36. About fourteen hundred times the volume of the Earth.

37. About ten hours.

38. About twelve times as long as our own year.

39. Nine—four visible and five invisible.

40. The orbits of innumerable particles which revolve around the planet.

41. Probably, yes.

42. Nine.

43. In 1930.

44. A tenuous body of gases, sand grains, pebbles, and blocks of metal and stone, which travel in a long and narrow orbit over the heavens.

45. Nothing more serious than a dazzling shower of meteors.

46. The tiniest of the solid bodies in the heavens—a mixture of stone and metal and other crystals and minerals—probably the remainders of a disintegrated comet.

47. The light-year—the distance covered in one year by a ray of light traveling at the rate of 186,000 miles a second.

48. The fourth dimension of space—the measurement of space in motion.

49. Relative.

50. So far as science can foretell, yes.

BIOGRAPHICAL SKETCHES OF GREAT ASTRONOMERS

Thales (c. 624–c. 548 B.C.). Greek philosopher. The father of science and philosophy. Born in Miletus, he studied in Egypt and came back to Greece as a teacher of philosophy, geometry, and astronomy. He was the first philosopher to explain the origin of things in reference to natural rather than supernatural causes. Among his contributions to astronomy were his calculations of the length of the year and of the interval between the solstices and the equinoxes. He is believed to have predicted an eclipse of the Sun.

Ptolemy (Claudius Ptolemaeus). Flourished about A.D. 139. He was a native of Egypt and lived for a number of years in Alexandria. Nothing is known about his personal life. He was, however, the last great astronomer of antiquity, and his works were classic textbooks until the fifteenth century. He evolved a theory that the Earth was the center of the universe and around it revolved the Sun, the Moon, and the Stars. His system held sway until it was overturned by the teachings of Copernicus. In addition to his work in astronomy, he constructed twenty-six individual maps and a general map of the world.

Copernicus, Nicolaus (1473–1543). Father of modern astronomy. Born in Prussian Poland, he was brought up at the home of his uncle Lucas, the Bishop of Ermeland. He studied science, the, ology, and medicine at the universities of Cracow, Bologna, and Padua. He settled in Frauenburg, East Prussia, where he had been nominated canon of the cathedral. He is said to have practiced medicine, to have served as town bailiff, military governor, and vicar general. He achieved fame as the author of a treatise describing the Sun as the center of the universe and the Earth as one of the planets revolving around it. This treatise, *De Revolutionibus Orbium Coelestium* (*On the Revolutions of the Celestial Spheres*), is the foundation upon which present astronomy is built. He died a few hours after seeing the first printed copy of his treatise.

Brahe, Tycho (1546–1601). Born in Knudstrup, then a part of Denmark, he lived to become one of the most celebrated astronomers of the sixteenth century. He perfected the instruments of astronomers and added classic data on the position of the planets. He built a famous observatory on the island of Hven, from which he carried out his investigations. His system was a middle-of-the-road compromise between the Ptolemaic and the Copernican. He believed that the Sun revolved around the Earth, but that five planets moved around the Sun. He discovered a new star in the constellation of Cassiopeia, observed the "variation" of the Moon, and was one of the earliest to compute tables of refraction.

Galileo (1564–1642). Born and educated at Pisa, Italy, he was appointed professor of mathematics at the university of that city, where he proved his famous theory that all falling bodies descend with equal velocity. Compelled to resign from the university because of the jealousy of his colleagues, he taught mathematics and astronomy (1592–1610) at the University of Padua. In his lectures he corroborated the view of Copernicus that the Earth moves around the Sun, and made a number of additional important observations about the planets and the stars. He was called to Florence (1610), where he was appointed "philosopher and mathematician extraordinary" to the Grand Duke of Tuscany. Here he continued his "heretical" teachings until the members of the Inquisition compelled him, at the age of seventy, to abjure his scientific creed of the Earth's planetary motion around the Sun. He retired to Arcetri, near Florence, lost his hearing and sight (1637), and continued his researches—in spite of these infirmities—until his death.

Kepler, Johannes (1571–1630). German astronomer. Educated at the University of Tübingen, he became professor of astronomy and mathematics at Graz and subsequently the assistant of Tycho Brahe in his observatory near Prague. Upon the latter's death, he published the results of Brahe's observations, contributing celebrated laws of his own. Among other things, he explained the action of the tides, and he formulated the law that the orbit of each planet is an ellipse. In general, he devoted his life to popularizing the theories of Copernicus.

Römer, Olaus (1644–1710). Danish astronomer, celebrated for his investigations of light. A friend of Newton and Halley, he became royal mathematician and professor of astronomy in Copenhagen. He made an estimate of the velocity of light while observing eclipses of the satellites of Jupiter. He revealed that light, far from traveling instantaneously through the universe, takes a definite amount of time in its movement. Among other things, he devised the first valuable transit instrument for measuring the movement of stars.

Halley, Edmund (1656–1742). British astronomer. He is celebrated for having calculated the orbit of the comet of 1682, which bears his name. In 1676 he traveled to St. Helena, and he catalogued 341 stars of the Southern Hemisphere. He was friendly with Newton and at his own expense published the great physicist's *Principia.* He identified the comet of 1682 as the one recognized in 1305, 1456, 1531, and 1607. He predicted its return in 1757. Actually he miscalculated its reappearance by two years. He became royal astronomer in 1720, and for the next eighteen years he carried on highly significant investigations dealing with the revolutions of the Moon.

Herschel, Sir William (1738–1822). British astronomer. Outstanding student of the stars. Born in Hanover, Germany, he went to England as a young man and became a music teacher. During his spare time he studied astronomy and constructed telescopes with which he investigated the sky. On March 13, 1781, he discovered a new planet, afterward called Uranus. Chosen astronomer to King George III, he built a telescope with a 48-inch mirror and a focal length of 40 feet. He penetrated the vast reaches of space, discovering the sixth and seventh satellites of Saturn. He catalogued over eight hundred double stars and conducted important researches in the field of nebulae.

Laplace, Pierre Simon, Marquis de (1749–1827). French astronomer. He rose to high positions in the service of his country. He became professor of mathematics in the Ecole Militaire of Paris. He was appointed vice-president and chancellor of the Senate. He served as president of the Académie Française. As an astronomer and mathematician, he devoted his life to finding an answer to the mechanical problem of the universe. The result of his research, which established the truth of Newton's theory of gravitation, was published in his celebrated work, *Mécanique Céleste.* His name is associated with the nebular hypothesis. He contributed classic data on the theory of the satellites, the motions of the Moon, Jupiter and Saturn, and the theory of the tides.

Huggins, Sir William (1824–1910). British astronomer. He devoted his life to the study of the chemical constitution of stars by spectrum analysis. He was a pioneer in the use of the spectroscope. Carrying on his investigations from an observatory at upper Tulse Hill, London, he learned from the spectra of certain comets that the principal part of the light was emitted by luminous vapor of carbon. He discovered that the light of certain nebulae came from a mass of glowing gases. He was one of the first to delve into spectroscopic photography, obtaining an image of the spectrum of Sirius. Among other things he developed a method of examining areas of the Sun. He was knighted in 1897. From 1900 to 1905 he served as president of the Royal Society.

Jeans, Sir James Hopwood (1877–1946). British astronomer and physicist. Born in London, he was educated at Cambridge University. He taught applied mathematics at Princeton and Cambridge universities from 1905 to 1912, and was later professor of astronomy at the Royal Institution. He is known for his work in the application of mathematics to astronomy and physics and for his gaseous-tidal hypothesis for the origin of the Earth, which he developed with Harold A. Jeffreys. He has written a number of books which popularize science.

CAREERS IN ASTRONOMY

Astronomy is a field for scholars. In most cases a degree of Ph.D. is desirable, and the period of professional training in astronomy is as lengthy as in medicine. The most qualified astronomers usually teach at universities or direct a limited number of observatories throughout the world. In addition, the government provides opportunities for astronomers with the National Almanac and for consultants in the Navy Department. There is a civil service rating for junior astronomers whose duties consist chiefly of laboratory observations, assisting with publications, and caring for equipment.

Generally speaking, astronomy is a field for students who are not too demanding of material awards. There are opportunities for women as well as for men.

While long years of education are usually a prerequisite for the profession, there have been instances of amateur astronomers achieving recognition. Clyde Tombaugh, one of America's foremost astronomers, was the son of an impoverished Kansas farmer. He entered the field as an amateur, studied the heavens with self-made equipment, and was invited to assist at an Arizona observatory. Here he discovered a new planet—Pluto—at the age of twenty-four. As a result he was awarded a scholarship at the University of Kansas, where he proceeded to train himself academically.

BIBLIOGRAPHY: BOOKS ON ASTRONOMY FOR FURTHER READING AND STUDY

Baker, Robert Horace: *Astronomy: A Textbook for University and College Students.* New York, 1946.
——: *Introduction to Astronomy.* New York, 1947.
Bartky, Walter: *Highlights of Astronomy.* Chicago, 1935.

Barton, William Henry, Jr., and Joseph Maron Joseph: *Starcraft*. New York, 1938.

Beet, Ernest Agar: *A Textbook of Elementary Astronomy*. Cambridge.

Bergh, G. Van den: *Astronomy for the Millions*, tr. from the Dutch by Joan C. H. Marshall and Th. de Vrijer. New York, 1937.

Chant, Clarence Augustus: *Our Wonderful Universe*. London, 1940.

Duncan, John Charles: *Astronomy: A Text Book*. New York, 1946.

Fath, Edward Arthur: *Elements of Astronomy*. New York, 1946.

Grondal, Florence Armstrong: *The Romance of Astronomy*. New York, 1937.

Grover, Frederick Warren: *The Pageant of the Heavens*. London and New York.

Jacoby, Harold: *Astronomy*. New York, 1929.

Jeans, Sir James Hopwood: *The Stars in Their Courses*. 1931.

——: *Through Space and Time*. New York, 1934.

——: *The Universe Around Us*. New York, 1944.

Moulton, Forest Ray: *Astronomy*. New York, 1931.

——: *Consider the Heavens*. New York, 1935.

Newcomb, Simon: *Astronomy for Everybody*. New York.

Pendray, Edward: *Men, Mirrors, and Stars*. New York, 1946.

Phillips, Theodore E. R., and W. H. Steavenson: *Splendor of the Heavens*. London and New York.

Reichenbach, Hans: *From Copernicus to Einstein*, tr. by Ralph B. Winn. New York, 1942.

Shapley, Harlow: *The Universe of Stars*. Cambridge, Mass., 1929.

—— and H. E. Howorth: *A Source Book in Astronomy*. New York, 1929.

Skilling, William T., and Robert G. Richardson: *Sun, Moon, and Stars*. New York, 1946.

Smart, William Marshall: *Astronomy*. London.

Stetson, Harlan True: *Man and the Stars*. New York, 1930.

Thomas, Oswald: *Heaven and Earth*, tr. by Bernard Miall. New York, 1930.

Williams, Henry Smith: *The Great Astronomers*. New York, 1930.

Wylie, Charles Clayton: *Astronomy*. New York, 1942.

CHAPTER TWO

geology—the story of the earth

THE BIRTH OF OUR PLANET

Our Earth is—so to speak—a "blood relation" to the stars. For all of them are composed of the same substances and are derived from a single source.

There are various theories as to the origin of the Earth. The one that is most widely accepted, as we have already noted, is the so-called *tidal wave theory*. At some time in the past—about five thousand million years ago—a great star came too close to a little star in the course of its journey. This "near collision"— actually they were millions of miles apart at the moment—produced a tremendous tide of gases upon the surface of the smaller star, now known as the Sun. The tide stretched out like an arm of fire toward the gravitational pull of the larger star. And then, as the pull became irresistible, the arm was wrenched away from its parent star. But not too far away. As the larger star receded, its attraction grew less and less powerful, and the disconnected filaments of gas became "tied into several knots" that fell once more under the attraction of the Sun. And thus began the separate existence of the solar planets and of their elliptical revolution around the Sun.

At first the particles of these globular knots were much more tenuous than they are today. They were held together by mutual attraction. But little by little they became "cemented" into solid spheres.

And they were continually being bombarded by the "leftovers" from the tidal wave that had been swept into space by the passing of the great star. This bombardment is believed to have continued for many thousands of years. And thus the solar planets "grew" in size from birth to maturity. The Earth, for example, possessed at the outset—all this, of course, is theory—a diameter of only about two or three thousand miles.

According to this theory, the Earth at first consisted of gaseous matter. Later it became condensed into liquid; and still later, solidified into rock.

And thus the Earth began as a chunk of the Sun, and it grew to its present proportions through the gradual admixture of star dust into its caldron of boiling rocks.

But how did the Earth get its air and its water? They came, according to the theory advanced by Professors Chamberlin and Moulton, from outside the Earth. At first there was no atmosphere above the Earth and no moisture upon its surface, for the Earth was too small to attract the molecules that could be combined into air and water. But as the Earth grew larger, it began to draw these particles out of the depths of space. And thus the Earth became covered with a mantle of air, and the air became saturated with clouds. And the clouds dissolved, and the rain fell upon the Earth and poured into the hollows and turned them into lakes and rivers and oceans.

According to this theory, therefore, our planet originally was all land. And the seas at first were very much smaller than they are at present. But gradually they grew larger and larger until there were only narrow bridges of land holding the continents together. Finally these bridges disappeared under the spreading waters and the land became separated into the "island continents" of Eurasia and Africa and America and the many smaller islands that protrude above the surface of the sea.

This is merely one of several theories. Yet there is ample scientific evidence to sustain the hypothesis of a single continent or at least of a group of continents connected by a number of land strips. The bones of the same prehistoric animals—such as the dinosaur, for example—have been discovered both in the Eastern and in the Western hemispheres. Also the fossils of the same kinds of plants have been found in all the continents under similar conditions of climate and soil. It is inconceivable that a separate process of evolution created the same sorts of animals and plants in separate continents at about the same time. It is equally inconceivable that the dinosaurs swam across the ocean or that the seeds were carried across by the waves or the winds. The most plausible deduction, therefore, is that in prehistoric times the continents were not separated by the ocean but formed a single continuous body of land.

THE MIGRATIONS OF THE CONTINENTS

One day in 1910 the German meteorologist, Alfred Wegener, was examining the maps of Africa and of South America, when he was struck with an interesting idea. *These two continents looked as if they had once been together and had drifted apart.*

"He who examines the opposite coasts of the South Atlantic Ocean," wrote Wegener, "must be somewhat surprised by the similarity of the shapes of the coast-lines of Brazil and Africa." These two coast lines *complement* each other. They can be fitted

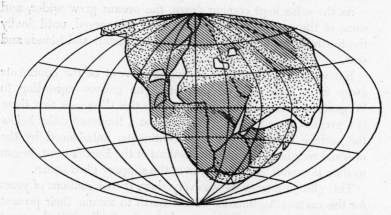

How the large land masses of the Earth appeared millions of years ago, according to the Theory of the Displacement of Continents.

together, like the pieces of a Chinese puzzle, to make a *complete whole*. "Every projection on the Brazilian side corresponds to a similarly-shaped indentation on the African side; and, conversely, every indentation on the Brazilian side has its corresponding projection on the African." It is as if a single sheet of paper had been irregularly torn in half. So closely, indeed, do the two coast lines dovetail into each other that "experiment with a compass on a globe shows the dimensions [of the projections and their corresponding indentations] to be in perfect agreement."

Shortly after making his observation, Professor Wegener came across a book in which the author discussed the similarities in the prehistoric plant and animal life of Africa and of South America. All these factors, Professor Wegener concluded, seemed to point to a definite theory. He formulated it as the *theory of the displacement of continents*. Briefly stated, this displacement hypothesis is as follows:

The Earth, in its formative period, consisted of one united continent dotted here and there with a river, a lake, or an inland sea. South America and Africa were one continuous stretch of land. Later on, as the rains came down, a narrow stream began to flow in their midst. And then the two banks began to drift apart like two drifting icebergs. South America floated away to the west of Africa. And, in a similar manner, North America floated away to the west of Europe.

As the rains kept coming down, the oceans grew wider, and some of the smaller tracts of land were submerged, until finally the Earth assumed its present form of continents and islands and seas.

But what was the cause of this movement of the continents away from their original position? The answer—according to Wegener and the others who adhere to this theory—is that there is a great ocean of "molten glass" about a thousand miles below the surface of the Earth. The continents, unbalanced by the unequal weight of the various portions of the Earth's crust, began to *slide downhill*, so to speak, over the slippery glass ocean.

This gliding movement was very slow. It took millions of years for the various "landmarks" of the Earth to assume their present positions. And these positions are being gradually shifted around even at the present time.

In this continual shifting, believe the adherents of the displacement theory, there is a corresponding commotion in the Earth's crust. At some points where the land glides against a barrier at the bottom of the sea, there is a tremendous pressure which results in the upheaval of a mountain chain like the Andes or the Rockies. At other points the grinding of the Earth in its motion may force a mountain to crumble into dust or the surface to be split asunder for an inrush of the sea. All this would explain the presence of sea shells on mountaintops. These mountaintops were once covered with water but have been "hoisted up" by the pressure of the moving continents against the sea.

This theory—and it is far from established as yet—would discard the older explanation of the origin of the mountain chains. According to the older theory, the mountains resulted from the shriveling of the Earth's surface, just as a baked apple shrivels as it cools. In any case, the Earth's surface is not static but dynamic. Mountains, like flowers, unfold and fold up again and are crumbled into dust. And there is nothing permanent under the sun.

The crust of the Earth—and this is pretty well established—is warping all the time. Some parts of it, like the Pacific coast, for example, are rising at the present time; and other parts, like the Atlantic coast, are sinking. But there is no immediate ground for apprehension on the part of those of us who live in Boston or Baltimore or New York. For these cities will remain above the sea for many, many centuries to come. At one time—millions of years ago, perhaps—Manhattan was a mountain whose summit was considerably higher than the top of the Empire State Building. And the Hudson River tumbled over a precipice into the sea. But the mountain was leveled, and the waterfall straightened out, in the everlasting shift of the scenery that decorates the revolving stage of our tragicomedy called Life.

THE FOUR ICE AGES

For reasons which the scientists have not as yet been able to explain—another of the many gaps in the continuity of our human knowledge—the Earth has been visited by four extensive periods of glacial weather. At those periods enormous formations of ice gathered at the poles and kept spreading toward the equator until they covered the greater part of the Earth's surface. At times these blankets of ice reached a thickness of several thousand feet. We know this from the fact that there are regions in British Columbia where the traces of ice can still be seen upon the mountains a mile above the level of the surrounding plain.

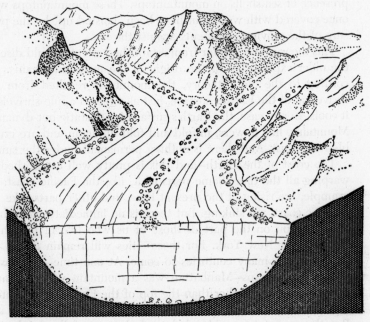

A glacier in the Swiss Alps. In time the mass of ice will move on, leaving a deep, smooth surface.

These four great freezes—known as *Ice Ages*—came at periods that were millions of years apart; and each of them lasted more than a thousand centuries. The fourth of these cold periods, the *Pleistocene Ice Age,* is still upon us. We seem to be passing through the closing phases of this global freeze. When it is completely over, the Arctic regions will probably be warm enough for human habitation, and the North Pole may become transformed into a garden of roses. Such is but one of the many prospects held out for us by the stranger-than-fiction forecasts of our scientific investigators.

But if the Arctic regions should become *habitable* in the final melting of the icecaps, many regions of the present Temperate Zone would become *uninhabitable,* for the melted ice would have raised the level of the oceans by about one hundred feet; and cities like Boston and London and Los Angeles and New York would have become completely submerged.

This prospect, however, is a long way off—perhaps twenty-five or even fifty thousand years. For many generations to come, our seasonal climates and our present earth levels are likely to remain unchanged.

THE FORMATION OF LAKES AND RIVERS

When the height of the glacial season had passed, the ice began to recede. That is, it began to melt at the edges. And the waters, as they trickled down from the diminishing icecaps—this process took thousands of years to develop—finally turned into a succession of cataracts and filled all the hollows in the Earth as they rushed over its surface. The pools thus formed by the melting ice kept on being replenished by the streams that tumbled into them continually along the narrow clefts of the Earth. And in turn, as the water kept rising in the lakes, it o 'erflowed their shores at the lowest points and formed a succession of new rivers.

This process is still continuing, so that, as times goes on, old lakes are emptying themselves into new rivers, old rivers are running dry, and old glaciers are melting into the hollows of the Earth to form new lakes. Thus, to paraphrase the words of Tennyson's *Brook* and to make the poet's meaning more scientifically correct, "waters may come and waters may go, but *the process of change* goes on forever."

To take but a single example: at one time the region now covered by Lake Erie and Lake Ontario was a sheet of solid ice. So, too, was the area now known as Niagara Falls. When the ice melted, the two lakes were formed in the hollows, and the surface of the land between them was comparatively dry. At least it had no enormous waterfall. But later on, as the two hollows became overfilled, Lake Erie began to flow out in the direction of Lake Ontario. Now somewhere along the course of this outflow the water started to fall over a precipice—at first in a slender stream, then in a small cascade, and finally in a mighty cataract that developed into the present majesty of Niagara Falls.

Thus far Lake Erie has emptied itself to such an extent that its greatest depth is only 210 feet as compared to the depth of Lake Superior, which reaches down to a maximum of about 1100 feet. In time to come—not too long a time on the geological scale —Niagara Falls will have disappeared and Lake Erie will have become a stream valley—an extension of the Niagara River.

The above is but a general outline of the story of such bodies of water as Lake Erie and Niagara Falls. It takes into account only a few of the many factors that went into their creation, their present form, and their future possibilities. In the entire field of geology, as of all the other branches of science, we are dealing with a bushel of theories based upon a thimbleful of facts. Thus our geologists have unearthed the fact that the rocks at the bottom of the Great Lakes were not always covered with water. They have found definite "landmarks" upon these rocks. And they have further evidence of traces left upon the surrounding regions by the recession of melted glaciers. It is upon these and similar facts that they have built up their largely conjectural picture of the rivers and the waterfalls and the lakes.

As time goes on, and more and more facts become available, the picture grows more distinct and emerges gradually out of the realm of theoretical imagination into the province of scientific knowledge. Our present picture of the creation of the inland waters —a picture which has been reinforced by considerable scientific evidence within recent times—is that of a glacial process taking hundreds of millions of years, modeling the clay surface of the Earth, filling up the hollows, scooping out the river beds, and hurling the cataracts over the precipices. A glacial period comes and goes, the face of the Earth is subjected to a new massage, and the features become completely changed—until the treatment of the next glacial period. Thanks to the grinding and the melting of the Earth's gigantic icecaps, our planet presents a kaleidoscope of ever-changing variety.

And of never-resting power. The mightiest mechanical shovel devised by the brain of man is as nothing compared to the melting prong of a glacier. With a single scoop—geologically speaking, of course—the glacier plows into the Earth, and the Mississippi with all its tributaries is born. Another scoop of the ice shovel, and the sea carves out the channel of Long Island Sound. For each of the ice prongs—known geologically as *lobes*—carries along with it a pressure of billions of tons as it melts.

And—this is very important—the melting takes hundreds of thousands of years. What makes the power of the Earth so tremendous is not only the weight of its pressure but the duration of its activity. Even a drop of water can dissolve a rock, if repeated consecutively over a long enough period. Time and motion are the parents of all change.

As to the causes that produced the four Ice Ages, and as to the question whether there will be any more Ice Ages in the future, the scientists are still in the dark.

THE EARTH'S CRUST

The crust of the Earth, from the top of the highest mountain to the greatest depth of solid rock underneath the surface, is about thirty miles thick.

This crust, or outer shell, consists mainly of two types of substance: light rock, such as granite, and heavy rock, such as basalt. The surface of the crust reaches different levels at different places, depending upon the weight of the rocks. The heavier rocks press down to produce the depressions covered by the sea. The lighter rocks remain on top and, as the sagging at the bottom continues, become grouped into mountain chains.

And thus the continents may be regarded as ships—with the mountain peaks as their masts—that "ride above the sea" because their material is lighter than the material sunk underneath the ocean floor.

But how was the surface crust formed in the first place? By the cooling of our molten planet after its departure from the Sun.

The chemical elements upon the surface became gradually crystallized into minerals and solidified into rock. The minerals —there are about two thousand of them—are (as a rule) built upon a definite pattern. Their crystals possess not only a symmetrical outline but an atomic symmetry—a regular design— in their internal structure. But the non-crystalline substances of the Earth's surface are composed of atoms that are heaped together very much like piles of bricks, without any structural design.

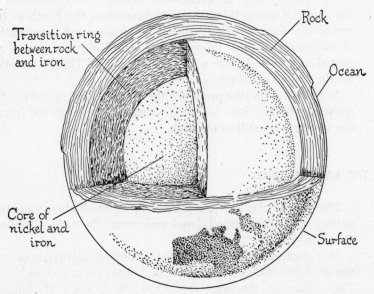

What the interior of the Earth may look like. It is thought that materials making up the Earth are relatively light near the crust and grow heavier and heavier toward the center.

In addition to the hard substances of the crust we have the softer materials—mud and clay and soil and sand. These are disintegrated rocks, "ashes" of minerals and mountains that have been pulverized into dust.

And thus the bedrock of the crust, as it undergoes its process of weathering, becomes covered with a mantle soft enough and varied enough to sustain life.

But the weathering of the rocks *from above* is only half of the story regarding the Earth's crust. The other half of the story is the transformation of the rocks *from below*. The tremendous pressure at the "roots" of the rocks, the activity of the fires within the Earth, and the gases and the lava erupting through the surface from the molten matter underneath—all these factors continually change the rocks from one type to another.

Thus, for example, limestone as it undergoes the alchemy of nature becomes transformed into richly tinted marble. Volcanic ashes are sheared into slates of silvery green. Carbon becomes crystallized into diamonds. Basalt is carved out of lava and finally chiseled, as in the Giant's Causeway and in Fingal's Cave, into huge prismatic columns of brown or greenish black. And sandstone is compounded out of "secondhand" material—remnants of disintegrating quartz and mica and feldspar cemented into a new substance by the perpetual interlocking of the elements.

And so we find the crust of the Earth to consist of an upper layer of soil or sand, a platform of lighter rocks that have stretched up to various levels above the surface of the water, and a flooring of heavier rocks that have settled down to the bottom. Our next step is to read the history of the Earth as we see it engraved upon the pages of the rocks.

SERMONS IN STONES

The trained geologist can read a rock as easily as you and I can read a book. For example, when he sees in a limestone the fossil traces of corals or of sea shells, he knows that formerly this stone was part of an ocean floor and that the surrounding land, therefore, was once submerged under the waves. Or when he sees in a pile of rocks a column of glassy basalt, he knows that at some time in the past there was an active volcano in the vicinity.

In the syllables inscribed upon the rocks by the hand of time the geologist can decipher the story of evaporated oceans and melted glaciers and desiccated lakes. In the arteries of coal under

the Earth's surface he can read the biography of dead and buried
forests once teeming with luxuriant growth. And in the craterlike
pittings of the more pliable rocks he can see the recorded foot-
prints of the rain.

The geologist can understand the changing face of the Earth;
and he can trace the course, if not always the cause, of these
changes. He knows, for instance, that the climate in England was
not always mild. For he finds, in the excavations made for the
London tubes, fossils of tropical vegetation and reptiles and
shells. And he knows, too, that the weather in Central Africa was
not always hot. For he has discovered, even in the densest of its
jungles, the traces of prehistoric glaciers.

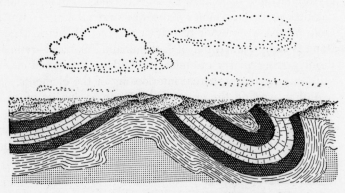

*A cross section of a mountainous region. The shading represents
layers of rock more durable than the unshaded portions. The durable rock was better able to withstand the effect of wind and water;
this accounts for the unevenness of the surface.*

The rocks have been compared, in this section, to the pages of
a book. This comparison is even more scientific than poetical. For
a good many of the rocks are *stratified.* That is, they are piled
up, layer upon layer, just like the sheets of a manuscript. And
often the worn-down edges of the various layers protrude so
distinctly one above the other that it is possible to read the
consecutive messages written down upon them by the passing
centuries.

And thus the ages pile up their record, layer upon layer upon layer. Every page tells the story of its period; and very often the story is illustrated by the fossils embedded in the rock. "The principle of identifying the ages of strata by their fossils," writes Professor Arthur Holmes, "has now been firmly established all over the world." When we find the same fossils in various rocks distributed throughout the world, we know that all these rocks tell a story of the selfsame period. And thus we can get a pretty good idea of the general condition of the Earth during that period.

And by means of the *different* fossils found in the various layers of the rocks we can get a general picture of the passage of geological time. In the book of the Earth, every rock page begins the chapter of a new epoch.

THE BREATHING OF THE EARTH'S SURFACE

Many geologists believe that they have discovered a definite rhythm in the surface changes of the Earth. There is a regularity in the rising and the falling of land waves as well as of sea waves. The rocks of Utah and Nevada, for example, contain the evidence of lakes that covered them on more than one occasion. This would mean, most likely, that the Earth in such regions—and perhaps elsewhere—has contracted and expanded in a motion similar to that of a breathing creature. When the Earth contracted, the hollows were filled with water; when it expanded, the water spilled over. And these motions—each of them covering a period of perhaps millions of years—were repetitious. In other words, the so-called *changes* of the Earth are in reality *cyclical oscillations*.

Moreover, these oscillations of the Earth's surface appear to take place upon a basis of regulated balances. Underneath the solid crust of the Earth, according to this theory, there is a layer of plastic rock in a semimolten state. The Earth's crust, as it floats over this elastic "sea of glass," exerts a great pressure upon it. At every point where the downward pressure is heaviest, the matter below is pushed away to find an outlet at some point where the pressure is lighter. And at the new outlet the lower layer in turn begins to press against the upper crust. In this way there is a tendency on the part of the Earth to maintain a constant equilibrium. A depression in one region produces a bulge in another region. The heavier rocks of the Earth descend into a gorge, the lighter rocks rise into a mountain, and the Earth is kept moving along on an even keel, and continually "breathing" as it moves. For the crust is always contracting somewhere and expanding somewhere else.

UNDERGROUND WATERS

Until recent times there was a theory to the effect that water, when it entered the Earth, kept going down until the steam in the interior turned it into vapor and sent it back to the surface. This theory has been abandoned except for such areas as contain hot beds of lava. In these areas the water that flows into the Earth spurts up again in the form of geysers. Elsewhere on the Earth, where there is no lava close to the surface, the water seeps into the ground and remains embedded in the crust. For the rocks at the bottom of the crust are so solid that the water cannot penetrate them to the semimolten layer underneath. Thus there is very little moisture to be found in most mine shafts below the one-mile level.

The water that flows into the non-volcanic areas of the Earth keeps percolating through the pores and the fissures of the rocks. It gathers into reservoirs, or flows off into subterranean rivers, or seeps along a slope in the Earth's crust until it trickles out in a spring on the hillside.

Some of these springs and subterranean rivers empty into the ocean underneath its surface. Silver Spring in Florida is the mouth of such an undersurface river.

A cross section of "Old Faithful" geyser in Yellowstone National Park. Water, heated by lava, enters the bottom of the geyser and rises to a point about forty-five feet below the surface. Here it generates steam, which blows the water above it high into the air.

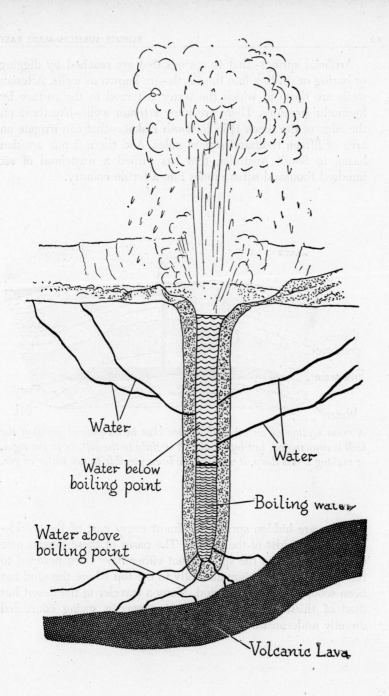

Artificial springs—that is, springs that are reached by digging or boring or drilling into the Earth—are known as *wells*. Artesian wells are those in which the water is forced to the surface by hydraulic pressure. There are some artesian wells—like those on the edge of the Black Hills in South Dakota—that can irrigate an area of fifteen thousand square miles. And there is one artesian basin, in South Australia, that has turned a wasteland of six hundred thousand square miles into a fertile country.

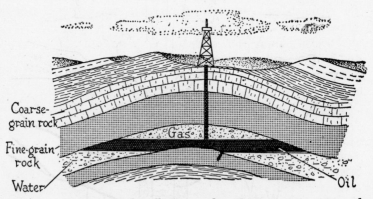

A cross section of an oil well. Notice that in its present position the well is drawing oil, but by locating it slightly to the left, or to the right, or making it less deep, it would have been possible to tap water or gas.

There are hidden springs in almost every part of the world—even in the midst of the deserts. The oases of these deserts owe their vegetation to the springs that either have been pumped to the surface or have risen naturally to the top where the sand has been scooped out by the wind. Many a traveler in the desert has died of thirst with his head resting over a spring concealed directly underneath.

SUBTERRANEAN CAVERNS AND PALACES

When the rain water seeps into the rocks underneath the Earth's surface it acts as a carrier for the various chemicals that it has gathered up from the soil. These chemicals flow along with the water through the fissures of the crust, decomposing the softer portions and seeking for a natural drainage along the flooring of the harder rocks, until they find an exit—sometimes at a very great distance from the start.

Then fresh waters, with new supplies of chemicals, pour along the channels carved out by the original current. The channels grow wider and more varied, branching out into new directions and seeking always for additional passages and exits. And thus the Earth's crust becomes honeycombed with a network of tunnels and grottoes and caverns—a world underneath the world.

One of the most striking of these subterranean networks is the Mammoth Cave of Kentucky, with its decorative tapestry of stone. This cave consists of a number of connecting chambers, covering an area of thousands of acres—almost an entire city in extent. And its underground scenery is as varied as that of a city above the ground—with its squares and its streets, its rivers and its reservoirs, its fountains and its bridges, its castles and cathedrals and domes. Some of the chambers of this fantastic "underland" are festooned with *stalactites* ("icicles" of stone), and their floors are adorned with *stalagmites* ("candelabra" built up from rock deposited by chemical action).

Another famous example of this subterranean architecture is the Carlsbad Cavern in New Mexico. The "King's Chamber" of this "Underground Palace" is 4000 feet long, 600 feet wide, and 300 feet high. And its decoration is beyond the fantasy of the most gifted of stage designers. Minarets and statues and pyramids and totem poles and thrones—a gigantic jewel box of the nether world.

There is a continual shifting of scenery in this enormous underground drama of rivers and rocks. When the water has worn away the roof of a cavern, the structure collapses, and new cisterns and tunnels and gorges and ravines are carved out to replace the old. Sometimes only a part of the roof breaks down, and a natural bridge is left hanging over the chasm some thousands of feet in depth. At other times the water, as it tumbles down the cavern, changes its direction from the harder to the softer rock. But it leaves its mark upon the wall over which it has recently traveled, and we have what has often been described as a "frozen cascade."

In short the caverns in the rocks are (again geologically speaking) as transitional as the hollows in a cloud. The only difference between the melting of a cloud and the fusion of a rock is the matter of relative speed.

RIVERS, VALLEYS, AND LANDSLIDES

The tendency of land, like that of water, is to flow downward. For both alike are subject to the attraction of gravity. In order that a river may form, there are two necessary conditions: a sufficient supply of water and an adequate slope.

The water of a river is supplied entirely by the rain and the snow. (Some rivers, to be sure, originate in glaciers; but the moisture that freezes into a glacier comes first to the Earth in the form of snow.) And the course of a river is determined by the

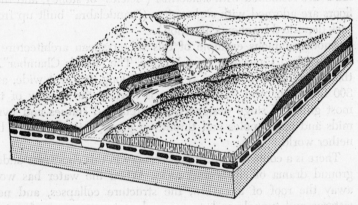

Diagram showing how a river has worn a deep canyon into formerly level terrain.

downward warping of the Earth's crust. In some cases, like that of the Mississippi and the Congo, the slope is ready-made for the downflow. In a good many other cases, however, the rivers and their tributaries must dig out their own channels as they drain down toward their outlet.

The general drainage of a river is from the hillside to the sea. And its general development depends upon the rainfall, the grading of the slope, and one other factor—the consistency of the rocks over which it flows. A soft rock will readily erode and make room for a widening of the channel; but a hard rock will offer a resistance that tends to dam up the flow of the water.

As the river travels down its channel it carries along with it a continual cargo of "rock waste"—disintegrated minerals which it gathers up in its course or which the rain washes into its current.

As the rock waste continues to be carried away by the river, the slopes upon the banks gradually "dissolve" into the current, and a valley is thus formed along the course.

But here and there, throughout the valley, there are rocks and ridges too stubborn for the water to erode. Therefore the valley becomes cut up into various levels and begins to present a diversified landscape to the eye. In time, however, even the harder rocks undergo the process of erosion, and the scenery keeps on changing until the entire land is brought down to a uniform level. This gradual process is called the *cycle of erosion*.

Thus the land and the rivers move always downward to the sea. Even where there are no rivers present there is a continual downslope movement of the Earth. This is brought about by the rainfall, the frost, the undersurface activity of various living organisms such as worms and moles, and the force of gravity. We frequently see examples of this slow-motion picture of a hillside—the tilted fences, the warping walls, the curving tree trunks just above the roots. All these objects are temporarily "suspended" in the course of their descent.

When the hillside is formed over a steep incline, and the accumulation of the unbalancing forces has reached the final thrust, the soil and the rocks are propelled into a gigantic landslip known as an *avalanche*.

Sometimes it is possible to forecast the approach of an avalanche and by proper timing to avert the loss of many lives. At about the beginning of this century, for example, a narrow crack was observed on a mountainside near Bellinzona, Italy. Several years later the crack had developed into a fissure about six feet wide. But the widening had been so gradual that no immediate danger was apprehended. The measurements were taken several times a day, and every significant change was carefully noted. Then one day in 1927 the fissure was observed to have suddenly extended to about fifteen feet. The mountain was definitely in motion. A warning was broadcast for the danger zone to be evacuated. When the avalanche descended, two days later, all the inhabitants and their livestock had been removed to a place of safety.

And thus, as we observe, there is nothing that is permanently solid in the world. Everything flows. The rivers of water dissolve the "rivers of rock," and everything is finally carried down to

Two stages in the formation of a plateau by erosion of surrounding land.

the sea. The amount of soil that is being freighted annually into the ocean is almost *three billion tons.*

But we need not get unduly alarmed over this picture. For the average thickness of the Earth's crust that is being thus dumped into the ocean is only about one foot in thirty thousand years. At this rate it will take a matter of seventy million years before the Earth becomes entirely submerged.

VOLCANOES AND EARTHQUAKES

Of greater immediate danger—to some of us—is the possibility of volcanic eruptions and of earthquakes.

Volcanoes are treacherous things. Some of them, apparently dead for several hundred years, come unexpectedly to life again. In the fall of 1538 a quiet valley near the Bay of Naples suddenly burst into flame. Within a week a new "mountain" of lava, almost five hundred feet high, had risen above the plain. It was the re-awakened upheaval of a volcano whose cone had been worn away and whose very existence had been forgotten.

A similar eruption of an "extinct" volcano took place in Mexico in the fall of 1759. The scene was a level plateau covered with sugar plantations and indigo. It was about thirty-five miles away from the nearest known volcano. The eruption—or rather, the series of eruptions—lasted several months; and at the end of the period there were six new mountains towering above the plateau. Twenty years later it was still possible to light a cigar in the lava a few inches below the surface.

These volcanic eruptions may sometimes occur in the middle of the ocean, or even in the ice fields near the poles. And the lava does not necessarily come out of a crater at the mountain-top. Indeed, it is not the volcano that produces the eruption; it is the eruption that produces the volcano. To be more exact, the volcano builds its mountain, or cone, as a result of its eruption. The eruption may spurt out of a mountaintop, or it may shoot up through the level ground. The explosion takes place wherever there is a sufficient pressure of gases and molten rocks to tear apart the surface.

Among the most devastating of these surface explosions within

historic times were the eruption of Mount Vesuvius in A.D. 79,
and of Mount Pelée, on the island of Martinique, in 1902. The
first of these eruptions obliterated two entire cities—Hercu-
laneum and Pompeii—and killed almost half a million people; the
second wiped out the city of St. Pierre and took a toll of thirty
thousand lives.

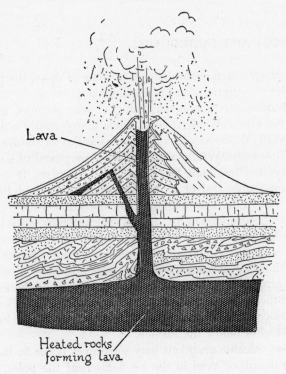

Lava

Heated rocks
forming lava

A cross section of a volcano.

Yet the totality of destruction due to volcanoes is but a drop
in the ocean as compared to the destructiveness of war. Many
generations may live under the shadow of a Vesuvius without
experiencing a single eruption. But there is hardly a generation
anywhere that has not been exposed to the explosion of at least
one war.

At the present time there are about five hundred active volcanoes in the world. Two thirds of them are situated on the shores and on the islands of the Pacific. Several of them are scattered over the Mediterranean region. The Atlantic coast is comparatively free of volcanic hazards. Yet in the middle of the Atlantic there are several islands—the Cape Verde group, Iceland, St. Helena, the Azores, the Canaries—which contain a number of extinct or still active volcanoes.

The region of extinct volcanoes, indeed, is almost world-wide. Deposits of lava, the sputum of extinct volcanoes, are to be found in eastern and central Canada, in Wisconsin, Wyoming, Minnesota, Washington, Colorado, New Mexico, Oregon, New Jersey, Germany, Scotland, France, England, and the diamond fields of South Africa.

A volcano becomes extinct when the supply of gas underneath the fissure has been exhausted, and the lava immediately over it has solidified into a stopper that plugs up the bottleneck of the flow. But it sometimes happens that a fresh supply of gas accumulates—over a period of thousands of years perhaps—and finally blows off the stopper at the surface. Thus a volcano that has been regarded as extinct for many centuries may suddenly explode into a new eruption.

Sometimes the eruption of a volcano emits gases or cinders instead of lava. Thus, in 1912, the volcano Katmai, in Alaska, hurled into the air a column of ashes which darkened an area of about ten thousand square miles for almost three days. An even more violent explosion of vapor and ashes, in 1883, disintegrated two thirds of the island of Krakatao, near Sumatra, blew a cubic mile of rock into dust, and scattered it over the world so that nearly every country experienced dusky sunsets for almost half a year.

And thus the cinders of a single eruption may sometimes travel around the Earth. An explosive stroke of Nature's brush, and the entire color of the Earth is changed.

And also its shape. For the Earth, let us remember, keeps constantly "breathing." Its surface, like the surface of the sea, keeps rising and falling all the time. As a rule, this rising and falling of the Earth's crust is imperceptible because the motion is very slow. But sometimes it can be observed within the course of a few centuries. Thus about two thousand years ago the Romans built a temple on the seashore near Naples. After a time the worshipers began to notice that the temple was slowly sinking, like a ship in the ocean. This sinking continued for several generations until the marble columns were surrounded by sea water to a depth of twenty-one feet. And the process went on until the entire temple disappeared in the sea.

Then it began to rise again. In 1741 the roof became visible above the surface of the water. The rising continued until 1835, when it began to sink once more—a downward process which has been going on to the present day.

This up-and-down movement of the Earth's crust is more rapid in some places than in others. Thus the Italian island of Palmarola, in the Adriatic Sea, rose over two hundred feet in three quarters of a century. Sometimes the rise is very sudden, especially in an earthquake. One such earthquake lifted the shore of Disenchantment Bay, in Alaska, almost fifty feet in the space of a few minutes. And, while some parts of the world rise in an earthquake, other parts sink. In 1762 an area of sixty square miles dropped below sea level during an earthquake on the coast of India.

Earthquakes are much more frequent than is commonly supposed. Every year about thirty thousand of them are actually felt and many more thousands are recorded by seismographs. There is no region in the world—and no hour of the day—that is altogether free from these incessant tremors.

An earthquake in Chile as recorded on a seismograph thousands of miles away in Harvard University.

But there are certain sections—or belts—which are most frequently exposed to the recurrence of violent upheavals. These are the sections of active and of passive volcanoes—the Pacific area, the Atlantic islands, and in general those regions where "very high mountains tower above very deep valleys." For these regions are so far out of balance that their surface is continually subject to "equilibrization"—that is, a leveling off through sudden and devastating earthquakes.

Earthquakes and volcanoes are very closely allied. An eruption of lava is often preceded by tremors in the surrounding area. The inhabitants of ancient Pompeii, who were buried under the explosion of Vesuvius, might have saved themselves if they had heeded the warnings of a constant succession of earthquakes that lasted over a period of thirteen years. Many of the inhabitants had wanted to abandon the city, but the politicians and the merchants persuaded them to stay.

Yet there is something to be said for the politicians and the merchants of Pompeii. For there was a method to their madness. Although many an eruption is preceded by an earthquake, not every earthquake is followed by an eruption. The San Francisco earthquake of 1906, for example, was due not to a volcanic disturbance but to a shifting in the position of the Earth's crust. Every once in a while the giant Earth "rouses itself," gives a deep breath, and readjusts itself to a more "comfortable" position.

Sometimes the readjustment comes in a single quake; more often, in a series of "shiftings and tremors and groans." These "groans" are caused by the grinding of subterranean rocks as their surfaces are crushed against one another. One such series of earthquakes produced over seventeen hundred shocks in Missouri from December 16, 1811, to March 16, 1812. The largest of these shocks threw the Mississippi River "back upon itself"—this quotation is from *The Story of Geology,* by Allan L. Benson —caused it "to run uphill a moment," and then sent it "rushing back in waves thirty feet high."

During that entire period of three months the land on the banks of the Mississippi kept rising and falling like the sea. Lakes disappeared into the Earth, and other lakes sprang into sudden existence.

And thus the solid Earth, like the liquid sea, is a scene of surface waves in perpetual motion. This motion of the Earth is less perceptible, because it is less rapid, than the motion of the sea. But it is none the less real. There is a continual change of expression on the moving face of the Earth.

Our knowledge as to the predictability—or as to the cause—of earthquakes is very inadequate as yet. We do not know just where or when or how the next serious earthquake is likely to break out. But we do know, as a general thing, that the greatest danger spots are on the coasts and in the islands of the Pacific—particularly in Japan, the region surrounded by a "circle of [volcanic] fire" and founded upon a "sieve of hollow earth." For this is the area of highest mountains and deepest seas. It would seem, then, that the surface of the land, like the surface of the water, is forever seeking its own level—a leveling down and a leveling up to an even keel.

WIND AND WEATHER

One of the most important freight carriers in the world is the wind, for it keeps constantly shifting the soil and changing the face of the Earth. A single sandstorm in 1901 transported about fifty thousand carloads of dust from the Sahara Desert to Europe. Every spot on the Earth contains some soil that has been carried there by the wind from some other—and oftentimes very distant —spot. This is but a further reminder that nothing on Earth, neither water nor soil nor sand nor stone, remains unchanged for (geologically speaking) any great period of time. This Earth of ours, like all other material objects in the universe, is (again geologically speaking) no more solid than a cloud. The rocks become transformed into soil, the soil keeps constantly moving on the wings of the wind, and the generations of men are treated to a drama whose scenery is forever on the shift.

For the Earth is wrapped in an envelope of air, and the air is practically always in motion—from the light breeze of only a mile an hour to the hurricane of over a hundred and fifty miles an hour.

And the winds, in their motion, carry loads of broken rock and grains of sand and particles of dust from place to place. The dry winds of the desert are able to pick up greater loads of dust and sand and pebbles than the moist winds of the lowlands. Thus a hurricane on a Pacific island may uproot trees and destroy villages and kill people; but it is prevented by the moisture and the grass from picking up much of the soil and carrying it across the sea.

The dry winds, on the other hand, can carry tremendous loads of dust, and to tremendous distances. Thus a strong wind blowing northeast from the Colorado "dust bowl" will produce hazy sunsets in Vermont. And a single storm traveling only a couple of days from New Mexico may deposit a million tons of dust in the region of the Great Lakes.

Among the most interesting "wind loads" in the shifting of the soil on the Earth's surface are the sand dunes of the Southwest. These sand dunes range in height from eight feet in Texas to four hundred feet in Colorado. In general a dune is produced by the whirling of the wind-blown sand around the barrier of a bush, a clump of grass, a mesquite tree, a rock, or even a pile of tin cans. Incidentally, it is among the sand dunes of Colorado that some of the "Sahara" scenes are taken for the motion pictures.

Many of the sand dunes in the deserts of the Southwest—composed perhaps of volcanic ashes—are of a pinkish hue. Many others, however, are almost as white as snow. This is especially true of the dunes along the northeastern seacoast of the United States. Here the waves carry the sand from the sea to the shore, and the wind blows the sand inland.

All sand dunes, whether in the desert or on the seacoast, are constantly subjected to the movement of the winds. And thus the dunes keep shifting in a kaleidoscopic succession of shapes and sizes. They are almost as variable as the sea waves. In the Baltic village of Kunzen, for example, a dune began to form around a church in 1809. By 1839 the entire church, including the steeple, was buried under the sand. By 1869 the sand had blown completely away, and the church "rose" once more into the air. Many an ancient city has been "drowned" in the sands, only to emerge again in the passage of the winds across the centuries.

For the Earth is like a plastic ball of clay that is continually being modeled by the wind and the weather—the rain, the snow, the heat, and the cold.

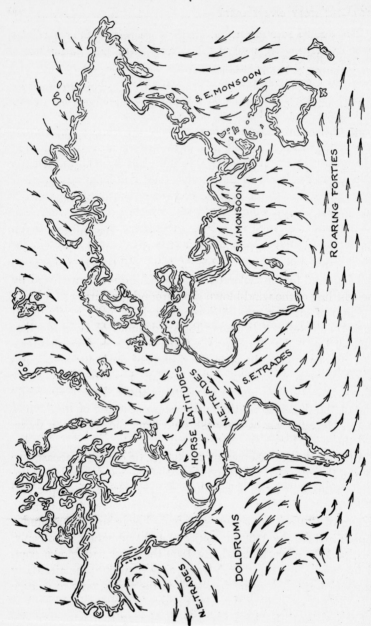

The prevailing winds and air currents of the world, as they are in July of the year.

The annual rainfall on the Earth is very unevenly distributed over its surface. In some of the deserts there may be no rain at all throughout the year. In southern California the rainfall may be from 4 to 16 inches; in some sections of India, such as the watershed of the Ganges, the precipitation may reach almost 500 inches—a veritable perennial deluge.

As to the power of the rain in carving the Earth's surface, it is interesting to note that one inch of rain exerts a pressure of about 113 tons of water to the acre. Multiply this by 500—the average rainfall on the banks of the Ganges—and you have a pressure of over 50,000 tons to the acre every twelve months. This results in an incessant displacement of the soil, which is dredged out in one section and deposited elsewhere along the course of the stream.

The rain, no less than the wind, is a powerful agent in the modeling of the Earth's surface. And the rain is closely related to the wind. Indeed, without any wind there would probably not be any rain. It is only when the wind carries the particles of dust into the clouds that the mists gather around these particles and become transformed into raindrops. Nearly every drop of water that falls from a cloud has its nucleus of dust at the center. It is possible, of course, to produce a dustless drop of rain in the laboratory. But the manufacture of these artificial raindrops requires an atmosphere more saturated with moisture than is contained in the mist of a natural cloud.

A raindrop, therefore, is generally a combination of dust and mist. This seems to be true also of a snowflake. But the pressure of snow is so much lighter than the pressure of rain because the snow contains so large an admixture of air. A snowfall of 12 inches may contain only an inch, or even less than an inch, of water.

Yet a heavy fall of snow, especially when it is packed down, may cause considerable damage. In February 1916 a snowfall of 30 inches crushed the dome of the St. James Cathedral in Seattle. And in January 1922 a snowfall of 28 inches brought the roof of the Knickerbocker Theater, in Washington, D.C., down upon the heads of the audience. And many of us can still remember the wrecked roofs—in the suburbs of New York and of other big cities along the Eastern seaboard—during the "Great Snow" of December 1947.

As a result of these and of similar accidents, flat roofs and domes are now fortified to resist any foreseeable snowstorm in the more temperate climates. As for the colder and especially the mountainous regions, roofs are generally constructed with such a high pitch that the snow tends to slip down their sides instead of piling up to any considerable weight.

The snow, like the rain, is a perpetual sculptor of the Earth's face. But its action, on the whole, is less pronounced. For in its gradual melting it carves out the shallower furrows in the soil and slowly replenishes the rivers which a sudden rainfall would transform into impetuous torrents.

Furthermore, the snow serves as an equalizer of the summer's heat. For, lying on the mountaintops, it tempers the passing winds which in turn carry the coolness to the overheated valleys below.

In other words, the snow-laden winds cool the surface of the Earth while the sunshine heats it. For heat, according to the present scientific theory, does not come to us directly from the Sun, but is radiated back to us indirectly from the Earth. The Sun does not heat the air; it heats the Earth's surface, which then transfers the heat to us.

Heat consists of motion. It is the motion within the molecules of which all matter is composed. But the matter which composes the air is so thin that it contains a minimum of molecules—so few, in fact, that their combined agitation is insufficient to produce any perceptible degree of heat.

The molecules at the Earth's surface, on the other hand, are sufficiently numerous to produce heat in their agitation under the Sun, or under a fire. The more intense the sunshine or the fire, the more rapid the agitation of the molecules, and the greater the degree of heat which they radiate back to us.

And so, many scientists believe, the Sun gives the heat to the Earth, and the Earth gives (a part of) the heat back to us. Thus you will notice—if you walk barefoot on the sand, for example— that the ground is much hotter than the air.

Indeed, the higher we go, the less intense the heat. This is because the air becomes thinner as we go up. The air at the mountaintop is thus cold enough for a blanket of snow while the valley underneath may be broiling under a temperature of more than 100 degrees in the shade. Ten miles above the Earth, even at the equator, the temperature is about 110 degrees below zero. And beyond the thin envelope of our atmosphere there is a perpetual, windless, and silent cold. For in those empty regions of space, though they are nearer to the Sun, there is no molecular action to produce any radiation, no heat, no life.

PLANT AND ANIMAL FOSSILS

The word "fossil," from the Latin *fossilis,* means *something dug up.* In modern geologic phraseology "fossils are the remains of prehistoric plants and animals that have been buried and preserved in the rocks," to be "dug up" later on.

The story told by the fossils is one of the most interesting chapters in the text book of the Earth. As far back as twenty-five hundred years ago, when the Greek historian Herodotus was traveling in Africa, he observed fossil sea shells in the Libyan Desert. Being of a scientific turn of mind, he concluded that the desert had once been covered by the sea. About two thousand years later the artist Leonardo da Vinci found similar fossils in Milan and reasoned that a part of Italy, too, must have been at one time submerged under the sea.

Yet their contemporary "professional scientists" scoffed at both Herodotus and Leonardo. They called their idea "fantastic." In 1696, when the remains of a mammoth were discovered in Germany, the doctors of science and of medicine dismissed the evidence by ascribing the skeleton to a "freak of nature." Ten years later, when a mastodon tooth was unearthed in the United States, Governor Dudley of New York wrote to Cotton Mather that this tooth, though it "measured 6 inches in height and 13 inches in circumference," had belonged to a "human body" drowned in the Old Testament flood.

It remained for our own Thomas Jefferson, another "amateur" scientist like Herodotus and Leonardo, to establish the study of fossils upon a logical basis. In 1799 he read before the American Philosophical Society a paper on the subject and illustrated his findings with a number of specimens that he had collected. Jefferson's paper may thus be regarded as a preface to the science of *Paleontology*—the study of the fossil remains of ancient life.

From Jefferson's day to the present many fossils have been discovered, and in every stage of preservation. In the frozen soil of Siberia about fifty mammoths have been found with their skeletons—and in some cases even with their flesh and skin and hair—almost intact. And all along the Atlantic coast, from Maine to Florida, fossil shells have been found with their original structure and coloring practically untouched.

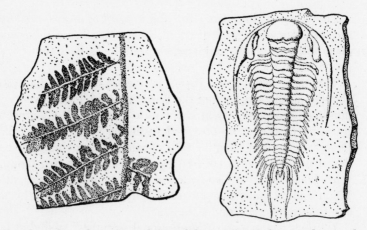

Fossils such as these (fern, left; trilobite, right) help us to know what forms of life existed on Earth many thousands of years ago.

Most of the fossils—especially those that date very far back—are petrified. Thus coal is petrified or mineralized vegetable matter. A good many fossils, however, show the traces rather than the bodies of ancient creatures. Thus we have, in New Jersey, the evidence of a dinosaur which literally, about two hundred million years ago, "left its footsteps in the sands of time." The wet red sand in which the dinosaur walked became, in subsequent ages, cemented into stone. And the footsteps have remained intact to this day—a distinct message transmitted to us from the morning of the world.

At the present time the geologists are able to read quite a number of similar messages—the tracks of prehistoric crabs and gigantic snails, the excrement of long extinct reptiles and fishes, the "gizzard stones" of enormous winged creatures as yet untaught to fly, and the hunting holes of trilobites that grubbed for their worms in the primitive mud flats now hardened into slabs of shale.

And thus Nature keeps preserving the story of the centuries in the time capsule of the rocks. The books that men write are but the fragmentary and garbled quotations from the universal book of Nature.

REVIEW QUESTIONS IN GEOLOGY

1. What, according to the "tidal wave theory," is the parentage of the Earth?

2. What is meant by the "displacement of continents?"

3. Is the Earth's surface static or dynamic?

4. Is the North Pole likely to remain forever cold?

5. What, probably, will be the ultimate fate of cities like London and New York?

6. What was the original nature of Niagara Falls?

7. By what general processes did the Earth become modeled into its present shape?

8. How thick is the Earth's crust?

9. What is its general nature?

10. What is the "raw material" of marble?

11. What is the "raw material" of diamonds?

12. How can we identify the ages of the various layers of rocks?

13. About how far down can water be found in mine shafts?

14. What is an artesian well?

15. What is a stalactite?

16. What is a stalagmite?

17. How solid are the "solid" things of the Earth?

18. What are the two necessary conditions for the formation of a river?

19. How are river valleys formed?

20. About how much soil is being annually freighted into the sea?

21. What comes first, the volcano or the eruption?

22. About how many active volcanoes are there in the world today?

23. Where are most of them situated?

24. Is an "extinct" volcano likely to remain always extinct?

25. What is the site of the so-called "submerged temple" of the Romans?

26. What is the annual number of earthquakes throughout the world?

27. What areas are most frequently exposed to earthquakes?

28. Is there any connection between earthquakes and volcanoes?

29. Are earthquakes, like the weather, predictable?

30. What is one of the leading carriers of matter in the world?

31. How are sand dunes formed?

32. What is the average annual rainfall in southern California?

33. In some sections of India?

34. What is the pressure, per acre, of 1 inch of rain?

35. Could there be any rain without any wind?

36. What is the nature of a raindrop?

37. About how much water is there in a snowfall of about 12 inches?

38. How are roofs in the colder regions built in order to resist the snow?

39. How does the snow on the mountains temper the heat in the valleys?

40. Does the heat of the Sun come to us directly *from* the Sun?

41. State a simple test to substantiate your answer to Question 40.

42. What is the temperature at the equator about ten miles above the Earth?

43. How did Herodotus discover that the Libyan Desert had once been submerged under the sea?

44. What is a fossil?

45. Who established the study of fossils upon a scientific basis?

46. What is the scientific name for the study of fossils?

47. What is the peculiarity of the fossils discovered in Siberia?

48. What is coal?

49. What sort of dinosaur fossil has been discovered in New Jersey?

50. Mention some of the other fossil traces that enable the geologists to read the story of the past.

ANSWERS TO THE QUESTIONS IN GEOLOGY

1. According to this theory, the Earth was pulled away, in a tidal wave, from the Sun.

2. The gradual drifting apart of continents that originally had existed together.

3. Dynamic. It changes continually.

4. No.

5. The scientific probability is that they will be submerged under the sea.

6. A sheet of solid ice.

7. By the glacial process and the action of streams, rivers, and wind.

8. About thirty miles.

9. A layer of soil or sand at the top, a layer of light rocks in the middle, and a layer of heavy rocks at the bottom.

10. Limestone.

11. Carbon, or coal.

12. By their fossils.

13. About a mile down.

14. A well in which the water is forced to the surface by means of hydraulic pressure.

15. A conelike rock deposited by the action of subterranean waters and hanging, like an icicle, from the roof or the side of a cavern.

16. A similarly shaped rock projecting from the floor of a cavern.

17. Nothing is solid on Earth. Everything keeps changing like a cloud—but more or less rapidly, depending on its nature.

18. A sufficient supply of water and an adequate slope.

19. Through the dissolution and abrasion of the minerals upon the banks by the waters of the river. The valley is thus "scooped out" of the rocks.

20. About three billion tons.

21. The eruption.

22. About five hundred.

23. On the shores and on the islands of the Pacific.

24. Not necessarily.

25. On the seashore near Naples.

26. About thirty thousand, on an average, are actually felt and many more are recorded by seismographs.

27. The Pacific area, the Atlantic islands, and the deepest valleys surrounded by the highest mountains.

28. Frequently, but not always, a series of earthquakes is followed by a volcanic eruption.

29. No.

30. The wind.

31. By the whirling of the wind-blown sand around a barrier of bushes or rocks or other obstacles.

32. From 4 to 16 inches.

33. Almost 500 inches.

34. About 113 tons.

35. Probably not.

36. A ball of mist with a nucleus of dust at the center.

37. It may be as low as 1 inch or even less.

38. With a steep slope, so that the snow may slide down to the ground.

39. By cooling the passing winds, which in turn carry the coolness to the valleys.

40. No. The Sun does not heat the air; it heats the Earth's surface, which indirectly transfers the heat to the air.

41. If you walk barefoot on the sand you will notice that the ground is much hotter than the air.

42. About 110 degrees below zero.

43. He found fossil sea shells in the desert.

44. A fossil is the petrified form—or trace—of an ancient animal or plant dug up from the earth.

45. Interestingly enough, Thomas Jefferson.

46. Paleontology.

47. The fossils of about fifty mammoths, discovered there, were almost intact.

48. Petrified vegetable matter.

49. The imprint of the dinosaur's footsteps imbedded in the sand, which became cemented into stone.

50. The tracks of gigantic crabs and snails, the excrement of reptiles and fishes, the gizzard stones of prehistoric birds, and so on.

BIOGRAPHICAL SKETCHES OF GREAT GEOLOGISTS

Steno, Nicholas (1638–87). Danish scientist. Born in Copenhagen, he adopted a career in medicine. Anatomy was his particular specialty. He was appointed physician to the Grand Duke of Florence. But he abandoned his practice, entered the Church, and was appointed a Roman Catholic bishop, assigned to northern Germany. Besides his contributions to medicine and to the Church, he is famous for his investigations in the field of geology. He was the first to demonstrate the nature of fossil animals. He described the stratification of rocks, in writing of the crust of the Earth, and classified them as of volcanic, mechanical, or chemical origins.

Buffon, Georges Louis Leclerc, Comte de (1707–88). French naturalist. Born at Montbard, Burgundy, he studied law at the College
of Jesuits at Dijon. At thirty-two he became the curator of the
Jardin du Roi and of the royal museum. He spent the remainder
of his life preparing a tremendous study, *Natural History,* which
was published in forty-four quarto volumes. Among other things,
he developed a theory of the Earth in this work which, while con-
troverted afterward in its details, nevertheless set forth the true
geological concept that the Earth is the product of continuous
change which can be traced by recognizable phenomena. He
wrote five volumes on minerals alone. Buffon was a member of
the French Academy and a fellow of the Royal Society of London.

Hutton, James (1726–97). Scotch geologist. Born in Edinburgh, he
studied medicine but abandoned it in favor of agriculture. Practically singlehanded he formulated the science of modern geology.
He did extensive pioneer research in the history of the Earth,
tracing it from the records of minerals and rocks. He investigated
the conditions of the atmosphere, paying particular attention to
the phenomenon of rainfall.

Werner, Abraham Gottlob (1750–1817). German geologist. Born
in Saxony, he entered a mining school at Freiburg and proceeded
afterward to Leipzig, where he studied mineralogy and law.
At twenty-five he was appointed teacher and inspector in the
Freiburg mining school and held the position for forty years.
Generally considered the father of German geology, he taught
the doctrine of geologic succession with particular regard to
rocks. His theory of the aqueous origin of rocks was rebutted
by a hostile school of geologists and a historical controversy arose.
Despite the errors of some of his theories, Werner's contributions
to the science of geology have a lasting value.

Sedgwick, Adam (1785–1873). British geologist. Born in Yorkshire, the son of a parson, he was educated at Cambridge University and assumed the chair of geology. He contributed significant research on the strata of the Yorkshire coast and the geology
of the Isle of Wight. To the most ancient group of fossil-bearing
strata he gave the name Cambrian. In collaboration with Murchi-

son he carried out investigations dealing with the culm measures of Devonshire. He introduced the nomenclature Devonian for the grits, limestones, and slates discovered in Devon, Cornwall, West Somerset. In 1827 he was chosen president of the Geological Society. He lectured at Cambridge until his death.

Murchison, Sir Roderick Impey (1792–1871). British geologist. Born in Scotland, he was educated at the Great Marlow military college and he took part in several military campaigns. In 1825 he joined the Geological Society of London and commenced intensive researches in the field. He went on tours of exploration through England, Scotland, France, Italy, Austria, and Switzerland. He collaborated on a classic paper dealing with the geological structure of the Alps. Among other trips, he went on a journey to Russia and collaborated on a significant publication, *Russia and the Ural Mountains.* In 1855 he was appointed director of the geological survey, of the Museum of Practical Geology, and of the Royal School of Mines. He founded a chair of geology and mineralogy at Edinburgh University.

Lyell, Sir Charles (1797–1875). British geologist. Born at Kinnordy, Forfarshire, he studied law but devoted his life to geology. He divided a geological system of shells into several groups, giving them terms that have become famous—Eocene, Miocene, Pliocene. He incorporated this system in his book, *The Principles of Geology.* He followed this with *Elements of Geology,* which served as a standard work on paleontological and stratigraphical geology. He explored the early history of the human race in his book *The Antiquity of Man.* At forty he became president of the Geological Society. Among his extensive voyages were two trips to America during which he investigated Niagara Falls, collected data on the delta of the Mississippi, and studied vegetable deposits in Virginia. He was created a baronet in 1864. Toward the end of his life he became blind.

Chamberlin, Thomas Chrowder (1843–1928). American geologist. Born in Mattoon, Illinois, he studied at Beloit College and later taught at the college. Following an active career as geologist, first with the Wisconsin Geological Survey and then with the United

States Geological Survey, he became president of the University of Wisconsin in 1887. In 1892 he was made head of the department of geology at the newly organized University of Chicago. Chamberlin's major contribution to geology is his formulation, with F. R. Moulton, of the so-called planetesimal hypothesis of the origin of the earth.

CAREERS IN GEOLOGY

Geologists study the history of the earth as it is recorded in the rocks, study the composition of the soil, draft topographical maps, and estimate available water supplies. Universities, museums, and a number of government bureaus employ geologists.

The majority of geologists, however, work for industry. A large number of them have jobs in the petroleum industry. The danger of exhausted oil wells is acute and the duty of the geophysicist, as the geologist in this field is called, is to locate new oil deposits. Still others work for mining companies, charged with the task of finding new mineral deposits. Coal technologists—specialists in the processing and utilization of coal—are highly esteemed. Many of these experts transfer from industry into government service to map out the country's coal resources. Still others work as engineer geologists. They are experts on the geological conditions of the ground over which roads and bridges and railroads are to be constructed. They advise the construction engineers. In addition, they assist engineers in the collection and conservation of water supplies. Still other geologists make agriculture their career, becoming specialists in the science of soil management as the prime factor in the production of crops. They do expert research in fertilization, irrigation, and conservation.

Whether he works for the government, a university, a museum, or for coal companies, the metal industry, or in the field of oil or engineering, the occupations available to the student of geology are fully satisfying ones.

coal technologist
EXPERIENCE REQUIRED: Graduate fuel technologist. Thorough knowledge of properties of fuels.

DESCRIPTION OF JOB: Directs preparation, processing, and utilization of coal as a raw material other than for direct combustion.

OPPORTUNITIES FOR ADVANCEMENT: Fuel engineer, plant manager, sales engineer.

WHERE TO APPLY FOR JOBS: Coal companies, steel companies, coke and by-product companies, gas manufacturers, coal producers.

engineering geologist

EXPERIENCE REQUIRED: College degree. Graduate work desirable. Thorough knowledge of mathematics, chemistry, physics.

DESCRIPTION OF JOB: Investigates geologic conditions of ground under consideration for building purposes. Investigates deposits of building stone, clay, roofing materials, etc. Studies underlying rock bed in highway and railroad construction.

OPPORTUNITIES FOR ADVANCEMENT: Consultant.

WHERE TO APPLY FOR JOBS: Engineering firms, construction companies, government.

geophysicist

EXPERIENCE REQUIRED: College degree. Graduate specialization desirable. Thorough training in geology, physics.

DESCRIPTION OF JOB: Applies physical methods to determination of oil and mineral locations.

OPPORTUNITIES FOR ADVANCEMENT: Assistant head of a field party, research head.

WHERE TO APPLY FOR JOBS: Oil and mining companies, research institutes, colleges and universities, federal and state bureaus.

mining geologist

EXPERIENCE REQUIRED: College degree in mining geology. Graduate study desirable. Thorough training in geology and mineralogy. Working knowledge of chemistry, physics, mathematics.

DESCRIPTION OF JOB: Concerned with finding mineral deposits. Collects samples of minerals for laboratory research. May guide mining operations.

OPPORTUNITIES FOR ADVANCEMENT: Administrative, executive.

WHERE TO APPLY FOR JOBS: Metal mining companies, United States Geological Survey.

petroleum geologist

EXPERIENCE REQUIRED: College degree and experience in oil or mining industry. Thorough training in all branches of geological sciences desirable.

DESCRIPTION OF JOB: Oil scouting, reports on geological conditions. Maps new districts. Advises production department. Engaged in intensive subsurface work.

OPPORTUNITIES FOR ADVANCEMENT: Department head, executive, administration, consultant.

WHERE TO APPLY FOR JOBS: Oil companies, universities, government.

x-ray crystallographer

EXPERIENCE REQUIRED: College degree, major in geology, physics, chemistry, engineering, plus experience in X-ray diffraction.

DESCRIPTION OF JOB: Designs equipment for X-ray production to explore minerals.

WHERE TO APPLY FOR JOBS: Government.

BIBLIOGRAPHY: BOOKS ON GEOLOGY FOR FURTHER READING AND STUDY

Bateman, Alan Mara: *Economic Mineral Deposits.* New York, 1942.

Benson, Allan Louis: *The Story of Geology.* New York, 1927.

Bradley, John Hodgdon: *Autobiography of the Earth.* New York, 1935.

Branson, Edwin Bayer, and W. A. Tarr: *Introduction to Geology.* New York, 1941.

Croneis, Carey Gardiner, and William C. Krumbein: *Down to Earth.* Chicago, 1936.

Daly, Reginald Aldworth: *Architecture of the Earth.* New York, 1938.

Fenton, Carroll Lane: *Our Amazing Earth.* New York, 1938.

——: *The Story of the Great Geologists.* New York, 1945.

Gamow, George: *Biography of the Earth.* New York, 1941.

Holmes, Arthur: *Principles of Physical Geology.* New York, 1945.

Hotchkiss, William Otis: *The Story of a Billion Years.* New York, 1932.

Jeffreys, Harold: *The Earth: Its Origin, History, and Physical Constitution.* New York, 1929.

Lahee, Frederic Henry: *Field Geology.* New York, 1941.

Lee, Willis Thomas: *Stories in Stone.* New York, 1926.

Mills, Enos A.: *Romance of Geology.* New York, 1926.

Morrel, Martha McBride: *When the World Was Young.* Boston, 1941.

Pirsson, Louis Valentine, and Charles Schuchert: *A Textbook of Geology.* New York, 1929.

Reeds, Chester Albert: *The Earth.* New York, 1931.

Schuchert, Charles, and Carl O. Dunbar: *Outlines of Historical Geology.* New York, 1941.

Shand, Samuel James: *Earth-Lore.* London, 1933.

Thompson, Henry Dewey: *Fundamentals of Earth Science.* New York, 1947.

CHAPTER THREE

geography—a survey of the earth

BY THE DAWN'S EARLY LIGHT

Geographically speaking, we of America have been a rather illiterate nation. Separated from the rest of the world by the Atlantic on the one side and by the Pacific on the other, we have been unable to see this world in its proper—that is, its geographic —perspective. We are just beginning to recognize this fact as a result of the last war—a war we might possibly have avoided with a better knowledge of geography and of its political, economic, and social implications.

But now our soldiers have fought nearly all over the face of the earth, and our minds have become more clearly focused upon its features and its resources. Thus we are beginning to see it under the dawning of a new light. Greece, Turkey, Guadalcanal, the Aleutian Islands, Greenland, Hawaii, Iran—these are no longer mere names of faraway places. They are the intimate features of a world that directly concerns our everyday existence. They are becoming more and more closely impressed upon the map of our intellectual equipment. For the first time in our history we are learning to think geographically—or, to be more precise, *geopolitically*. Our country is a related part of the earth; and it is our business, for our own safety, to examine the nature of this relationship.

Geography, in other words, constitutes a vital part of our present-day training in American citizenship—in *world* citizenship. We are becoming interested not only in the events that take place but in the places that occasion the events. Why are certain outposts on the Mediterranean so vital to the peaceful development of international trade? What is the meaning, in terms of your welfare and mine, of the geographical situation of Alaska, of the Azores, of Guam? What are the "gateways" to some of the strategic areas of the world? In peacetime? In time of war? What are the sea lanes and the air routes best adapted for travel, for commerce, for defense? What is the political effect of the geographical distribution of coal, iron, rubber, manganese, uranium, oil? How does this distribution influence our daily lives? How can the balance be maintained to keep the world at peace?

These are but a few of the many geographical questions that confront us constantly in our daily activities. Whether we realize it or not, a very great part of our thinking is geographical. The news that we read, the editorials that we ponder, the ideas that we select or reject in the computing of our mental ledgers—all these are founded largely upon geographical data. The locations of our cities are determined by geographical factors—the proximity to the ocean, the meeting place of rivers, the convergence of roads between industrial or agricultural areas. Our political thinking is determined, to a great extent, by the places where we live—the prairies, the seacoast, the cotton belt, the mining regions, the oil fields, the hills.

Our very civilization, in short, is a series of geographical adjustments—a gradual and painful adaptation of man to his environment. It is over the highways of geography that we are slowly traveling to wisdom. The civilization of the human race is a progressive discipline in the art of *sharing*, rather than *plundering*, the important geographical regions of the earth.

HOW THE EARTH LOOKED TO OUR ANCESTORS

The Homeric poets, writing about three thousand years ago, regarded the earth as a platter surrounded by the sea and covered by the inverted bowl of the sky. This is the primitive view of childhood when you live in a little world bounded by the horizon, and your experience has not as yet penetrated beyond its circular rim. All the early Greek maps were constructed upon this conception of the earth as a flat, round disk, with the Pillar of Atlas in the center supporting the sky.

It was not until the end of the fifth century B.C. that the Greek philosophers—notably Plato and Aristotle—began to look upon the earth as a spherical body. But as to the geographical features of this body, they were almost entirely in the dark. For their travels had not taken them beyond the Mediterranean basin. They knew very little of the lands and the oceans that lay beyond.

The first scientific student of geography was Claudius Ptolemaeus, known to us as Ptolemy. In the second century A.D. he produced twenty-six maps of the world, as well as a number of tables denoting the geographical positions of the principal rivers and mountains and cities. This collection of maps, though it marks a definite advance over the earlier geographies, represents a picture of the world which is still very distorted and incomplete.

After Ptolemy, the study of scientific map making was discontinued for nearly a thousand years. The scholars of the Middle Ages discarded the spherical conception of the earth and returned to the primitive picture of a disk-shaped world—a sort of tent floor covered by the hangings of the sky. Most of the medieval maps were either circular, depicting the "circuit of the earth," or rectangular, delimiting the "four corners of the earth." But all of them were based upon the notion of a *flat* world, with Jerusalem situated in the center and Paradise tucked away in the Far East.

In the eleventh century, however, there was an impetus toward the making of more accurate maps as a result of the Crusades. The horizons had opened up and the world had become larger and at the same time more familiar. Charts were carefully constructed for the guidance of soldiers and traders.

In addition to the charts, the geographers of that period prepared a number of "sailing books"—compilations of harbors, bays, gulfs, shoals, tides, currents, and other matters of topographical interest to navigators.

And then "the world was flooded with light." It was the dawn-

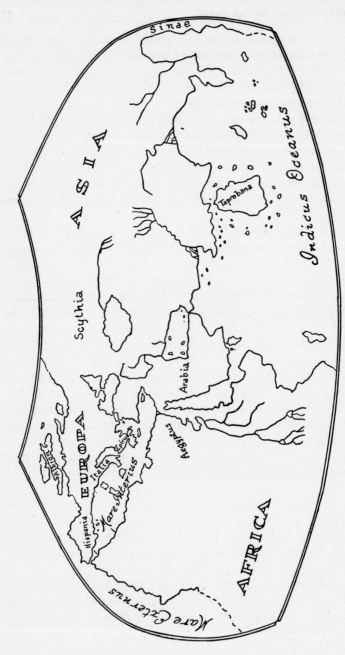

A map by Ptolemy of the world known in his day—the second century A.D.

ing of the Renaissance, or the Revival of Learning, in the latter part of the fifteenth century. Along with the restoration of classical art came the rediscovery of classical science. During the next three hundred years the geographical works of Ptolemy were republished again and again. His old maps were corrected, and new maps were added as rapidly as new lands were explored. The world was rounding into shape, and its inhabitants were becoming more and more intimately acquainted with one another.

It was in 1492, the year of the discovery of America, that the first global map of the world was constructed. The author of this map, Martin Behaim, appropriately called it *Erdapfel,* which means *Apple-shaped Earth.*

And thus the geographers followed the explorers, retracing their steps, surveying their discoveries, and collecting the maps

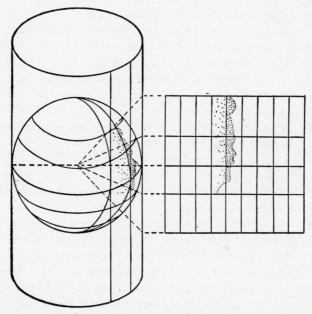

How an area on the globe is mapped on a flat surface. The globe is divided up into small sections, like the pieces of an orange. These are then projected onto the surface of a cylinder, which is then rolled flat. Notice the distortion of the dotted area on the flat map.

into atlases—the first of these atlases, by Mercator, was published in 1595—until they came to the so-called "golden age" of geography.

This "golden age" in map making was largely the product of the Dutch geographers. These hardy pioneers, in the mental as well as the physical sphere, were among the first to get a definite picture of the totality of the earth. They looked upon it as a "global theater"—*theatrum orbis terrarum.* (It is interesting to note the similarity between this geographical conception and the Shakespearean metaphor, *the world's a stage.*) The greater part of the earth had now been encircled and measured out. Some of the maps of this "golden" period—the seventeenth century—are not only works of scientific erudition but masterpieces of artistic conception. Their coloring is brilliant, and their margins are embellished with figures of sea monsters and savages, animals and clouds, and chariots and ships. These maps are highly prized as wall decorations even at the present time.

Yet the picture of the world, as presented in these maps, is still far from accurate. It shows, among other things, a connecting strip of land between America and Asia, a large inland body of water in the American Northwest, and an island, instead of a peninsula, in the region now known as Lower California.

These inaccuracies were gradually eliminated, as the nations tried to outdo one another in the acquisition of colonies and in the detailed study of their terrain as a protection against the encroachment of their neighbors. But this advance in geographical knowledge was not without its drawbacks. The exaggerated nationalism of the eighteenth and the nineteenth centuries resulted in a shortsighted policy of isolation. The one world, as visualized in the studies of the pioneer geographers, was becoming split up into alien—and often hostile—territories. While more and more maps were being constructed for the development of highways and canals in *this* or in *that* country, fewer and fewer maps were being prepared for the understanding of *all* the countries.

This lack of interest in the world beyond the horizon was carried into the twentieth century. People everywhere were getting excellent township views, county views, state views, and forgetting all about their world view. In 1919, as a result of World War I, people became international-minded—geographically speaking

—for a while. But this was a passing phase. Within a very short time the vision of one world became once more overshadowed by the cloud of a provincial isolationism.

And it took the catastrophe of Pearl Harbor, in 1941, to awaken America, and indeed all the other countries, to the nearness of the most distant places. The majority of us are becoming geo-political-minded. We see the world in its united kinship. No spot is now regarded as isolated from any other spot. We are entering upon the enlightened age of global geography. We are beginning to find our way to our neighbors over the newly charted sea, land, and air routes of the world.

A MODERN GLANCE AROUND THE WORLD

Our present view of the world discloses to us the fact that it has no geographical center, but that every location is relative to every other location. It shows us, moreover, that there is a direct line of communication—through the air—between any one locality and all the rest of the world.

It will be interesting, therefore, to take a brief airplane view of the world as we know it today and to fix in our minds the picture of its global unity.

The surface of the earth, as we thus examine it from our vantage point in the encircling plane, is about three fourths water and one fourth land. Most of the land, we observe, is centered in the northern latitudes. Yet even here the extent of the water surface is far greater than that of the land surface.

And now, as we look at the pattern of this picture, we note that it is divided into four principal areas:

1. The larger bodies of water known as *oceans*—the Atlantic, the Pacific, the Arctic, the Antarctic, and the Indian.
2. The smaller bodies of water known as *seas*—nearly thirty of them.
3. The larger bodies of land known as *continents*—North America, South America, Africa, Europe, Asia, Australia, and Antarctica.
4. The smaller bodies of land known as *islands*—several thousand of them.

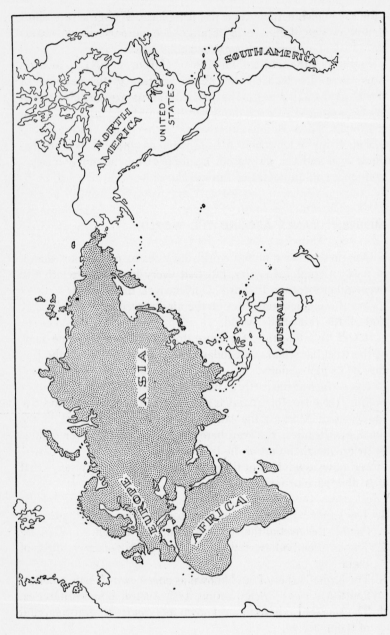

The shaded areas make up the Triple Continent, the largest single land mass in the world.

Strictly speaking, however, the entire land surface of the earth is insular. Our human habitation consists of a group of islands and of island continents—"houseboats" of various shapes and sizes anchored in the middle of the sea.

Of these "houseboats," the seven largest—or the continents—are divided into three groups: a triple continent, Afro-Eurasia; a double continent, North and South America; and two single continents, Australia and Antarctica.

The Triple Continent—Afro-Eurasia—is the most extensive single land mass in the world. Eurasia is one continuous body—from Spain on the Atlantic, through the Balkans into Russia, on to Siberia and China, and as far as Vladivostok and Hong Kong on the Pacific. On the south, Eurasia is united to Africa at the Isthmus of Suez and separated from it by a narrow strait at Gibraltar. And thus the Mediterranean, which lies between Eurasia and Africa, is often regarded not as a dividing sea but as a connecting lake—a water-route for the commerce of the various countries in the Triple Continent.

And it was this idea—the continuity of the Triple Continent along with its political implications—that was brought home to us, at so costly a price, as a result of World War II. We now realize that Europe is no longer a continent all by itself, but merely a small segment of the enormous land mass geopolitically known as Afro-Eurasia.

This Triple Continent, when closely examined, stands out as a feature of tremendous importance in our global picture. It covers about two thirds of the land surface of the world. Eurasia alone, without Africa, is more than three times as large as North America; and the entire continent of Afro-Eurasia is almost three times the size of North America and South America combined.

Moreover, this Afro-Eurasian continent is surrounded by all the five oceans. And thus it contains an outlet to every possible avenue of commercial traffic. To return to our earlier metaphor, it is the only one among the "houseboats" with windows opening on every side.

The Triple Continent is thus the *largest,* and the *most strategically situated,* of all the land areas in the world. And—this, too, is of the greatest importance—*it contains seven eighths of the world's population.*

Potentially, therefore, the Triple Continent could become the most influential politically and commercially, as it is the most favored geographically, of all the land areas in the world. United, it could exert an irresistible military power or create a veritable paradise on earth. The fate of its inhabitants lies in the wisdom of their own choosing.

Slightly less favored, geographically, than the Triple Continent of Afro-Eurasia is the Double Continent of North and South America. Of these two members of the Double Continent, North America is by far the more closely connected to the Triple Continent, and hence the more intimately concerned with its social and political and military history. At its extreme point in the northwest, the United States territory of Alaska is separated from the Russian territory of Siberia by the river-wide channel of Bering Strait. When this strait is frozen in winter, it is possible to cross it on foot. And, since the winters are very long in that district, the United States and Russia are practically "land neighbors" for the greater part of every year.

Thus, at its western extremity, there is but a negligible stretch of water between the Double Continent and the Triple Continent. At its eastern extremity, the stretch of water is considerably wider—about eighteen hundred miles between South America and Africa.

But North America is connected to Europe by a continental "shelf"—that is, a land bridge which stretches under shallow water all the way from Labrador to France, and which rises above the surface in the island "steppingstones" of Greenland, Iceland, the Faroes, Ireland, and Britain.

This "land-studded approach" between North America and Europe was used extensively in World War II. Our ships carried troops and supplies over this route to the war zone, and our planes formed a protecting "umbrella" over the ships from their island air bases. And even in peacetime this air route is regarded as one of the best, because it contains the biggest number of resting points between the most important cities of the two largest continents.

This development of sea routes and air routes along strategic points is gradually transforming the Double Continent, though smaller and less populated than the Triple Continent, into a political and commercial power of the utmost importance. Here, too, the possibilities are unlimited if only the inhabitants can become united in wisdom.

And now, in our rapid survey of the world, we come to the two single continents—Australia and Antarctica. Of these two continents, Australia alone is inhabited by man. And—this is an important distinction—of all the continents in the world, Australia is the only one that is dominated by a single political power.

Commercially, Australia is in a vital position because it lies across the principal streams of traffic between the Pacific and the Indian oceans.

The last of the continents, Antarctica, is little more than an enormous ice field. Indeed, it is impossible to determine whether it consists of one continuous stretch of land or is a collection of islands linked together by a permanent bridge of ice.

Owing to its inclement weather, this continent has provided no haven for shipping and has played no part in world events. With the advent of the air age, however, the strategic picture of this continent may possibly undergo a radical change. For it may provide adequate air bases both for commercial and for military ventures in the years to come.

So much, then, for the continents of the world. And now, a brief glance at the eight largest islands—Greenland, Baffin Island, New Guinea, Borneo, Sumatra, Madagascar, Honshu, and Britain.

Greenland and Baffin Island lie mainly in the Arctic Circle and, like the Antarctic continent, are too cold for extensive human exploitation. The southern part of Greenland, however, has already been developed as a base for Atlantic air travel. For—as we have noted above—this island is one of the "steppingstones" in the continental shelf between America and Europe.

Of greater strategic importance than Greenland and Baffin Island are the tropical islands of the Pacific—New Guinea, Borneo, Sumatra, and Madagascar. These islands lie along the direct route of some of the most profitable world traffic; they possess good harbors for the refueling of ships; and they can serve as convenient springboards for air travel both in peace and in war. They are therefore regarded as "prize packages" in the international "grab bag" of political and economic aggression. These, like many of the smaller islands that lie scattered in strategic positions over the seas or are rich in material resources, have become the meeting places of traders and the battlefields of fighting men.

But all these important islands are mere pawns in the global picture of our geographical survey. They pale in comparison with Honshu and Britain, the two islands which are physically the smallest but politically and economically the most ambitious of the Big Eight.

The reason for their global ambition is due largely to their geographical situations. Britain, the core of the British Empire, lies at the gateway to Europe; and Honshu, the nucleus of the Japanese Empire, guards the approaches to Asia. This continental proximity makes their inhabitants land-minded; yet their insular positions make them sea-minded as well.

Moreover, the density of their population—about 500 per square mile—necessitates a great volume of sea trade for the maintenance of a standard level of existence. Hence the development, in these empires, of a large and powerful fleet, and the great hunger for colonial expansion.

Indeed, this hunger for expansion—the desire for space in which to grow and for food and luxuries upon which to grow fat —has been one of the leading factors in the geographic "globalization" of the world. It has resulted in the invention of rapid transportation; it has combed the seas for every large and every small island that may contribute to the welfare of the various nations; it has enriched the world with the interchange of commerce and deluged it with oceans of blood.

But it has also made the world smaller and more conformable to another human hunger—the spiritual hunger for mutual understanding, for harmonious collaboration, for concerted action in the harnessing of nature to our human needs. Our increasing and applied knowledge of geography as a global science is very likely to develop within us a united vision of one world.

THE TRIPLE SPHERE OF OUR PLANET

We are accustomed to think of the earth as a single sphere. Actually it is a triple sphere: the *geosphere*, or the land globe, which forms the core of our planet; the *hydrosphere*, or the water globe, which is pierced here and there by the projections of the land globe in the form of continents and islands; and the *atmosphere,* or the air globe, which adheres closely to the other two globes and rotates along with them around the sun.

All three globes form a single unit, and all of them are equally necessary for our human existence. We live on top of the geosphere, we get much of our subsistence from the hydrosphere, and we breathe at the bottom of the atmosphere.

And the atmosphere in itself is a combination of three spheres, or hollow shells: the *troposphere,* or the region of the winds, the clouds, the rain, the snow, and the dust; the *stratosphere,* or the region of the cloudless frosts; and the *ionosphere,* or the upper shell of rarefied and extremely cold gases that stretch into the outer darkness of the universe.

In the study of our global geography we are mainly concerned with the troposphere, or that section of the atmosphere which is subject to the changes of wind and weather. For the wind and the weather play a great part in the selecting of our human habitations and in the adjusting of our human lives. The seeds of our plants and the moisture that makes them grow are transported from place to place by the winds. And our health, our clothes, our shelters, our inventions, our activities, our plans, our very moods, are determined largely by the weather.

Thus the history of the human race, from a geographical point of view, is the story of a series of migrations to those localities where the wind and the weather are likely to insure the most abundant food, the most comfortable living place, and the most effective stimulant to the satisfaction of our human needs.

CLIMATE

Many of us, in our everyday conversation, confuse the three terms—*wind, weather,* and *climate.* A brief definition of these terms will enable us to understand the difference between them:

Wind is air in motion. It is caused by the tendency of heated air to rise, and of colder air to rush into the gaps that are thus left vacant.

Weather is the condition of the air—wet or dry, warm or cold, calm or stormy, nebulous or bright—at a given time in a given place. Thus, yesterday it was rainy weather in Boston; today it is clear weather in Detroit.

Climate is generalized weather—the average condition of the air in a given place over an extended period of time. Thus New York—over an extended period of years—has a temperate climate; Miami has a semitropical climate; the Sahara Desert has a very hot climate.

The climate of a locality depends, to a great extent, upon its latitude and its altitude—that is, its distance from the equator and its height above the sea. Thus, a high mountaintop near the equator may be considerably colder than a low-lying valley some thousands of miles to the north or the south of the equator.

In addition to the latitude and the altitude of a region, there are several other factors that may influence its climate. Some of these additional factors are: the distribution of its land and water areas; the nature of its soil, vegetation, and rainfall and the direction of its winds; and its possible proximity to a protecting wall of mountains, or to a warm-water channel such as the Gulf Stream that flows diagonally across the Atlantic and tends to soften the climate of the western coast of Europe and of the eastern coast of North America.

But the most important factor that determines the climate of a locality is its latitude. And it was for this reason that the ancient geographers divided the world into *climatic* or *latitudinal* zones.

These zones, or imaginary girdles of the earth, are five in number: the Torrid Zone (with the equator in the middle), the North and the South Temperate zones, and the North and the South Frigid zones. The sun shines most directly upon the Torrid Zone, somewhat slantingly upon the Temperate zones, and most obliquely upon the Frigid zones. Hence the differences in the climate of these different zones.

The above method of dividing the world into five climatic zones has been used by geographers from about 450 B.C. down to the present century. But, as we have seen above, the climate can vary to a considerable extent within the different localities of the same zone. And therefore it has been found expedient, within recent years, to *subdivide* the zones in accordance with their surface characteristics. For different kinds of surfaces mean different kinds of climate.

On this basis of surface characteristics, each zone may be subdivided into five parts: ocean, coast line, mountain region, plain, and plateau.

In this way it is possible to get a fairly accurate picture of the diversified climates in the different parts of the world.

Yet this is a general picture. Actually no two places in the world have precisely the same climate. This is due to the fact that no two places in the world have precisely the same features or are exposed to precisely the same atmospheric conditions.

And if you want to study *all* the climates of the world in any *one* place, you can take Mark Twain's advice and spend a single day in New England. This witticism of Mark Twain's is not merely facetious; it is, to a certain degree, factual. There are few places in the world so subject to extreme and sudden changes in the weather; for New England, while it lies in the Temperate Zone, is exposed all along its coast line to the cold, wet winds from the northeast, and is at the same time protected by the tropical warmth of the Gulf Stream. Moreover, much of New England has a mountainous surface, and thus it offers a meeting place, so to speak, for all the various climates that drift in from the Frigid, the Temperate, and the Torrid zones. It is Nature's laboratory for the brewing of the world's worst, and best, weather.

As a general rule the climate is more variable in the Temperate than in any of the other zones. Near the equator it is—with the exceptions as specified above—uniformly hot; near the poles, uniformly cold. In between these two regions the temperature varies from the torrid in the height of summer to the frigid in the dead of winter. And this variation in temperature serves to invigorate the body and stimulate the mind.

And thus the temperate regions of the world have become the important highways of human progress.

SOIL AND PLANT LIFE

The soil—or spongy layer of earth between the air and the rocks—is largely responsible for our sustenance and our life. It absorbs the rain, cradles the plants, covers the rocks, softens our paths, and supplies the bricks for our walls, the wood for our ceilings and our floors, and the vegetation for our food.

Soil is a mixture of powdered rock and decayed animal substance. It is the animal substance—or the organic matter—that gives "life" to the soil and enables it to transfer this life to growing things.

The formation of the soil is a very slow process. It takes thousands of years for the rock to become pulverized and "organized" into a single inch of soil. The more solid the rock, the longer it takes for the soil to "grow" out of it. However, the soil may be carried from place to place by the waters and the winds, so that many a hard rock may be covered by a shipment of thick, soft, fertile earth.

The care and conservation of the soil are, in the opinion of the leading geographers, "the most serious of all our duties to our descendants." For the destruction of the soil can be much more rapid than its formation. Because of its looseness and its light weight, it can easily be dissolved by a heavy rainfall or a running stream. This is especially true of sloping land, where the rain shovels the earth down to the bottom of the hill.

And the more cultivated the soil—that is, the more it has been loosened by the plow—the more rapidly it can be destroyed. There are many sloping fields in the United States where a single torrential rainstorm can wash away two or three inches of soil. These "vulnerable" hillsides are colloquially known as "twenty-year" fields, "ten-year" fields, or "five-year" fields—depending upon the period during which their soil may become completely destroyed.

Soil erosion is a very serious matter. If it continues in the United States at the present rate, about two thirds of our fertile land will become useless. But it is possible, even on the sloping hillsides, to retard the erosion of the soil. This can be done through the planting of trees or of other vegetation with compact roots, for the roots will keep the clods of the earth together. A thickly wooded slope can generally withstand the onslaught of the rain.

But the onslaught of the wind is quite another matter. The wind can carry the soil away even from the level fields. In the

1930s the Dust Bowl of America—the region extending roughly from Texas to Nebraska—was almost "swept clean" of its topsoil by a devastating succession of dust storms.

Yet even the clouds of dust had their silver lining. For the loss to Texas and Nebraska meant a gain to Indiana and Pennsylvania. The earth, carried away from the West, settled down in the East; and thus the increased barrenness of one section resulted in the added fertility of another section. Moreover, the seriousness of the wind action in the Dust Bowl induced the United States Congress to authorize a nationwide study of soil conservation. This study has already brought about the saving of millions of acres of land.

The saving of land for cultivation may mean the saving of the land's civilization. One of the principal reasons for the present-day eclipse of China, Spain, Syria, North Africa, and Greece is that their ancient fertility has been seriously damaged through the erosion of the soil. These countries, especially China, have more people than food—hence too much poverty, ignorance, superstition, and despair.

For the soil determines the life of the plants, and the plants determine the life of man. Our fuel, clothing, shelter, medicine, newspapers, magazines, books, the pencil with which I write this manuscript, the eraser which rubs out the mistakes, the desk *at* which and the chair *upon* which I sit—all these are derived, for the most part, from growing things. Things that grow *out of the soil*. We feed upon plants, or upon animals that are in turn fed by plants. And the nature of every plant depends upon the climate and the soil. Our march to civilization, therefore, is a continual search for, and adjustment to, those localities where the soil and the sun and the wind and the rain can contribute most effectively to the nourishment of our bodies and the stimulation of our minds.

MINERALS AND NATIONS

Plants feed our bodies; minerals feed our machines. If you want to follow the trend of international politics, fix your mind upon the geographic distribution of the world's important minerals.

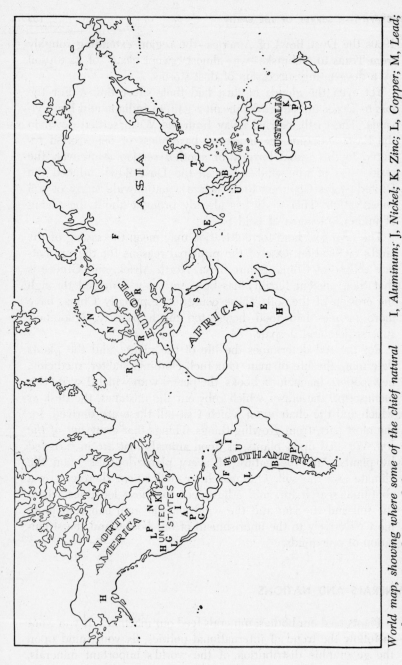

World map, showing where some of the chief natural products are found: A, Asphalt; B, Tin; C, Hemp; D, Antimony; E, Mica; F, Platinum; G, Silver; H, Gold; I, Aluminum; J, Nickel; K, Zinc; L, Copper; M, Lead; N, Iron; O, Coal; P, Wool; R, Flax; S, Cotton; T, Silk; U, Rubber.

It is the location of the minerals that is threatening constantly to plunge the leading nations into new wars. For each nation is determined in its efforts to secure control of such minerals as coal, iron, and oil.

It is our human misfortune that the minerals of the earth are unevenly distributed. The Alps, for example, are poor in minerals. And this has been a primary cause for the colonial expansion of such countries as Italy—"to get our share of the minerals and to equalize the wealth of the nations." Much of the international unrest of the twentieth century has been due to the unequal distribution of oil among the various countries. The *have-nots* have always been hungry to take away the "surplus" from the *haves*. Thus the world is periodically besmeared with oil and deluged with blood.

But let us get a closer view of some of the important minerals and of the inequality of their geographical distribution.

iron

Iron is one of the most widely distributed minerals in the world. There is hardly a country without some deposit of iron ore. Yet even in this case the deposits are uneven in quantity and unequal in quality. Five countries—the United States, Germany, Russia, Great Britain, and France—produce about seventy-five per cent of all the iron ore in the world. And the quality of the pig iron produced in these five countries is far superior to that of any other country.

Of all the iron deposits in the world, the greatest amount and the highest grade are to be found in the Lake Superior region of the United States. This district alone accounts for one fourth of the entire world supply of this important metal.

Almost equal in amount, though inferior in quality, to the deposit of the Lake Superior region is that of the Minette section of northeastern France. Another great production center of iron ore is the Kiruna-Gallivare district in Sweden.

There are extensive deposits of iron ore in Russia. But the exact information as to the quantity and quality of such deposits has thus far been withheld from the rest of the world. And thus we can get no accurate picture of the industrial and military strength of the Soviets. We do know, however, that this strength is potentially very great.

In the manufacture of iron into high-grade steel, it is necessary to use various alloys—such as manganese, nickel, chromium, tungsten, and vanadium. In the production of some of these alloys, Russia is the most favored among the nations. And Turkey is a close second. The former Axis countries—Germany, Japan, and their allies—are the least favored.

And these factors enable us to understand some of the motives that dominate the actions of men. The comparative absence of steel-making minerals in the Axis countries accounted—in part, at least—for the German attack on Russia and the Japanese invasion of China and the Philippines. And the rich deposits of chrome ore in Turkey may help to explain her strategic position in the political jockeying of the world's leading nations.

aluminum

Aluminum—or its mineral source, bauxite—has recently become one of the most important metals in the world, for it possesses the two essential qualities for rapid transportation—lightness and durability.

The production of aluminum has made gigantic strides within the past century. And, with the development of air travel, it promises to make even greater strides in the years to come. We shall probably see, in the near future, a twofold race among the leading nations—for air supremacy and for aluminum with which to build the planes.

Just now the leading centers of aluminum production are in the United States, South America, the eastern part of Europe, and the Dutch East Indies. In addition to these centers there are large deposits of aluminum—as yet unexploited—in Africa. It will be interesting to watch these regions of hidden wealth and hidden dangers in the development of the power politics of the world.

tin

The occupation of southeastern Asia by the Japanese in World War II was a most serious blow to the United States. Among other things, the Japanese through that invasion gained control of seventy-five per cent of the world's supply of tin. Many of us still remember the almost total disappearance of food in cans from the grocery shelves. But this is only half the story. Not only was our pantry depleted, but our machinery was impaired. For tin is a necessary ingredient in the making of bearings to reduce friction. As a result of the Japanese occupation, we were obliged to look to Bolivia, the only other producer of tin on a fairly large scale. But our supply of tin from a new source was almost too little and too late.

coal

The largest deposits of this important fuel mineral are to be found in the Appalachian plateau of the United States, and in the great Central Plain of Europe that stretches from France across Germany and into Russia. And, since the political boundaries of Europe do not always correspond with its geographical conformation or its mineral deposits, the inhabitants of that continent—and, indeed, of the entire world—are periodically subjected to "wars of adjustment." It is interesting to note that one of the chief sources of Germany's military power during the two World Wars was the great deposit of coal within its borders. That, and the deposits of iron in Sweden and in France. Since coal is so much bulkier than iron, the iron ore is sent to the coal regions for manufacture into pig iron. This explains, in part, the ability of Germany to amass such great quantities of iron from France and from Sweden for the building of its own military machine.

And, too, the military machine of Japan was largely the product of an available supply of coal. The Japanese controlled the coal mines of Manchuria. This Asiatic coal region, though less extensive than the coal regions of Europe and of America, has one great advantage. The coal in Asia lies just underneath the surface, is easily mined, and possesses a high grade of efficiency.

oil

Within the past hundred years our conception of geography, our entire standard of living, has been revolutionized through the exploitation of the two energy-producing minerals—coal and oil. These minerals move our engines, heat our homes, control our industries, and determine our political thoughts. Now, little by little, oil seems to be supplanting coal as the major source of energy both in peace and in war. It is hardly an exaggeration to say that the geopolitical map of the world today is a picture painted in oil. For oil is the power that keeps our air-minded and motor-minded civilization on the go.

It is for this reason that so much of our international politics is concerned with the strategic oil centers of the world.

The most productive of these oil centers are to be found in the United States. Our oil pools have thus far supplied over sixty per cent of all the petroleum used throughout the world. This, however, does not necessarily mean that over sixty per cent of the world's potential oil fields are concentrated in this country. It means merely that thus far we have *discovered* more oil in the United States because we have *drilled* for more. Geologically, there are many spots—called "structures"—all over the earth where reservoirs of oil may possibly be concealed. But there is only one way to *prove* the possibility—through a drill. And this is a difficult and expensive process—a "gamble" that appeals only to the most adventurous of prospectors. And America has led the way in this adventure. For every prospective hole drilled in all the other countries, ten have been drilled in the United States alone.

Yet there are several important oil centers outside of the United States—notably in the Caribbean countries, the Dutch East Indies, Rumania, Russia, Saudi Arabia, Iraq, and Iran.

The hunger for oil was one of the principal reasons for the German invasion of Russia and the Japanese invasion of the East Indies.

At the present time there is no country in the world that can produce all the oil it needs. This condition applies even to the United States. And therefore the oil-producing centers of the world are among the danger spots that may precipitate another war.

THE INDUSTRIAL MAP OF THE WORLD

The chief industrial areas of the world are included in a belt which extends irregularly all the way across the North Temperate Zone. For this belt contains the most invigorating climates and the richest mineral deposits.

Foremost among the industrial nations—largely because of its favored geographical position—is the United States. This country, though it possesses less than a tenth of the world's population, performs almost half of the world's work. The United States is first in the manufacture of iron and steel, in the building of ships and aircraft, the making of railway and motor cars, the production of machine tools, the development of electrical power, and the transformation of chemicals into industrial goods.

But there is another country which, potentially at least, bids fair to challenge the manufacturing supremacy of the United States. That country is Soviet Russia. Ever since the Revolution of 1917 the Russian government has been launched upon a campaign of exploitation and production: the exploitation of the vast resources of raw material deposited under the Russian and the Siberian soil, and the production of this raw material into finished goods. Great industrial cities have sprung up, almost as if by the magic of an Aladdin's lamp, across the mountains and the ice fields and the steppes of the Soviet republics, from the Arctic down to Mongolia, Iran, and the Black Sea, and from the Baltic all the way to Manchuria and the Pacific Ocean. The twentieth-century pioneers of Russia seem to have been inspired with the same fanatical zeal that moved the nineteenth-century pioneers of the United States.

Prior to World War II, however, the leading industrial country in Europe was not Russia but Germany. This industrial supremacy was bound to be temporary, since Germany was obliged to import about ninety per cent of her raw materials from other countries. It was the awareness of this situation that prompted the Kaiser in 1914, and Hitler in 1939, to gamble everything in an effort to conquer the world.

And thus the industrial picture of the world is at present a sort of Chinese puzzle. Some countries, like the United States and

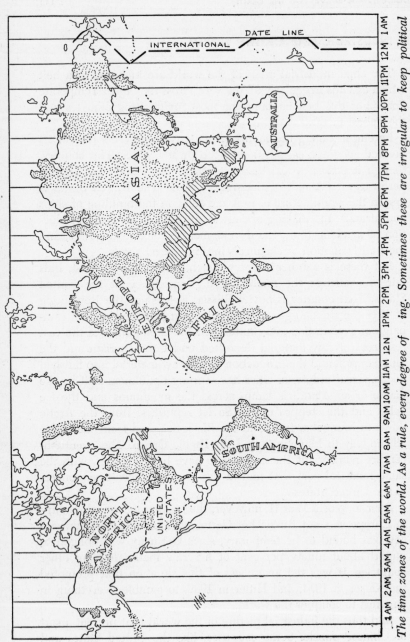

1AM 2AM 3AM 4AM 5AM 6AM 7AM 8AM 9AM 10AM 11AM 12N 1PM 2PM 3PM 4PM 5PM 6PM 7PM 8PM 9PM 10PM 11PM 12M 1AM

The time zones of the world. As a rule, every degree of longitude represents four minutes of time. The hour zones are shown in alternate stripes of white and shad-ing. Sometimes these are irregular to keep political units in the same time zone. The diagonal lines are areas in which there are half-hour differences.

Russia, are able to groove their raw materials into their manufacturing needs. But other countries, like Germany, England, Italy, France, and Japan, must rely upon outside resources to further their mechanical growth. Hence the quest for empire, the jockeying for power.

GEOGRAPHY AND TRANSPORTATION

Transportation is one of the principal factors in the study of geography, since it deals with the effort to put in balance the distribution of the world's food, raw materials, and manufactured goods. And, through the changes in transportation, the geography of the world has undergone a continual change—a progressive readjustment in the relationship between places, resources, and men. We have gradually advanced from the multitudinous little horizons of the men in the primitive oxcarts to the one-world horizon of the man in the modern airplane.

The horizons of our prehistoric ancestors were beset with all sorts of barriers—rivers that couldn't be navigated, mountains that couldn't be scaled, forests that couldn't be penetrated, deserts that couldn't be crossed. But little by little our ancestors conquered these barriers. They built rafts, leveled forests, tamed horses, and made roads, and thus they widened their horizon and increased their knowledge of "the lay of the land." They began to exchange ideas and goods, and to recognize the world across the mountains and beyond the seas. They developed a system of roads for conquest and war, and they built a number of cities at the strategic meeting places of these roads. These cities—Babylon, Athens, Carthage, Constantinople, Venice, Alexandria, Rome— came to dominate the highways, the rivers, and the seas. They were the geographic "centers" of the ancient and the medieval world.

But it was, as yet, a comparatively small world—a narrow ring of land that surrounded the Mediterranean Sea. For their transportation was still confined to horses, camels, cartwheels, paddles, and sails.

And still, in spite of these primitive methods of transportation, the spirit of adventure carried our European ancestors to the Far

East. But this was a long and hazardous journey overland; and so the traders of the Middle Ages began to seek a simpler route—a *sea route*—for the transportation of the "fabulous wealth" from the East to the West. Most of the geographers of the day, having forgotten the spherical earth theory of Plato and Aristotle, believed that the only way to reach the Orient was to sail eastward. And many an attempt was made to develop this eastward sea route all the way down the western coast of Africa and up again toward Asia—a journey of almost prohibitive difficulty and length.

But a few of the geographers—notably Toscanelli—suggested that the best way to reach the *East* was to sail *west*. For the earth, he maintained, is round; and therefore, "a person sailing persistently westward will arrive at the Orient where the spices are found."

But neither Toscanelli nor Columbus, who acted upon his suggestion, had any idea that a man sailing westward would revolutionize the geography of the world through the discovery of a new continent.

A new conception of the world, and new methods of transportation. Steamships, railroads, motorcars, and airplanes. From our vantage point in America we now enjoy a fresh outlook upon the world. The early settlers of America were obliged to look eastward, toward Europe, for their resources, their trade, and their thoughts. But now, whether we turn east or west, our horizon is world-wide—Europe and Africa and Asia across the Atlantic, Asia and Africa and Europe across the Pacific. And the Arctic Circle to the north, and the Antarctic to the south, connecting us by air to the rest of the world. Whichever way we look or travel, we encompass the picture of a global geography, an interrelated unit, one world.

This new global geography, especially since the arrival of the airplane, is entirely different from any of the geographical systems of the past. For the earth, as we see it now, is no longer a jumble of localities divided by oceans and rivers and mountains and lakes. It is an affiliated system of trading centers united by an encircling and navigable ocean of air.

And the picture of this global connection of trading centers, as viewed from the standpoint of aerial transportation, is somewhat as follows: a unit of land masses centering largely around the

Arctic Ocean, with the North Pole as a focal point for the radiation of many of the air routes between Eurasia and America. On this map we can clearly visualize the intimate neighborliness of such widely separated places as, for example, Seattle and Calcutta. The sea distance between these two cities, across the

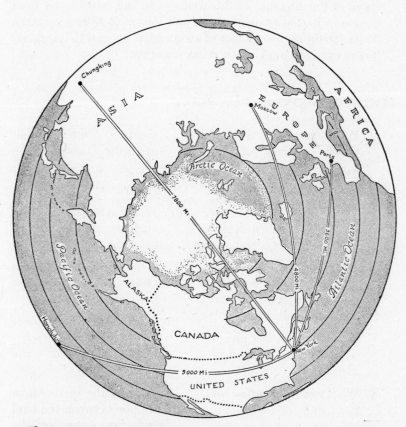

The coming of the long-distance airplane has made it necessary for us to think of the world in terms of routes which ignore the barriers of land and water. Here is the Northern Hemisphere shown as if you were looking straight down on the North Pole. Notice the different orientation required for such a map; compare it with the world map on page 106.

Pacific, is twelve thousand miles; the air distance, across the Arctic, is only seven thousand miles. A similar abbreviation of air distance, as compared with sea or land distance, exists between such cities as Chicago and Bombay, or Moscow and New York.

As for the rapidity of air transportation between any two parts of the world, it is rash to make any predictions. For almost every day brings new revolutions in the atmospheric and stratospheric speed of the airplane. At this writing you can travel faster from Boston to Berlin by plane than from Boston to Miami by train. As for the future possibilities of air travel, it staggers the imagination of even our most adventurous scientists.

REVIEW QUESTIONS IN GEOGRAPHY

1. What was the ancient Greeks' concept of the earth?

2. How did Plato and Aristotle look upon it?

3. Who was the first scientific student of geography?

4. Why was there a revival of interest in geography during the tenth and the eleventh centuries?

5. When was the first global map of the world constructed?

6. Who was the author of this map?

7. What century is known as the "golden age" of geography?

8. When did America first become, geographically speaking, "international-minded"?

9. What caused this state of mind?

10. What subsequent event emphasized this geopolitical point of view?

11. What is the geographical center of the world as we know it today?

12. What is the most direct line of communication between all the parts of the world?

13. What is the quantitative relation between the land and the water of the world?

14. How many oceans are there?

15. How many seas?

16. How many continents?

17. What is the name of the Triple Continent?

18. How much of the land surface of the world does this Triple Continent cover?

19. Why is this Triple Continent the most strategically situated?

20. How much of the world's population does it contain?

21. What is the Double Continent?

22. At what point are the territories of the United States and of Russia nearest to each other?

23. What is the distance, across the Atlantic, between South America and Africa?

24. What is the "continental shelf" between Labrador and France?

25. Why was the route across this shelf so important during World War II?

26. What transportation factor has greatly contributed to the political and commercial importance of the Double Continent?

27. Which one of the continents is uninhabited by man?

28. Which one of the continents is dominated by a single political power?

29. Why is Australia important commercially?

30. Why is it important from a military standpoint?

31. What are the eight largest islands?

32. Which are the two most important?

33. What chief factor is responsible for the "globalization" of the world?

34. What is the spiritual importance of geography as a global science?

35. What is the triple sphere of the earth?

36. What are the subdivisions of the atmosphere?

37. What is the distinction between wind, weather, and climate?

38. What are the two main factors that largely determine the climate of a locality?

39. What are the climatic zones?

40. What are the subdivisions of each of the zones?

41. Why has civilization made the most rapid strides in the Temperate Zones?

42. What, in the opinion of some of the leading geographers, are "the most serious of our duties to our descendants?"

43. What is one of the important reasons for the present-day eclipse of many great countries of the past?

44. What is one of the chief causes of war?

45. What regions are richest in (a) iron, (b) aluminum, (c) tin, (d) coal, (e) oil?

46. Why are the oil-producing countries a source of danger to the peace of the world?

47. In what geographic "belt" are the chief industrial areas of the world situated?

48. What country is foremost among the industrial nations?

49. What country is most likely to challenge this leadership?

50. What is the sea distance between Seattle and Calcutta? The air distance?

ANSWERS TO THE QUESTIONS IN GEOGRAPHY

1. A flat, round disk, covered by the inverted bowl of the sky.

2. As a spherical body.

3. Ptolemy.

4. Because of the Crusades.

5. In 1492.

6. Martin Behaim.

7. The seventeenth century.

8. In 1919.

9. Our involvement in World War I.

10. The attack on Pearl Harbor.

11. The world has no geographical center.

12. The air route.

13. One fourth land, three fourths water.

14. Five — Atlantic, Pacific, Arctic, Antarctic, Indian.

15. Nearly thirty.

16. Seven.

17. Afro-Eurasia.

18. About two thirds.

19. Because, surrounded by the five oceans, it contains outlets to all avenues of commercial traffic.

20. Seven eighths.

21. North and South America.

22. At Bering Strait, where Alaska is separated from Siberia by a narrow stretch of water.

23. About eighteen hundred miles.

24. An underwater land bridge, which rises above the surface in the islands of Greenland, Iceland, the Faroes, Ireland, and Britain.

25. Because our ships carried troops and supplies over this route, and our planes protected them from the island air bases.

26. The development of sea routes and air routes along the strategic points.

27. Antarctica.

28. Australia.

29. Because it lies across the traffic between the Pacific and the Indian oceans.

30. Because it serves as a base for military operations on a global scale.

31. Greenland, Baffin Island, New Guinea, Borneo, Sumatra, Madagascar, Honshu, and Britain.

32. Honshu (Japan) and Britain.

33. The human hunger for territorial expansion.

34. This global view of geography is likely to give us a united vision of one world.

35. The geosphere, the hydrosphere, and the atmosphere.

36. The troposphere, the stratosphere, and the ionosphere.

37. Wind is air in motion. Weather is the condition of the air in a given place at a given time. Climate is the average condition of the air over an extended period.

38. Latitude and altitude.

39. The Torrid, the North and the South Temperate, and the North and South Frigid.

40. Ocean, coast line, mountain region, plain, and plateau.

41. Because of its variable and invigorating climate.

42. The care and the conservation of the soil.

43. The erosion of the soil.

44. The unequal distribution of mineral resources throughout the world.

45. (a) The United States, Germany, Russia, Great Britain, France, and Sweden. (b) The United States, South America, the eastern part of Europe, and the Dutch East Indies. (c) Southeastern Asia and Bolivia. (d) The Appalachian plateau of the United States, the Central Plain of Europe, and Manchuria. (e) The United States, the Caribbean countries, the Dutch East Indies, Rumania, Russia, Saudi Arabia, Iraq, and Iran.

46. Because no country in the world can produce all the oil it needs.

47. In the North Temperate Zone.

48. The United States.

49. Russia.

50. Twelve thousand miles; seven thousand miles.

BIOGRAPHICAL SKETCHES OF GREAT GEOGRAPHERS

Herodotus (c. 484–c. 425 B.C.). Greek historian and geographer. Born at Halicarnassus in Asia Minor, he embarked upon extensive travels from the age of twenty. His voyages embraced practically all of the world known to his times. In various regions he collected extensive facts, anecdotes, geographical descriptions for a tremendous history. His chief travels occupied approximately seventeen years. His history of the Greco-Persian wars is a massive project. He interwove into the narrative descriptions of practically every nation of antiquity, describing the countries, their people, climate, crops, and customs. Indeed, Herodotus has been called the father of geography.

Eratosthenes (c. 276–c. 194 B.C.). Greek geographer and astronomer. Born in Africa, he was educated in Alexandria and Athens. He was appointed librarian in Alexandria and commenced scientific investigations which made him a celebrity of his times. He measured the size of the earth and his estimate was uncannily close to the actual answer. He published three volumes on geography in which he made the first recorded efforts to deal with it mathematically and experimentally. He is considered the founder of accurate chronology, since he attempted to fix the dates of the principal events in history from the fall of Troy to his own times. It is believed that he starved himself to death after going blind.

Strabo (c. 64 B.C.–c. A.D. 19). Greek geographer. Born at Amasya in Pontus, he studied the works of Aristotle and went to live in Rome. During his lifetime he traveled widely over much of the then known world. He wrote a 43-volume work in history which is no longer extant. His epochal *Geography* has come down to us. It is one of the most important studies of geography of ancient times. It is constructed on a relatively scientific basis, comprising seventeen volumes. The seventh volume has been lost, but a summary has been preserved.

Münster, Sebastian (1489–1552). German geographer. Born in the Palatinate, he taught theology and Hebrew at Heidelberg University and was preacher at the Heidelberg court. At the University of Basel he taught mathematics. He wrote the first scientific and lucid description of the world in German. In compiling this work, *Beschreibung aller Länder* (*Report on All Lands*), he called upon the services of over a hundred research assistants. He died of the plague in Basel at the age of sixty-three.

Mercator, Gerhardus (1512–94). Flemish geographer. Mercator was essentially a cartographer and plied his trade in the days of the great explorations. His great contribution is his map of the world with the parallels and meridians represented as straight lines intersecting at right angles. This map, the principle of which is still used today, has been of particular value to navigators, since from it they can find the true direction in which they are traveling. However, for general use the map is not accurate, for it distorts the areas which are at some distance from the equator.

Varenius, Bernhardus (1622–50). German geographer. Born in Hanover, he prepared himself for medicine at Königsberg and Leyden. But he abandoned medicine for a career in geography. He formulated the study of geography on a broad, scientific basis, classifying it into (a) absolute geography, dealing with mathematical data concerning the earth; (b) relative geography, concerning the effect of the sun and the climate upon the earth, the phenomenon of time; (c) the actual divisions of the earth, cartography, longitude, etc. One of his publications was a translation of a contemporary writer's account of Siam. It contained, in addition, data on the religions of various peoples.

Anville, Jean Baptiste Bourguignon d' (1697–1782). French geographer. Born at Paris, he became one of the greatest cartographers of all time. He reformed the inaccurate practices of map making, instituting a rigorous historical method. In 1743 he issued a map of Italy which corrected innumerable errors in the previous works on that country. He made valuable investigations in ancient and medieval geography, and he mapped anew the leading countries of pre-Christian times.

Ritter, Karl (1779–1859). German geographer. Born at Quedlinburg, Prussia, he received his education at Halle University. In 1819 he was appointed professor of history at the Frankfort Gymnasium, and a year later he was made professor of geography at the University of Berlin, a position which he occupied until his death. He is said to have been the founder of comparative geography. He conceived of geography as a physiology of the earth. Mountains and rivers are anatomical organs; each country is a distinct structure, etc. His most important publication was his *Geography in Its Relations to Man's Nature and History.*

Richthofen, Ferdinand, Baron von (1833–1905). German geographer. Born in Silesia, he received his education at the universities of Breslau and Berlin. At twenty-three he commenced geological investigations in the Tirol, and three years afterward he undertook an expedition to the Far East. He became fascinated with the possibilities of exploring the Chinese Empire, and he ultimately made seven journeys, penetrating to every corner of it. Among other things he called attention to the significance of Kiaochow as a port, and of the coal fields of Shantung. He wrote a work in three large volumes, revealing the results of his expeditions to China.

Huntington, Ellsworth (1876–1947). American geographer. Born at Galesburg, Illinois, he was educated at Beloit and at Harvard. He received his Ph.D. from Yale in 1909. He served as instructor at Euphrates College, Turkey, and explored the canyons of the Euphrates River. He took part in a scientific expedition to Turkestan and to Chinese Turkestan. Returning to Yale, he joined the faculty as geographer, and headed an expedition equipped by the university to Asia Minor and Palestine. He followed this with researches in the climate of the United States, Central America, and Mexico. From 1910 to 1913, he served as research associate of the Carnegie Institution of Washington, D.C. He is known particularly for his studies dealing with the effect of climate on culture.

CAREERS IN GEOGRAPHY

World War II spurred a tremendous interest on the part of the American public for geography and geographers. Newspapers and magazines teemed with maps and geographical surveys. Personnel were trained in geography by the Army and the Navy. The State Department, the Intelligence Service, the Board of Economic Warfare added geographers to their staffs. By the end of 1943 more than two hundred were employed in government agencies alone.

Year by year as the nation becomes more world-minded, the demand by industry for students trained in this specialty increases. There is a growing demand for cartographers—map makers—for students trained in transportation or industrial geography, vegetation studies, and terrain analysis. Many large businesses have developed, or are planning to develop, an extensive foreign commerce. They need economic geographers to study the world markets.

BIBLIOGRAPHY: BOOKS ON GEOGRAPHY FOR FURTHER READING AND STUDY

Bowman, Isaiah: *Geography in Relation to the Social Sciences.* New York, 1934.

Calahan, Harold Augustin: *Geography for Grown-ups.* New York.

Carter, William Harrison: *Economic Geography.* New York, 1939.

Case, Earl Clark: *College Geography.* New York, 1940.

Colby, Charles C.: *Geographic Aspects of International Relations.* Chicago, 1938.

Davis, Darrell Haug: *The Earth and Man.* New York, 1942.

Horrabin, James Francis: *An Outline of Political Geography.* New York, 1942.

Lawrence, Chester Henry: *New World Horizons: Geography for the Air Age.* New York, 1942.

Renner, George Thomas: *Global Geography.* New York, 1944.

Smith, Joseph Russell: *Industrial and Commercial Geography.* New York, 1946.

Spilhaus, Margaret Whiting: *The Background of Geography.* Philadelphia, 1935.

Stamp, Lawrence Dudley: *The World: A General Geography.* London, 1943.

Strausz-Hupé, Robert: *Geopolitics: The Struggle for Space and Power.* New York, 1942.

Van Cleef, Eugene: *Geography for the Businessman.* New York, 1943.

Van Valkenburg, Samuel: *Elements of Political Geography.* New York, 1939.

White, Charles Langdon: *Geography.* New York, 1936.

Whitbeck, Ray Hughes: *Economic Geography.* New York, 1941.

CHAPTER FOUR

chemistry—the composition of the world

Chemistry is the science which deals with the composition of substances, and with the changes in this composition resulting from the interaction of the various substances upon one another. Chemistry is thus the study of *matter*, as opposed to physics, which is the study of *energy*. Matter is anything which has mass or weight and occupies space. Energy is the capacity for doing work or for producing motion.

From the material—or chemical—point of view, this world of ours contains two kinds of substances—elements and compounds. An element is a basic substance which cannot be decomposed, by ordinary chemical methods, into two or more substances. A compound is a substance which *can* be decomposed by chemical means into two or more simpler substances. For example, hydrogen and oxygen are elements, because neither of them can be further "divided" or broken up by ordinary chemical means. But water is a compound, because it can be broken up chemically into hydrogen and oxygen.

The elements known to the scientists of the ancient world were only seven in number—copper, gold, iron, lead, mercury, tin, and silver. Today the scientists recognize no less than ninety-six elements. Of these elements, about ten are gases, two (mercury and bromine) are liquids, and all the others are solids.

It is interesting to note, however, that the compounds are

entirely different in their characteristics from the elements of which they are made up. Thus, for example, water is liquid, but its constituent elements—hydrogen and oxygen—occur as gases.

The natural and manufactured compounds of our present-day world are close to seven hundred thousand. The possible compounds of the world of tomorrow may run, it is estimated, into many millions. And all this complicated world of ours is based upon a simple scale of ninety-six elements, just as a symphony of Beethoven is based upon a simple scale of seven notes, or a drama of Shakespeare is based upon a simple alphabet of twenty-six letters.

Yet there is this difference: all the composers use all the notes, and all the writers use all the letters of the alphabet. But not all the chemists use, or are even familiar with, all the elements. Some of these elements are mere curiosities today. But they may be of the utmost importance tomorrow. Let us remember that only yesterday—historically speaking—tungsten was but a name and radium was not even known. Today tungsten lights the world and radium has revolutionized the entire trend of scientific thought.

FROM ALCHEMY TO CHEMISTRY

Alchemy is the pseudo science of transmuting one element into another, especially some baser metal into gold. This gold-making endeavor, based upon a misunderstanding of the laws of chemistry, occupied some of the best minds from the third century to the sixteenth. The "father of alchemy," Hermes Trismegistus, is said to have written no less than twenty thousand books. He claimed to possess "three fourths of all the knowledge in the world." Yet the other fourth, "withheld from the human mind," contained the "secret of the Philosopher's Stone"—the preparation which, if added to lead or copper, would transform them into silver or gold.

This continual search for the "great secret" enlisted the patronage of many a king—including the famous Haroun al Raschid of *The Arabian Nights* (763–809)—who tried, by means of the Philosopher's Stone, to replenish their royal funds. They encouraged scientists and philosophers and even quacks to devote their lives to this hopeless quest.

Among those who were rumored to have been successful in the quest was the Arabian scientist, Avicenna. He discovered the Philosopher's Stone, maintained his disciples, but he kept the secret to himself—with the result, it is believed by some, that he was able to brew the nectar of everlasting life. And thus Avicenna, who was born in the tenth century, "is alive and rich"—in the fanatical belief of some of the oriental alchemists—"to this very day."

The interest in alchemy received an added impetus as a result of the Crusades, when the impoverished aristocracy entered upon a gold rush of "metal transformation" through the "magic" of alchemy. Many a nobleman in Christendom fell a prey to the charlatans who pretended that they possessed the Philosopher's Stone.

Yet it was not only the dishonesty of the charlatans that kept alive the belief in alchemy. Quite a number of honest philosophers, including Albertus Magnus (1205–80), Thomas Aquinas (1225–74), and Roger Bacon (1214–94), regarded the transmutation of metals as a settled fact. "Gold is the most perfect of metals," declared Bacon, "because in this metal Nature has finished her work. It is necessary, then, to imitate Nature; but here a grave difficulty presents itself. Nature does not count the cycles which she takes for her work, and to which the life-term of a man is but an hour. It is, then, important to find some means which will permit one to do in a little time that which Nature does in a very much longer time. It is this means which the alchemists call . . . the Philosopher's Stone. . . . With the help of this 'Secret of Secrets' experimental science has manufactured not only gold of twenty-four degrees, but gold of thirty, forty, and onward according to pleasure."

Many of the scientists of that period, including Bacon, believed that the study of alchemy offered the solution to a double secret. "It will enable mankind not only to produce gold by purging other metals of their baser elements, but to prolong life by cleansing the body of its more corruptible particles."

Throughout the Middle Ages the belief persisted in the Philosopher's Stone, known to the credulous by such other titles as the *One Thing*, the *Great Elixir*, the *Heavenly Balm*, the *Carbuncle of the Sun*, the *Divine Panacea*, the *Soul of the World*. Little by little, however, the scientists lost faith in this mythical manufacture of gold. But the conviction of the non-existence of the Philosopher's Stone, as Ernst von Meyer reminds us in his *History of Chemistry*, "made its way slowly" among the general public. The "cheats and the swindlers kept cultivating the [fictitious] field of gold-making" until almost the beginning of the twentieth century.

Yet today the transmutation of some of the elements, not through the Philosopher's Stone but through the fission of the atom, has become a scientific fact. The pseudo science of alchemy, through all its blundering, helped to pave the way to the genuine science of chemistry.

Indeed, the science of chemistry has developed out of the very mistakes of the alchemists. There is this peculiarity about our human quest for knowledge: in spite of all our missteps in the dark, we manage to grope instinctively toward the light. It is to the laboratories of the alchemists that we can trace the beginnings of chemistry. In their futile search for the one *mythical* element—the Philosopher's Stone—the alchemists discovered several of the *real* elements of nature and the principles of their various compounds. Roger Bacon, for example, learned how to make gunpowder, to purify saltpeter by solution in water and crystallization, and to produce inflammable vapors by subjecting organic substances to dry distillation. It was Roger Bacon, too, who discovered that air was necessary for the burning of a lamp. Another of the alchemists, Arnold of Villanova, discovered the poisonous nature of decaying flesh. By the twelfth century, the Arabian alchemists had become familiar with many of the substances now known as chemicals. It is to them that we owe such terms as *alcohol, alkali, borax, elixir*, etc. The more serious among the alchemists laid down the principle of ascertaining facts through scientific experimentation. These alchemists may have followed the wrong clue, but they paved the way to the science of modern chemistry: the interaction of the elements in the composition of our material world.

THE ELEMENTS OF NATURE

Chemical symbols are used to record and explain chemical action. Each element has a symbol, usually the initial letter or letters of its name (sometimes the English and sometimes the Latin name). The symbol of hydrogen is H, that of oxygen is O —the chemical *formula* of water is therefore H_2O, which means that a molecule of water contains two atoms of hydrogen to one of oxygen. The symbol of carbon is C. The composition of starch, an organic substance, may be represented by the formula $C_6H_{10}O_5$, which means that a molecule of starch contains six atoms of carbon and ten atoms of hydrogen to five atoms of oxygen.

The factor in chemistry which makes atomic elements combine in different ratios is called *valence*. The valence of an element is the power of its atoms, expressed by a number, to hold a certain number of atoms of other elements in combination. The valence of hydrogen is 1, and all elements which combine with hydrogen in the atomic proportion of one to one have the valence 1. Since oxygen combines with hydrogen in the proportion of one atom of oxygen to two of hydrogen, oxygen has a valence of 2. The following table lists all the known chemical elements, with the chemical symbol, atomic weight, valence, and density of each, where known. Names in small capitals are common elements. The others are very rare.

the chemical elements

NAME	SYMBOL	ATOMIC WEIGHT	VALENCE	DENSITY
ACTINIUM	Ac	227.(?)	3	?
ALUMINUM	Al	26.97	3	2.7
americium	Am	241	3	?
ANTIMONY	Sb	121.76	3 & 5	6.68
argon	A	39.944	0	.0018
ARSENIC	As	74.91	3 & 5	5.73
astatine	At	211	1, 3, 5 & 7	?
BARIUM	Ba	137.36	2	3.5

NAME	SYMBOL	ATOMIC WEIGHT	VALENCE	DENSITY
beryllium	Be	9.02	2	1.85
BISMUTH	Bi	209.0	3 & 5	9.78
boron	B	10.82	3	2.45
BROMINE	Br	79.916	1, 3, 5 & 7	3.4
CADMIUM	Cd	112.41	2	8.65
CALCIUM	Ca	40.08	2	1.54
CARBON	C	12.01	2, 3 & 4	2.25 (graphite)
cerium	Ce	140.13	3 or 4	6.9
cesium	Cs	132.91	1	1.87
CHLORINE	Cl	35.457	1, 3, 5 or 7	.0032
CHROMIUM	Cr	52.01	2, 3 & 6	7.1
COBALT	Co	58.94	2 & 3	8.9
columbium	Cb	92.91	3 & 5	8.4
COPPER	Cu	63.57	1 & 2	8.93 to 8.95
curium	Cm	242	3	?
dysprosium	Dy	162.46	3	?
erbium	Er	167.2	3	4.77
europium	Eu	152.0	2 & 3	?
FLUORINE	F	19.0	1	.0017
francium	Fa	223	1	?
gadolinium	Gd	156.9	3	?
gallium	Ga	69.72	2 & 3	5.91
germanium	Ge	72.6	4	5.36
GOLD	Au	197.2	1 & 3	19.32
hafnium	Hf	178.6	4	13.3
HELIUM	He	4.003	0	.00018
holmium	Ho	163.5	3	?
HYDROGEN	H	1.0081	1	.000089
illinium	Il	146.(?)	3	?
indium	In	114.76	3	7.28
IODINE	I	126.92	1, 3, 5 & 7	4.93 (solid)
iridium	Ir	193.1	3, 4 & 6	22.42
IRON	Fe	55.84	2 & 3	7.86
krypton	Kr	83.7	0	.0037
lanthanum	La	138.92	3	6.15
LEAD	Pb	207.21	2 & 4	11.35
lithium	Li	6.94	1	.534
lutecium	Lu	175.0	3	?
MAGNESIUM	Mg	24.32	2	1.74
MANGANESE	Mn	54.93	2, 3, 4, 6 & 7	7.2

NAME	SYMBOL	ATOMIC WEIGHT	VALENCE	DENSITY
masurium	Ma	98.(?)	?	?
MERCURY	Hg	200.61	1 & 2	13.55
molybdenum	Mo	95.95	2, 3, 4, 5 & 6	10.2
neodymium	Nd	144.27	3	6.95
NEON	Ne	20.183	0	.0009
neptunium	Np	237	3, 4, 5 & 6	?
NICKEL	Ni	58.69	2 & 3	8.9
NITROGEN	N	14.008	3 & 5	.80 (liquid)
osmium	Os	190.2	2, 3, 4, 6 & 8	22.48
OXYGEN	O	16.0	2	.00143
palladium	Pd	106.7	2 & 4	12.0
PHOSPHORUS	P	31.02	3 & 5	1.82 to 2.20
PLATINUM	Pt	195.23	2 & 4	21.45
plutonium	Pu	239	3, 4, 5 & 6	?
polonium	Po	210.0	2 & 4	?
POTASSIUM	K	39.096	1	.86
praseodymium	Pr	140.92	3	6.5
PROTACTINIUM	Pa	231.	5	?
RADIUM	Ra	226.05	2	5 plus
radon	Rn	222.0	0	.0097
rhenium	Re	186.31	7	20.53
rhodium	Rh	102.91	3 & 4	12.5
rubidium	Rb	85.48	1	1.53
ruthenium	Ru	101.7	2, 3, 4, 6, 7 & 8	12.2
samarium	Sm	150.43	3	7.7 to 7.8
scandium	Sc	45.1	3	2.5
SELENIUM	Se	78.96	2, 4 & 6	4.3
SILICON	Si	28.06	4	2.42
SILVER	Ag	107.88	1	10.5
SODIUM	Na	22.997	1	.971
STRONTIUM	Sr	87.63	2	2.6
SULPHUR	S	32.06	2, 4 & 6	1.96 to 2.07
tantalum	Ta	180.88	5	16.6
tellurium	Te	127.61	2, 4 & 6	6.24
terbium	Tb	159.2	3	?
thallium	Tl	204.39	1 & 3	11.85
THORIUM	Th	232.12	4	11.2
thulium	Tm	169.4	3	?
TIN	Sn	118.7	2 & 4	6.99
titanium	Ti	47.9	3 & 4	4.5

NAME	SYMBOL	ATOMIC WEIGHT	VALENCE	DENSITY
TUNGSTEN	W	183.92	6	19.3
uranium	U	238.07	4 & 6	18.68
vanadium	V	50.95	3 & 5	5.96
xenon	Xe	131.3	0	.0058
ytterbium	Yb	173.04	3	?
yttrium	Y	88.92	3	5.51
ZINC	Zn	65.38	2	7.14
zirconium	Zr	91.22	4	6.4

Those elements with zero valence are *inert;* that is, they do not combine chemically with any other elements. The fact that helium is an inert gas is of importance in aeronautics, for its lightness makes it desirable for use in dirigibles, and since it does not combine with any other element, it is of course not inflammable, as hydrogen is. The United States has the principal source of the world's supply of helium; the gas is commonly used in American dirigibles.

The figures for density in the preceding table are the number of *grams* per *cubic centimeter*. The gram and centimeter are units of measure in the so-called *metric system* of weights and measures, which is used in scientific work throughout the world. A cubic centimeter of water at 4° C. weighs exactly one gram; therefore these density figures also indicate the ratio of the weight of each element to the weight of an equal volume of water; that is, zinc, with a density of 7.14, weighs 7.14 times as much as an equal volume of water at 4°. A gram is equal to 15.432 grains; there are 7000 grains in a pound of avoirdupois. To convert density to pounds per cubic foot, it is only necessary to multiply the density of a given element in grams per cubic centimeter by 62½ (more exactly 62.4, the weight in pounds of a cubic foot of water).

The ninety-six elements are roughly divided into *metals,* which form compounds known as bases, and *non-metals* (sometimes called *metalloids*), which form compounds known as acids; some, however, form both basic and acid compounds. Only about twenty are non-metals, including oxygen, hydrogen, sulphur, nitrogen, carbon, silicon, and chlorine. The rest are metals. Mercury is the only metal which is not solid at ordinary temperatures; mercury occurs naturally as a liquid, commonly called quicksilver. Ten or so of the non-metals are gases. Bromine is a liquid. The rest of the non-metals are solids.

When the elements are arranged in the order of their ascending atomic weights, they form a series conforming to the so-called *periodic law*. This series is more exactly indicated by the *atomic numbers* of the elements, which are derived independently of the atomic weights. Elements thus group themselves together in families with similar valences and chemical properties.

MOLECULES AND ATOMS

A *molecule* is a group of two or more atoms, usually consisting of different substances. Thus a molecule of water is a group of two atoms of hydrogen and one atom of oxygen. A molecule is the smallest part of any compound capable of maintaining its

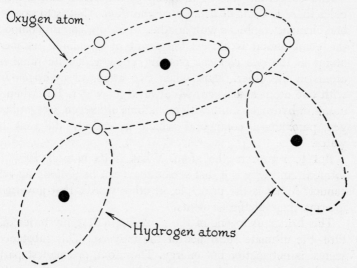

A molecule of water, consisting of two atoms of hydrogen and one atom of oxygen (H₂O). The nuclei of the atoms are shown by the heavy black dots, while the electrons in their orbits are shown as small outlined circles.

identity as that particular compound. Thus when you break up a molecule of water, you no longer have a particle of liquid, but three particles of gases (two hydrogen and one oxygen). Some molecules are composed of only two atoms; others, of many hundreds of atoms. Yet even the largest of molecules is smaller than a millionth of an inch. We can get an idea as to the relative size of the molecule from the following consideration: if a drop of water were to be magnified to the size of the earth, each molecule in this drop would be no bigger than a baseball.

An *atom* is part of a molecule. It is the smallest part of an element capable of maintaining its identity as that particular element. Thus we can talk about an atom of hydrogen, of oxygen, of sodium, of silver, or of gold. But we cannot talk about an atom of water, for water consists of molecules, or combinations of atoms, which in themselves are not water.

The term *molecule,* therefore, is used generally to denote the smallest particle of a compound, while the term *atom* is used to denote the smallest part of an element.

And concerning the relationship of the atoms and the molecules there is a *law of definite composition.* That is to say, when one element combines with another to form a certain compound, the combination is always the result of a definite number of atoms in the one element reacting upon a definite number of atoms in the other. Thus, when two atoms of hydrogen unite with one atom of oxygen, we always get water. But when two atoms of hydrogen unite with *two* atoms of oxygen, we get hydrogen peroxide—a compound which is entirely different from water.

But to return to the atom. What is its nature? How is it formed? And why is it that some atoms can be united and others cannot? What is the principle, in other words, that governs the intermarriage of the elements?

This brings us to one of the most fascinating mysteries of nature—the ultimate substance of the universe. This substance, it seems, is not matter but energy. The atom, or smallest particle of what we have been accustomed to regard as the material substance of the elements, is composed of electric charges. These electric charges are forms of energy which possess definite known weights.

Every atom, according to the modern theory, is a combination of positive and negative electric charges. The atom is a miniature solar system, with a nucleus of positively charged units, called *protons,* and planetary orbits of negatively charged units, called *electrons.*

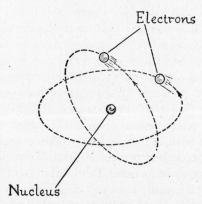

An atom of helium, showing electrons moving in their orbits around the nucleus.

These planetary electrons revolve very speedily—about 150,000 miles a second—around the solar nucleus of their protons. And thus an apparently solid and motionless object, like a lump of iron or gold, is in reality a union of solar systems, or atoms, each of them consisting of vast empty spaces and a whirlpool of rapid motion.

This motion of the negatively charged **units** of electricity around the positive charge in the center is **what** constitutes the body of the atom. And every atom of a definite element—such as hydrogen, for example—contains the same number of electrons. The atoms of the *different* elements, however, contain different numbers of electrons. Thus, the simplest atom, hydrogen, contains one electron; but the most complex atom, uranium, contains ninety-two electrons. It is this difference in the number of electrons that constitutes the difference in the elements.

In the atom, electrons will be found only at certain definite distances from the nucleus. These areas in which electrons exist are called principal orbits. In the lighter atoms with few electrons, there are few orbits; in the heavier atoms, there may be as many as seven orbits. The outermost orbit may hold as many as eight electrons. The ordinary free element is neutral, holding an equal number of protons and electrons. If, in addition, it has a completed outer orbit, with eight electrons, it is in a state of electrical equilibrium. It is stable. It has no tendency to add or lose electrons. Since chemical action involves the loss of electrons by one element to another, which gains them, such stable elements never enter chemical action. They are inert. Argon, neon, and helium are such inert elements. (If an element possesses one orbit only, it needs but two electrons to complete this orbit.)

If an electrically neutral atom has less than eight electrons in its outermost orbit, it tries to lose or gain enough electrons so as to acquire a complete outermost orbit. Thus, the sodium atom, with one electron in its outer, third, orbit (and eight electrons in its second orbit), easily loses this electron to an atom of chlorine, which has but seven electrons in its outer orbit. The result is a molecule of sodium chloride—ordinary table salt.

This, in brief, is the present-day theory about the process of atomic and molecular construction—the transformation of the electrons and the protons into the atoms of the elements, and the combination of the co-operative atoms into the molecules of the compounds. All chemical action, therefore, is a migration of electrons from one atom to another.

THE MORE FAMILIAR ELEMENTS

And now let us examine some of the more familiar elements— their structure, their characteristics, and the part they play in our everyday world.

oxygen

The discovery of oxygen marks the beginning of modern chemistry. In 1774 Joseph Priestley, an English clergyman, heated a substance—later known as red mercuric oxide—in a tube filled with mercury and inverted in a dish of mercury. The result was the production of a gas in which a candle burned with an "unearthly" brilliance, and a mouse frisked around with a "diabolical" activity. Priestley breathed some of this "strange air" and described his experience as follows:

"I fancied that my breast felt peculiarly light and easy for some time afterwards. Who can tell but that in time this pure air may become a fashionable article of luxury? Hitherto only two mice and myself have had the privilege of breathing it."

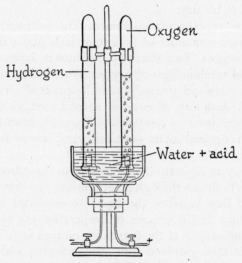

Obtaining hydrogen and oxygen through the electrolysis of water.

Priestley's conjecture has been realized—in a modified way. Oxygen has become not a "fashionable luxury" but a blessed necessity to humans exhausted by illness. As for Priestley himself, he received the compensation accorded to so many of our human benefactors. His house, his goods, his manuscripts, and his apparatus were committed to the flames, and he and his family were exiled from England because of his opposition to the orthodox fanaticism of his day.

But the scientists went on with the experiments initiated by Priestley. Antoine Lavoisier (1743–94), the "Father of Modern Chemistry," showed the relationship of oxygen to air and to the process of combustion. It was Lavoisier who first applied the name *oxygen* to this gas—from the Greek term for *producer of acid*. Lavoisier was wrong in his belief that oxygen is contained in all acids, but he was right in his contention that it forms an essential part of the air.

It is of painful interest to note that Lavoisier, like Priestley, fell a victim to the stupidity of his fellow men. His fate was even worse than that of his predecessor. He was executed—not, however, by the fanatical conservatives, but by the fanatical revolutionaries of his day.

But the experiments continued. The scientists went on to demonstrate a number of important facts about the newly discovered oxygen. Two thirds of the human body, they learned, consists of combinations of oxygen. Water contains about ninety per cent; earth and granite, about fifty per cent; air, about twenty per cent. And they discovered several methods for extracting pure oxygen from its compounds—especially from the air, which is now recognized as its most important source for commercial purposes.

· The way to separate the oxygen from the nitrogen in the air is to *liquefy* the air through great pressure at a very low temperature, and then to allow the liquid to evaporate by raising the temperature. In the process of evaporation the nitrogen, which is the more volatile of the two gases, escapes first. The remaining oxygen is then gathered into steel cylinders and stored away for commercial or medicinal use.

Oxygen is a gas without odor or color or taste. In its liquid state, however, it becomes light blue in color. At ordinary temperatures it is not very active, but at high temperatures it combines with almost every element.

When oxygen combines with one other element, as in water, the compound becomes an oxide. But when it combines with two or more other elements, as in potassium chlorate, the compound is not an oxide.

The combination of oxygen with another element is called *oxidation*. The oxidation may be slow, as in the *rusting* of metals, or rapid, as in the *burning* of metals. If you heat an iron wire until it becomes red and then insert it into a bottle of oxygen, the wire will flame (oxidize) into a shower of sparks. If you extinguish a lighted match and immediately introduce it into the bottle, the light will flare up again. The union of oxygen with any inflammable substance, such as fuel in a furnace, for example, will produce *combustion.* That is, heat and light. If the process of this oxidation is *very* rapid, as in a heap of oily rags or in a pile of wet coal, the heat thus generated will ignite the material into what is known as *spontaneous* combustion.

The uses of oxygen are many. To mention but a few of them, oxygen contributes to the maintenance of life through the burning of waste tissue; it helps in the disposal of sewage and in the transformation of fuel into light, heat, and power; it serves as the medium for the oxyacetylene torch whose flame cuts iron like a knife; and, compressed into cylinders, it sustains the aviator who travels through the attenuated air of the stratosphere. Above all, the oxygen tent enables the exhausted invalid to get the maximum amount of air with a minimum expenditure of effort.

hydrogen

Hydrogen was discovered one hundred and twenty-four years before the discovery of oxygen. In 1650, as he was treating iron with dilute sulphuric acid, Turquet de Mayerne noticed the formation of a separate substance which he called "inflammable air." It was Lavoisier, however, who first named it *hydrogen— producer of water.*

Hydrogen is rarely found free in nature, but it is present in almost all the organic compounds. Flames of hydrogen and calcium have been found to shoot out from the sun to a height of a million miles.

Hydrogen can be displaced from acids by a number of active metals. When such a displacement occurs a salt is formed. And the salt is always named after the acid from which it is formed: *chloride* from hydrochloric acid; *sulphates* from sulphuric acid; *nitrates* from nitric acid; *phosphates* from phosphoric acid.

Hydrogen can be very rapidly displaced from cold water by the more active metals, such as potassium and sodium. This displacement is so violent that you must take care against injury when you perform the experiment. For the heat of the reaction may ignite the hydrogen, melt the metal, and spatter the flaming particles in your face.

But the less active metals will displace hydrogen from water only when heated to a sufficient degree for the reaction to set in.

Hydrogen, like oxygen, is odorless, colorless, and tasteless. In appearance, liquid hydrogen is no different from water. But you can easily tell the difference when you place a cork upon its surface. The cork will sink in the hydrogen as rapidly as a stone sinks in the water. For hydrogen is the lightest of all the known substances. In its gaseous form it may be poured *upward* instead of *downward* from container to container.

Again like oxygen, hydrogen has many uses. Combined with nitrogen, it forms ammonia—the basis for the manufacture of fertilizers and explosives. United with petroleum or with lignite coal—the process is called *hydrogenation*—it materially increases the supply of gasoline. Reacting upon liquid fats, such as cottonseed oil, it transforms them into *solid* fats—Crisco, Spry, and other substitutes for lard. In the American homes about two hundred thousand tons of hydrogenated fats are consumed every year.

the halogen elements—bromine, chlorine, fluorine, and iodine

HALOGEN—from the Greek term that means *salt maker*—is the common name for those elements which, combined with metals, produce salts. These salt-producing elements are bromine, chlorine, fluorine, and iodine.

BROMINE was first recognized as a separate element in 1826. This liquid substance is found largely in the salt layers of the earth's soil, in sea water, and in saline springs. Bromine has a deep red color and a very offensive smell. Its chief uses are in the manufacture of aniline dyes, in the preparation of the sedative, potassium bromide, in the production of silver bromide, the sensitized surface of photographic plates, and in the making of tetraethyl lead as an "anti-knock" in motor gasoline.

CHLORINE, as a separate element, was discovered about half a century before the discovery of bromine. The name, derived from the Greek, means "greenish yellow."

This gaseous substance has a suffocating odor and is highly poisonous. Owing to its great activity in combining with other substances, it occurs in nature only as a compound, never as a free element. Its most familiar compound is salt, chemically known as sodium chloride. (Any combination of chlorine with another element is called a *chloride*.)

The combination of chlorine with sulphur, or sulphur chloride, is used in the manufacture of the fatal war weapon, mustard gas. In peacetime chlorine is used chiefly as a medium for the bleaching of paper and textiles, the cleansing of grease spots, the destruction of bacteria in polluted water supplies, and the extraction of gold from its ore compounds.

FLUORINE. The existence of this gas was known as early as 1670. But owing to its great activity—that is, its affinity for uniting with other substances—it was not until 1886 that the chemists were able to release it as a separate element.

A very small proportion of this element, if found in drinking water, helps to strengthen human teeth. But a somewhat larger proportion tends to destroy them.

The compounds of fluorine, or *fluorides,* are used in many ways. Aluminum fluoride serves as a disinfectant in breweries. Sodium fluoride is a powerful insect exterminator. In some of its liquid compounds, fluorine is used in the hardening of concrete and the making of opaque glass and enamel.

IODINE was discovered as an element at the beginning of the nineteenth century (1812), when Courtois released a violet vapor through the heating of the ashes of seaweed with sulphuric acid. Two years later Gay-Lussac named this element after the Greek word *iodes,* which means *like a violet*.

At room temperatures iodine is a solid. This element and its compounds are used extensively in medicine, photography, and the manufacture of dyestuffs. In its solid form it burns the skin; but diluted in alcohol, it forms the antiseptic tincture of iodine. A certain amount of the iodine compound known as *thyroxin* is found in the healthy gland tissue of man. A deficiency of this compound may result in goiter—a disease prevalent in countries where there is too little iodine in the soil.

sulphur

This is one of the earliest known elements. It is mentioned in the Bible as brimstone—the fuel for the burning of the sinners in hell. Among the alchemists it was regarded as one of the three fundamental substances.

This element is found in its free state in volcanic regions. It has two different kinds of structure—crystalline and amorphous (without definite shape).

Combinations of sulphur are found in all plants and animals. You can easily detect the presence of sulphur in decayed eggs by the offensive odor.

Yet in its free state sulphur is odorless as well as tasteless. It is a solid substance, pale yellow in color, insoluble in water, but very reactive upon most of the metals by the application of heat. It does not, however, combine with platinum or gold. Sulphur volatilizes—that is, it turns into vapor—at a moderate temperature.

Sulphur and its compounds—especially sulphuric acid—play a very important, perhaps *the most important,* part in our present-day activities. About fifty thousand tons of sulphur are used annually in the vulcanizing of rubber. The manufacture of matches and of various dyes depends upon sulphur. Free sulphur is used in the preparation of black gunpowder and of various disinfectants. (The disinfectant nature of sulphur was known to the Greeks in the days of Homer, about three thousand years ago.) Sulphur is a necessary ingredient in the bleaching of various fabrics, walnuts, and dried fruits.

Compounded with oxygen to form sulphur dioxide, it is used as a freezing agent in some types of electric refrigerators. And compounded into sulphuric acid, it has become one of the most important among all the chemicals. At present the United States uses annually almost ten million tons of sulphuric acid in a wide variety of industries—such as electroplating, the refining of petroleum, and the manufacture of fertilizers, dyes and coal products, paints and explosives, textiles, rayon, and cellulose film.

nitrogen

Nitrogen, discovered as an element in 1772, forms about four fifths of the atmosphere. Every square foot of ground sustains a column of nitrogen weighing almost a ton. Yet it is somewhat lighter than air, and it has no color, odor, or taste. Nitrogen is a necessary element in plant life and therefore, indirectly, in animal life. Absorbed by the bacteria that grow on the roots of clover and other herbs, it becomes converted into protein. When the clover is plowed under, the protein enriches the soil, the grain that grows in the soil feeds upon the protein, animals feed upon the grain, and thus the protein is ultimately transformed into muscle, which in turn is converted into the food of man.

But the cycle is not as yet complete. For, when animals and men decay, some of the original nitrogen returns to the air and the process begins all over again.

One of the important products of nitrogen is ammonia—a composition of one part nitrogen and three parts oxygen. The derivation of the word "ammonia" is interesting. This substance was

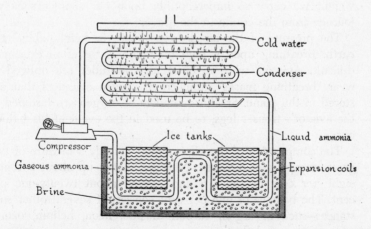

Ammonia (NH₃) used as a refrigerant. Ammonia, introduced in liquid form, is allowed to expand into a gas, meanwhile extracting heat from the surrounding water, thus freezing it. The compressor then changes the gaseous ammonia back to liquid form for re-use in the process.

first produced by the burning of camels' dung at the temple of *Ammon*, the Egyptian sun god. Hence the name *ammonia*.

Ammonia is still being utilized as an important ingredient in the preparation of fertilizers. And during World War I it was used extensively in the manufacture of nitric acid for explosives.

Yet nitroglycerine, the explosive agent in dynamite, can be made to serve as an agent of preservation as well as of destruction. Administered as a medicine in angina pectoris, it can promote the patient's comfort and prolong his life. Such are the paradoxical uses of chemistry as compounded in the crucible of the human mind.

In its industrial role ammonia is used for the hardening of steel through heating, and for the making of ice through freezing—another paradoxical exploitation of the forces of nature.

THE AIR WE BREATHE

The air around us appears to be so light that we are hardly aware of its presence. And yet there is a pressure of nearly fifteen pounds of air upon every square inch of the earth. This is the weight we carry so imperceptibly upon our shoulders as we journey from the cradle to the grave.

The pressure of the air decreases with its height above the earth. Breathing upon a high mountain is therefore extremely difficult. Aviators who travel at high altitudes are obliged to wear "breathing masks" attached to oxygen cylinders that are stored in the plane. Smaller cylinders of oxygen are fastened to the aviator's trouser legs, to be used in the event of his bailing out.

The composition of the air is almost entirely a mixture of two gases—oxygen and nitrogen. Nitrogen makes up about seventy-eight per cent of the air; and oxygen about twenty-one per cent. The balance of one per cent consists of several other substances—such as argon, carbon dioxide, neon, helium, ozone, water vapor, and dust.

All the above constituents of the air, it is important to note, form a *mixture* and not a *compound*. A chemical mixture is a blending of several ingredients without any alteration of the substances, each of which retains its own individuality. A chemical compound, on the other hand, is a fusion of substances which, in their reaction upon one another, lose their individual properties and form a substance differing in its properties from any of the ingredients. In the substance known as air each of the constituents retains its properties, regardless of the presence of the other constituents. To use a rough analogy, the air is to be compared to a boardinghouse of unrelated people rather than to the household of a related family.

The country air, when compared to the city air, shows less carbon dioxide—a substance that arises from decaying matter, the exhalations of animals and men, and the burning of fuel. But this is no cause for alarm to city dwellers. For the city air would have to contain many times its present amount of carbon dioxide before it could do any material harm to human beings by taking the place of needed oxygen.

And there is no possibility that there will ever be a dangerous amount of carbon dioxide in the air. Nature takes care of that. In the first place the plants "purify" the carbon dioxide in the air by "breathing in" the carbon dioxide and "rejecting" most of the oxygen. In the second place carbon dioxide is soluble in water, so that the ocean contains about thirty times as much of it as the air. So long as we have plants and water in this world, we shall be safe from an overaccumulation of carbon dioxide.

Of greater danger to human health is the presence of dust in the atmosphere. Dust is earth or any other substance reduced to a powder so fine and dry that it can be carried by the wind. The air in a city like New York may contain, at times, over half a billion dust particles per cubic foot. Mingled with this dust is the enormous quantity of sulphuric acid arising from the sulphur dioxide of burning coal.

Fortunately, however, there is a growing tendency in factories —and even in some homes—to "wash the air clean" by means of artificial "dust removers." These dust—and bacteria—removers blow the air through a spray of water; and thus they wash out the impurity and regulate the humidity and the temperature to the point of greatest comfort. This air conditioning should make no little contribution to the health, happiness, and productivity of the human race.

CARBON—THE LIFE-GIVING ELEMENT

Carbon is one of the most important among the elements. To date the chemists have discovered—or manufactured—almost half a million compounds of this substance. But even more significant is the fact that carbon is the basis of life. The chemistry dealing with carbon and its compounds is called *organic chemistry* because all organic, living (animal and vegetable) matter contains these substances.

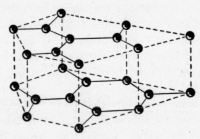

Carbon atoms as they are arranged in graphite, which is a crystalline carbon.

For a long time, indeed, it was believed that a carbon compound could be produced *only* within a living organism. But during the past hundred years the chemists have manufactured a great many of these compounds in the test tube of the laboratory.

We are brought into contact with carbon and its compounds in nearly all our daily activities. We find it in our food and our fuel, our dyes and our drugs, our lubricants, films, explosives, pencils, and ink. Nylon is basically a compound made from carbon, water, and air. Our stove polish, crayons, automobile tires, and phonograph records are treated with carbon black, familiarly known as lampblack.

In its crystalline form carbon occurs either as graphite or as the diamond. There are several amorphous—that is, formless or non-crystalline—kinds of carbon, such as soot, charcoal, and coke. In the democracy of nature, the black coal and the brilliant jewel are the selfsame essence under different disguises.

Under ordinary temperatures carbon is inactive. But when it is subjected to heat it combines with oxygen to form carbon monoxide or carbon dioxide. In a furnace fire, when there is little coke and much air, the prevalent compound is *carbon dioxide* (CO_2). But when there is much coke and little air, the predominant formation is *carbon monoxide* (CO).

CARBON DIOXIDE is found in the air (about 3 parts in 10,000), in oil wells, in the earth's crust, and especially in the sea. The easiest way to prepare carbon dioxide is to burn carbon—or coal, paper, or oil—with an excessive amount of oxygen. Caution: if the oxygen is *not* excessive, carbon monoxide may be formed.

Carbon dioxide has no color or odor. But its solution (in soda water) has a sharp and stimulating taste. If it is compressed to a liquid form which is then allowed to escape from an inverted cylinder, it vaporizes and cools very rapidly and part of it freezes into "dry ice." More than half a million tons of this carbon dioxide ice are sold annually in the United States.

Carbon dioxide represents an interesting cycle in the economy of nature. Expelled in the breathing of animals, it is absorbed by plants as a necessary food.

CARBON MONOXIDE has no color and practically no odor. And thus the victim exposed to its fumes has no way of detecting its presence. It can form in two ways: by burning carbon with insufficient air, as in a closed garage, or by exposing carbon dioxide to a very intense carbon fire. Its poisonous nature is due to its great affinity for hemoglobin—the coloring matter in the red corpuscles of the blood. It combines with the hemoglobin, neutralizes its oxygen-carrying function, and destroys the victim within a very short time. This carbon compound has been made into one of the deadliest weapons in war—phosgene, the poison gas manufactured out of carbon monoxide and chlorine.

THE CHEMICALS OF THE HUMAN BODY

It has been estimated that the human body consists of the following chemical elements:

Oxygen	65%
Carbon	18%
Hydrogen	10%
Nitrogen	3%

Calcium
Chlorine
Iodine
Iron
Magnesium   } 4% (approximately)
Manganese
Phosphorus
Potassium
Sodium
Sulphur

To express this in another way, we may reduce the chemical composition of a man to the following ingredients:

Enough water (oxygen and hydrogen) to fill a 10-gallon barrel.

Enough fat to make 7 bars of soap.

Carbon for 9000 lead pencils.

Phosphorus for 2200 matches.

Iron for 2 nails.

Lime enough to whitewash a chicken coop.

A few sprinklings of magnesium, potassium, sodium, sulphur, and so forth.

In other words, the makings of a man may all be sorted and labeled and stored away within a few bottles in the laboratory. In this composition there is only one thing missing—the man himself. That is, the mysterious life spark that transforms the chemicals into a human being. But that speculation is—and always will remain, perhaps—beyond the scope of our human knowledge.

Quite within the scope of our knowledge, however, is the chemistry of our physical energy. That is, the process of the replacement of worn-out tissue, of the generation of heat to keep the body alive, and of the absorption of food to maintain its growth.

For the human body is an engine that transforms fuel into work. And the chief sources of our fuel supply are six: water, air, proteins, fats, carbohydrates, and mineral salts. We get the water and the air directly; the proteins from milk, cheese, eggs, peas, beans, cereal, and fatless meat; the fats from milk, meat, nuts, and several of the vegetable oils; the carbohydrates from the starch of cereals, potatoes, and rice, and from the sugar in fruits, beets, and sugar cane; the mineral salts from meat, milk, nuts, vegetables, whole grains, and eggs.

In addition to the above foods, there is one other essential for the human body. This essential is known under the general name of *vitamins*—a group of substances whose precise function has not as yet been determined, but whose absence from a person's diet may cause serious damage. It is therefore unsafe to depend exclusively upon a diet of meat, bread, sugar, potatoes, and fats, since these articles are deficient in some of the most important vitamins. A more wisely balanced diet will include—together with the above items—milk, liver, eggs, carrots, tomatoes, green peas and the other green (uncooked) vegetables, fish liver oils, grains, lean pork, fruits (especially of the citrus kind), kidneys, and yeast.

METALS AND MEN

The past ages of history have been variously called the *Stone Age*, the *Bronze Age*, the *Iron Age*, and so on. But the present day may well be characterized as the *Metallic Age*. For our modern civilization is based, materially, upon nearly all the metals of the earth. We live and we work in buildings with iron frames; we travel in vehicles of aluminum and steel; we buy newspapers with copper and nickel and silver coins, and base their value upon a standard of gold; we keep iron from rusting by galvanizing it with zinc; we get our water through pipes of lead; our rings and our watches and our pens are made largely of gold; our electric bulbs are lighted with filaments of tungsten; and our atomic power has been developed—thus far—out of uranium.

It will be interesting, therefore, to consider briefly the nature and the uses of some of the leading metals.

aluminum

Nearly one thirteenth of the earth's crust consists of aluminum, which is the most widely distributed of the metals. It is not found free in nature but is contained as a compound in nearly all the rocks. The most important of the substances containing this metal is bauxite—a mixture of aluminum oxide (combined with some water), clay, iron oxide and silica.

Aluminum is a metal of great value because of its lightness, strength, ductility—that is, capability of being stretched out without breaking—and its resistance to tarnish. For a long time, however, the extraction of aluminum from its compounds was so expensive a process that this metal remained little more than a curiosity. A pound of aluminum about a hundred years ago sold for $160. Today, owing to the great advance of electrolysis—the chemical decomposition of substances by an electric current—the price of this metal has been reduced to less than twenty cents a pound.

The color of aluminum is similar to that of silver with a bluish glitter. It can easily be hammered into sheets or drawn into wire. Today there are almost half a million miles of aluminum cable in use throughout the world. And the number of aluminum vessels used for cooking is close to *half a billion* in the United States alone.

But these are not the only uses of aluminum. Owing to its lightness, beauty, strength, and resistance to corrosion, it has become one of the favored commercial metals. In its pure form it is used for automobile and airplane parts. Reduced to a powder and mixed with oil, it serves as a paint for metallic articles such as pipes, radiators, storage tanks, and the like. Combined with copper, it forms an excellent alloy for friction-resisting auto-truck gears. Aluminum and its alloys are also used extensively in the making of furniture.

The most successful of all the aluminum alloys is duralumin. Compounded of about ninety-four per cent aluminum, three per cent copper, and small quantities of manganese, magnesium, and silicon this alloy weighs only one third as much as steel but is equal to it in strength.

copper

This was perhaps the first of the metals known to man. Within recent times a piece of copper tubing has been excavated from the tomb of an Egyptian king who lived about five thousand years ago.

Copper is not only the longest-used metal but one of the most useful today. The world production of copper reaches close to three million tons a year. Of this total, about one third is produced in the United States. The rest comes from Africa, Canada, Chile, Japan, Mexico, Russia, and Spain.

In color, copper varies—according to the light—from greenish to red. Like aluminum, it is very tenacious and ductile. And it is also one of the best electric conductors among the less expensive metals. It is therefore used very extensively in the manufacture of wire for electrical purposes. But it also has other industrial uses—in copper roofing, in the making of electrotypes and the sheathing for ships and for coins, and in the alloys of bronze (copper and tin), and of brass (copper and zinc).

gold

Like copper, gold was known at a very early period in human history. And for the same reason: these two metals are so inactive that they are found practically free in nature.

Gold is one of the heaviest of the metals; and in malleability (or "hammerability") and in ductility it surpasses them all. One pound of gold can be beaten into about 8000 sheets the size of this book, or stretched into a wire about 220 miles long.

The largest gold-producing center in the world is the Transvaal in South Africa. The United States, Australia, and the Soviet Republics follow in that order. But there are some deposits of gold to be found in nearly every country—and, as has been recently demonstrated, even in the waters of the sea.

Since it is not susceptible to injury by air, gold has been selected as the basic metal for the minting of coins. Most of the world's leading countries have adopted gold as their monetary standard. And the gold reserve stored away for this purpose amounts to ninety per cent of the total annual supply.

The balance of the gold supply is diverted largely to ornamental uses. But in its pure state it is too soft for practical purposes; hence it is generally alloyed with such harder metals as copper or silver. Even our gold coins are not 24-carat—that is, pure gold; they are a mixture of ten per cent copper and ninety per cent gold. The general alloy of 18-carat jewelry is $18/24$—or seventy-five per cent pure.

iron

This is the commonest and one of the most useful of the metals. Although it was known to the Hindus as far back as 2000 B.C., it rarely occurs free in nature. Occasionally free iron is found in meteorites—metallic masses that have fallen to the earth from outer space. Perhaps it was through one of these meteorites that man first became acquainted with iron.

The richest iron mines in the world today are situated in the United States.

Much of the iron in use today is extracted from hematite—Fe_2O_3—an ore compounded of iron and oxygen. When the ore is taken from the mines, the impurities are melted away from the iron in gigantic blast furnaces. The "pure" iron—actually the smelting makes it about ninety per cent pure—is then cast into *pigs*, or oblong masses, for shipment to various parts of the world.

Arriving in this form at the foundry, the *cast iron* is remelted and molded into such articles as stoves, wheels, radiators, window frames, and the like.

Some of the cast iron, however, has to be further purified in order to become suitable for horseshoes, anchors, and other objects of a more pliable nature. This purification is performed by remelting the iron in a puddling furnace and then stirring it around with a "spoon"—like soup in a kettle—until every particle is exposed to the action of the flame and the "liberated" metal is brought into a plastic instead of a fluid form. It is then beaten by forge hammers into what is known as *wrought iron*.

But cast iron and wrought iron are neither strong enough nor elastic enough for the making of heavy structures such as boiler plates, bridges, railroad cars, office buildings, automobile bodies, and the like. These structures, and many smaller but equally durable articles, are made out of *steel*—an alloy of iron and about one per cent carbon. Sometimes there are other elements—such as chromium, manganese, nickel, tungsten, and vanadium—added to the iron and the carbon in the making of steel.

One of these alloys is the "stainless steel" of our table knives

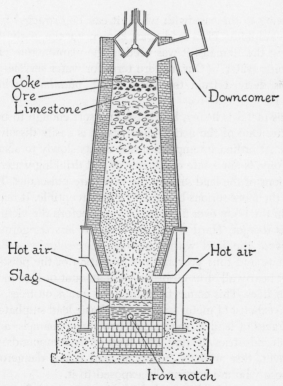

A cross section of a blast furnace. The coke, iron ore, and limestone are introduced at the top and the molten iron is drawn off at the bottom. This furnace, which is about ninety feet high, can produce up to 1200 tons of pig iron daily.

—a compound of iron containing about eighteen per cent chromium and eight per cent nickel.

Today steel is the most widely exploited form of iron, its use extending all the way from the tiny watch spring to the gigantic war vessel. But iron in any of its forms is of paramount importance among the metals. And this is due especially to one of its peculiar properties—magnetism—a characteristic which makes it so useful in the manufacture of the telegraph, the telephone, the motor, the compass, and the dynamo.

lead

Owing to the ease with which it can be extracted from its ore—the sulphide PbS—lead was known to the early Egyptians. Among the Romans, it was used in the manufacture of pipes for "running water." (Our modern term for water service—or *plumbing*—is derived from the Latin word, *plumbum,* which means *lead.*)

This metal is heavy, lusterless, and soft enough to be cut with a knife. One of the active elements, it is easily dissolved by hot acids. At ordinary temperatures it reacts slowly to acetic acid. A lead pipe is not a safe conductor of soft drinking water, since the solutions of the lead salts in the water are poisonous. This poison is all the more serious because it is imperceptible. It may accumulate in the body over a period of years before the victim is aware of his danger. Hard water, however, is less dangerous because it covers the lead with a coating of insoluble carbonate and sulphate and thus prevents the formation of the poisonous salts.

Yet nearly all of us absorb a small amount of lead in the course of our lives. This comes from the lead sprays on trees, lead oxide in the exhaust of motor vehicles, the basic lead sulphate in paints, the traces of lead in vegetables, linoleums, enamels, and textiles, and in industries dealing with lead or its compounds. As a rule, however, this ordinary intake of lead is not dangerous—except to those who are continually exposed to it.

Next to iron, lead is the least expensive metal. It has therefore been put to many uses. Owing to its airproof and moistureproof quality, it makes a good lining for vats, cisterns, and tanks. It is manufactured into type metal, electric fuses, toys, cable coverings, storage-battery plates, bullets and shot, and bolts that fasten metals to stone. And it is used extensively in potteries and paints, in the match and the rubber industries, and in the manufacture of collapsible tubes for pastes and shaving creams and the like. Lead arsenate is an insecticide; an alloy of lead and tin produces the metallic cement known as solder; and a mixture of lead and sodium forms a basis for tetraethyl—the anti-knock agent used in the better grades of gasoline.

nickel

This metal occurs in combination with arsenic or sulphur or both. The largest deposits of nickel are found in Canada, which produces about ninety per cent of the world's supply. The other ten per cent is produced in the Congo, India, Burma, and New Caledonia.

The reduction of nickel ore to pure nickel is a difficult process. But in its pure form it possesses four valuable qualities—hardness, malleability, resistance to tarnish, and a high susceptibility to magnetism. Its chief uses are in the minting of coinage, the coating of steel plates, the manufacture of "stainless" steel alloys, and the production of "permalloy." This alloy of four fifths nickel and one fifth iron is about thirty times as magnetic as soft iron in its pure state. Hence it is used extensively as a rapid conductor for underwater cables. A copper cable wrapped spirally with a narrow strip of permalloy can carry a message overseas four times as speedily as a cable without the wrapping.

silver

This element is found largely in the ore known as argentite, or silver glance—Ag_2S—a leaden-gray substance containing about eighty-six per cent of the pure metal. Small quantities of silver are also contained in ores of copper and lead. The leading producers of silver are Mexico, the United States, Canada, and South America.

When extracted from the ore, silver assumes a luster superior to that of gold. In ductility it is almost equal, and in malleability but slightly inferior, to gold. It may be beaten into plates so thin that it would take a hundred thousand of them to pile up to a thickness of one inch. It is resistant to air or moisture, but it is tarnished when exposed to sulphureted hydrogen.

As a conductor of electricity, silver is better than copper. But its comparative scarcity prohibits its general use in the manufacture of electrical instruments.

Its chief uses are in the minting of coins and the making of ornaments, the plating of the "less noble" metals, the silver surfacing of glass for mirrors, and the sensitizing of photographic films and plates with silver bromide. Hundreds of tons of silver are consumed in the picture industry every year.

tin

This metal (like iron, lead, and copper) is so easily extracted from its ore that it was known to the ancients. At present the chief deposits of tin are to be found in the East Indies, the Malay Peninsula, Siam, Bolivia, China, and Nigeria. Usually it occurs together with zinc, copper, and iron; and it is separated from these alloys by the simple heating of the entire mass to a point high enough for the melting of the tin but not high enough for the melting of the other metals. For the melting point of tin is only 232° Centigrade; of zinc, 419°; of copper, 1083°; and of iron, 1535°.

Tin is among the less active elements. It resists both water and air and is not easily tarnished. It is therefore used extensively as a coating for other metals in the manufacture of tin-plate. The sheets of metal—mostly steel—are dipped into melted tin and are then fashioned into kitchen utensils, tin cans, and the like. There are about *twenty billion* tin cans—actually they are tin-plated steel cans—manufactured in this country every year.

tungsten

Discovered in 1781, tungsten has become one of the most essential metals in modern industry. It has the highest melting point—3370°—of all the metals, is about as heavy as gold, and almost as hard as steel. Owing to its comparative infusibility, it is manufactured into filaments for electric lamps. These tungsten lamps can be maintained at a high temperature, with an expenditure of about 1.25 watts per candle power. This is only about one third the power expended for the same illumination with the old carbon filaments—a saving of about two billion dollars in the billion carbon lamps used in this country every year.

zinc

The annual production of zinc is about 1,200,000 tons, of which the United States supplies nearly one half. At low or high temperatures zinc is brittle. But when heated to a medium temperature of about 150°, it becomes very ductile and malleable. It can be rolled into thin sheets or drawn into fine wire. In its pure form zinc is used for the coating of steel, for roofing and rain pipes, and especially for the galvanizing of iron to save it from rusting. To galvanize iron, you remove the dust from the iron with sulphuric acid, and then you dip the iron into melted zinc.

As an alloy zinc combines with copper to form brass. As a zinc oxide—ZnO—it provides a filler for the rubber of automobile tires. Mixed with gutta percha and Venice turpentine, zinc oxide is used in the manufacture of surgical adhesive tape; and, united with phosphoric acid, it hardens into a dental cement. Among the other compounds containing zinc as an ingredient are white paint, celluloid, glue, glass, linoleum, ointment, and printer's ink. This metal cannot, however, be used as a food container, for the zinc salts are poisonous.

SYNTHETIC CHEMISTRY

The two chief processes in the chemical laboratory are *analysis* and *synthesis*—the *taking apart* and the *putting together* of the various natural and industrial compounds. In its earlier stages chemistry was largely a study of analysis. The students were—and still are—interested in learning *what* are the constituents in an unknown material (qualitative chemistry), and *how much* of each of these constituents is present (quantitative chemistry). Today, however, the tendency in chemical study is toward synthesis. Owing to the enforced shortages of many natural products during the two World Wars, it was necessary for the chemists to make synthetic products that would perform the same, or approximately the same, functions. And thus we now have synthetic rubber for tires, synthetic gas for fuel, synthetic ammonia for explosives, synthetic plastics, quinine, copper, cotton, silk—such as rayon and nylon—and other wearing apparel made out of synthetic wool, and fibers of glass with a diameter about one fourth the diameter of a human hair. A two-pound piece of glass can be spun into a thread that would encircle the earth.

Today the chemists are experimenting with many other synthetic possibilities which may be practical realities tomorrow. The goal of all this synthesis—and there are those who regard it as more than a mere dream—is to transform the chemical laboratory into a synthetic creator of life.

CHEMISTRY AND ELECTRICITY

A chemical compound may be decomposed by an electric current in a process known as *electrolysis*—a term which is derived from the Greek and which means *electrical separation*. When the electric current is passed through water, the water is decomposed into its constituents—hydrogen and oxygen. When it is passed through a liquid solution of ordinary table salt—sodium chloride —the salt is broken up into its constituent elements, sodium and chlorine.

The atoms of many compounds possess electrical charges and are called *ions,* from the Greek verb *ienai,* which means *to move* or *to go.* For these atoms *move away* from each other when the compound is dissolved in water.

There are two kinds of charges—positive and negative. As the salt is dissolved in water, there are produced sodium ions which are "positively" charged and chlorine ions which are "negatively" charged.

And here we note an interesting characteristic of electricity: similar charges repel each other, and dissimilar charges attract each other. Hence a union of two ions is possible only when one of them is positive and the other is negative.

In order to understand the electrochemical meaning of the terms *positive* and *negative,* let us glance at the construction of a simple battery cell—the instrument used for producing an electric current. This instrument usually consists of two strips of dissimilar metals—such as copper and zinc—in a vessel containing a solution of sulphuric acid. These metals are the *electrodes* of the cell, and the solution is the *electrolyte.* When the two electrodes are connected by a metal wire, the electric current passes through the solution and the connecting wire. The electrode by which the current flows *into* the electrolyte is called the *positive* pole, or *anode;* and the electrode by which the current flows *out of* the electrolyte is called the *negative* pole, or *cathode.*

And now, let us connect separate wires to the two electrodes and place these wires, which are now acting as parts of the electrodes, into a solution of salt—sodium chloride. As the electrodes convey the charge through the liquid, the *sodium* or the *positive* ions are attracted to the *cathode* or the *negative* pole, and the *chlorine* or the *negative* ions are attracted to the *anode* or the

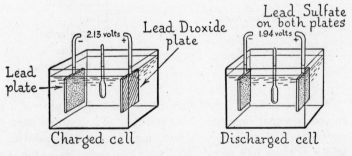

Simplified diagram of a lead storage battery. A negative lead plate and a positive lead dioxide plate are introduced into an electrolyte of diluted sulphuric acid. There is a flow of electrons from the negative plate to the positive plate. During discharge, lead and lead dioxide are changed to lead sulphate, and sulphuric acid is at the same time removed from the electrolyte. The specific gravity of the electrolyte, as measured by a hydrometer, is being constantly reduced and in time the battery must be recharged, during which the process is reversed, bringing the battery back to its original state.

positive pole. And this ionic migration, each to its electrode with the opposite charge, is, in brief, the entire process of electrolysis.

This process, in the experiment of sodium chloride dissolved in water, demonstrates another interesting phenomenon in electrochemistry. By itself water is a non-conductor—or, to be more exact, a very poor conductor—of electricity. But throw a pinch of salt into the water, and you will find that the current passes through it readily.

The same thing happens if you dissolve a number of other substances in the water. All the substances which *ionize,* or cause water to become conductive to an electric current, are called *electrolytes.* But there are several substances which have no such effect upon water. These substances are called *non-electrolytes.* Following is a partial list of the substances in each of the two classes:

ELECTROLYTES	NON-ELECTROLYTES
Acetic acid	Acetone
Ammonium hydroxide	Benzine
Hydrochloric acid	Cane sugar
Nitric acid	Chloroform
Potassium hydroxide	Ether
Silver nitrate	Ethyl alcohol
Sodium chloride	Glycerine
Sulphuric acid	Methyl alcohol

We have already noted that in the electrolytic process a substance becomes separated into positive and negative ions. And we can tell in advance which of these ions will be positive and which of them will be negative. Our knowledge as to the nature of the ions is derived from a series of experiments initiated (in 1887) by the Swedish chemist, Arrhenius. The atoms of all the metals and of the gas hydrogen, as these experiments have demonstrated, will form *positive* ions. The atoms of all the other elements will form *negative* ions. Thus, in the solution of sodium chloride in water, we can tell in advance that the atoms of the sodium (a metal) and the hydrogen will be positively charged, and that the atoms of the chlorine and the oxygen will be negatively charged. Similarly, in a solution of sulphuric acid—H_2SO_4—in water, we know that the hydrogen ions will be positive and that the sulphur and the oxygen ions will be negative.

This knowledge about the reaction of the ions—especially in the metals—has been of great value in the industrial development of electrolysis. It has led to the extensive use of the electrolyte process in the extraction of aluminum, sodium, nickel, zinc, and magnesium from their ores; in the refining of copper, lead, gold, silver, and tin; and in the making of various alloys, electrotypes, and electroplates. All these processes are the results of the discovery that the atoms of the various substances possess certain characteristics which enable us to harness them in the transformation of *chemical* energy into *electrical* energy.

NUCLEAR CHEMISTRY—ATOMIC POWER IN WAR AND PEACE

The latest researches in chemistry are largely concerned with the power of the atom. These researches have brought into being a new branch of the science—*nuclear chemistry*—the chemistry that deals with the changes produced upon an atom through the bombardment of its nucleus by a number of rapidly moving particles.

This nuclear bombardment can change the atom of one element into the atom of another element. And thus it revives the dream of the medieval alchemists about the transmutation of the "baser" into the "nobler" metals. Indeed, it is already possible to change mercury into gold—but at a prohibitive price. The day may not be far off, however, when the cost of such transmutation may be brought down sufficiently low to turn the possibility into an actuality.

But this is the least of the possibilities of atomic disintegration. The splitting of the atom—like the opening of Pandora's box—has released a power of almost incalculable dimensions. The explosion of a single atom of uranium produces about two hundred million electron volts of energy. In an atomic bomb weighing about four hundred pounds, the number of atoms that explode simultaneously is astronomical. The power thus unleashed by the disintegration of the atom—that is, by the conversion of mass into energy—may result in the deepest tragedy or the greatest blessing to the human race.

Let us briefly examine the process of atomic fission, the exploitation of atomic power to date, and the future possibilities of this power in war and in peace.

The atom, as we have seen, is a miniature solar system—with the nucleus as the sun and with the electrons whirling around it as its planets. Imagine our solar system suddenly torn asunder by some terrific bombardment from outward space. This is just what happens to the planetary system of the atom when it is bombarded from the outside.

The "bullets" with which the atom is bombarded—or the atom-smashing particles—are of various kinds: nuclei—or "hearts"—of helium thrown off by radium at a high velocity; nuclei of hy-

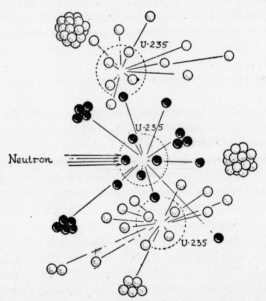

Schematic representation of splitting of atoms of Uranium-235 in chain reaction. The nucleus of the U-235 atom is split by a neutron "bullet." U-235's neutrons are thus released and they, in turn, become "bullets" which explode the nuclei of other U-235 atoms.

drogen whirled against the target by the passage of an electric current; nuclei of deuterium (heavy hydrogen); and, chiefly, heavy neutral particles, caused to be emitted from the nuclei of beryllium atoms, and known as "neutrons."

These bullets, or missiles, are shot out of a "gun" called a *cyclotron*—an atom-smashing instrument invented in 1931 by Dr. Ernest O. Lawrence, of the University of California. There are several different types of cyclotrons in use today.

The cyclotron is an accelerator of the atomic bullets. These bullets are held in a circular path by a tremendous magnet, and they are kept whirling around at an ever increasing rate until they reach—in some instances—a speed of 28,000 miles a second. And then, when the speed is at the highest, these bullets are flung out through a tube of the gun and into the atomic target. Millions of these bullets are shot out in a single discharge.

With the help of this atomic gun the scientists have been able (1) to break up the atom, (2) to disintegrate the elements and to transmute them into one another, (3) to manufacture the atomic bomb, (4) to produce artificial radioactivity—a bombardment of mysterious rays that can kill like an onslaught of bullets —and (5) to study the secrets of the atom for its industrial and medicinal possibilities.

1. *The breaking up of the atom.* As a result of Dr. Lawrence's invention, it was known as early as 1939 that a heavy atom of the element uranium (U-235) could be split into two parts, and that each of these parts would become the complete atom of an entirely different element. This knowledge gave rise to many researches into the structure of the elements and the possibility of their conversion into one another.

2. *The disintegration of the elements.* With the aid of the cyclotron it was soon possible to disintegrate many elements other than U-235, to transmute lithium into helium, beryllium into boron, and—as a matter of scientific interest rather than of practical value—mercury into gold.

3. *The atomic bomb.* The splitting of the uranium atom, it was noted, resulted in two important reactions: the release of

energy; and the beginning of a chain of bombardments—each atom in the explosion causing its neighbor to explode, and so on until the entire mass of the metal had blown up.

It was noted, furthermore, that under certain conditions the chain bombardment was very abrupt, and under other conditions very slow. It was the abrupt chain of explosions that was utilized in the development of the atomic bomb. In 1941 our government decided to draft the leading scientists, and to spend the necessary funds—over two billion dollars—in an all-out effort to invent this most destructive of military weapons.

The actual construction of the atomic bombs may remain, for some time to come, a military secret. But as regards the atomic bombs already exploded, this much seems probable: the Hiroshima bomb, based upon the uranium atom, was obsolete when the Nagasaki bomb was dropped; and the Nagasaki bomb, based upon the plutonium atom, was just as obsolete when the Bikini bombs were exploded. The atomic bomb in the process of construction today, as some of the scientists have hinted, may be a thousand times as destructive as the Nagasaki bomb.

4. *Artificial radioactivity.* The chain reaction resulting from atomic fission, as we have noted above, may be very rapid or very gradual. The *rapid* reaction has been utilized for destructive purposes in the atomic bomb. The *gradual* reaction may be utilized either for destructive purposes, in the military exploitation of radioactivity, or for constructive purposes, in the industrial and therapeutic manipulation of atomic energy.

The military exploitation of radioactivity, however, may prove to be as dangerous to the persons who use it as to those against whom it is used. For radioactivity is the release of a poison that spreads in every direction. Moreover, this poison remains active for a long time after its release. An area that has been saturated with radioactivity becomes unavailable for strategic purposes, not only to the victim but to the victor as well. A year after the atomic discharge at Bikini, it was still regarded as unsafe to board the radioactive ships that survived the explosions.

Let us not, however, exaggerate the dangers of radioactivity. All life, as a matter of fact, is radioactive. Nature is providing us with a small amount of this diet all the time. Through the action of the cosmic rays that come to us from outer space, the inert nitrogen in the air is transformed into radioactive carbon. This carbon is absorbed by all plant life, which in turn is absorbed by all animal life that feeds on vegetables. It is only the *excessive use* of artificially induced radioactivity—especially when it is not properly controlled—that constitutes a menace to human life.

And this brings us to the fifth and perhaps the most important result of atomic fission.

5. *Atomic power in industry and medicine.* During World War II the scientists concentrated their efforts on the destructive power of atomic disintegration. Today they are turning their attention more and more to its constructive possibilities. The extensive use of atomic power for industrial purposes seems as yet beyond the realization of the immediate future. But the human mind has always proved amazingly adept in the development of new inventions. When we remember the rapid evolution of the automobile, the radio, and the airplane—all of them inventions practically of a single generation—we can regard with a cautious hope the conjectures of the more optimistic scientists. These scientists tell us that perhaps within another generation atomic power will replace—or materially supplement—water, coal, oil, and electric power in the running of the world's industrial machine. The United States Atomic Energy Commission has been created to study this civilian—as well as the further military—development of atomic fission. Several laboratories have been built for extensive experiments in this field.

As to the possible results of these experiments, nobody can hazard a prediction. The general aim, however, seems to be the development of atomic energy for the propulsion of automobiles, airplanes, and battleships, for the production of new articles from hitherto unknown elements and compounds, for the installation of "atomic" heat and light in areas with inadequate access to coal and water power, and for the production—through atomic disintegration and reintegration—of a supply of food sufficient for the entire world.

But one of the greatest hopes for atomic energy lies in the field of medicine. It is already possible to use compounds of radioactive phosphorus as "tracers" in food that has been taken into the body. These tracers may be of great assistance in the study of the conversion of food into muscle, bone, and blood. By means of these or similar detectors, the physicians may ultimately be able to distinguish between foods that *build* and foods that *destroy* tissue. And this may be an important step in the diagnosis —and the possible prevention—of cancer and other degenerative diseases.

As for the *cure* of such diseases through radioactivity, this may be a long way off but it is a distinct possibility. There is a theory, based upon substantial evidence, that a cell of unhealthy tissue is more vulnerable to radiation than a cell of healthy tissue. Hence a radioactive medicine—that is, a substance with artificial radiation produced by atomic energy—may conceivably be injected into the body to destroy the diseased cells without at the same time injuring the normal cells. To take a specific example, most of the iodine in the human body tends to collect in the thyroid gland. If the thyroid should become cancerous, an injection of radioactive iodine would be attracted to the diseased spot and—conceivably—effect a cure by killing the abnormal growth. In actual practice the results to date have been far from conclusive. But the scientists in this field are going steadily ahead with their experiments and considerable sums of money have been diverted to the medical branch of atomic research.

And the most encouraging feature of all this atomic research is that it is *co-operative*. The best scientific brains have been united in an effort to harness atomic energy in the interests of peace, just as in 1941 they were united to harness it in the interests of war. While the need for speedy results is not so dramatically urgent today as it was in 1941, the brains and the willingness and the human urge for surmounting difficulties are the same as before. The conquest of atomic energy as an agent for greater comfort and better health may not be so far off as we think.

THE USES OF CHEMISTRY IN MODERN LIFE

In this chapter we have already touched upon the practical uses of chemistry. We shall now consider, briefly, some of the more important applications of chemistry in our everyday life.

abrasives

An abrasive is a substance that is employed for wearing down the surfaces of other substances by cutting, polishing, rubbing, or grinding. There are natural abrasives—such as diamond, corundum (crystallized aluminum oxide familiarly known as *emery*), garnet, and common sand and quartz. In addition to these there are artificial or synthetic abrasives—silicon carbide or *carborundum; carboloy*, a mixture of tungsten carbide crystals and powdered cobalt; and boron carbide or *norbide*, the hardest artificial abrasive on the market.

Abrasives are extensively used in the sharpening of our kitchen utensils, the filing and the cleansing of teeth at the dentist's office, the grinding of wood into paper pulp, the carving and surfacing of stones, the polishing of furniture and plate glass, the shaping and smoothing of plastic jewelry, and the co-ordinating of interchangeable machine parts by means of precision grinding wheels to equalize their measurement to the fraction of a thousandth of an inch. Abrasives are frequently mixed into concrete floors and steel stairways and other slippery surfaces as a precaution against accidents.

agriculture

Chemistry plays an important part in agriculture. Farmers can enrich their soil by the use of manufactured as well as of natural fertilizers—"soil foods" of phosphate and potash and calcium compounds; limestone and gypsum "binders" of the particles of loose clay in the heavier soils; and slaked lime to "sweeten" the soils that are too sour—that is, too full of acid.

Chemistry has also performed a great service in the control of the various pests that interfere with the health of plant life. Lead arsenate has, in the opinion of experts, saved our apple and pear crops from total destruction. Calcium arsenate has materially reduced the destructiveness of the cotton boll weevil and the potato beetle. Lime-sulphur sprays and fumigations of hydrogen cyanide have aided the productiveness of our peach and citrus fruit trees. Formaldehyde, solutions of mercuric chloride, and powders of copper carbonate have been applied, with satisfactory results, to various seeds in order to save them from fungus contamination. From the planting of the seeds, through the harvesting of the fruit, and down to the shipping of the crates to the market, chemicals are used as insect killers for the protection of the farmer, the middleman, and the final consumer.

Among the interesting experiments in modern agriculture is the so-called *hydroponics*, or *chemiculture*—the growing of plants without soil by submerging the roots in a solution of water and various amounts of mineral salts. Beans, tomatoes, and several other plants have been successfully produced through this method of hydroponics, or water planting.

clothing

Most of the textiles used for clothing are the products of nature. But the artificial silks known as rayon and nylon are the creations of the chemist.

The world's annual output of rayon is over a million tons. Most of this material is the so-called *viscose rayon*—a gummy fabric manufactured from bleached wood pulp or scraps of cotton by treatment with sodium hydroxide and carbon disulfide.

Nylon resembles silk even more closely than rayon. It consists of a compound of ammonia condensed with an organic acid and solidified through a nitrogen atmosphere into fine threads for stockings and the like, and into heavier fibers for paintbrushes or into bristles for toothbrushes.

The service of chemistry includes the dyeing and the cleansing as well as the making of textiles. In the washing of colored fabrics it will be observed that cottons "bleed" their colors while the colors of silks and woolens generally remain fast. It is therefore wise to avoid the laundering of cottons together with woolens, in order to save the wool from becoming permanently stained by the escape of the cotton dyes.

Moreover, it is well to avoid the use of soaps containing free alkali, since the alkali may not only change the colors but may even destroy the fabric. The mildest soaps are the safest for the washing of colored clothes.

In the elimination of stains it is important to use a cleanser that will remove the spot without injuring the garment. Following is a partial list of safe cleansers for various kinds of stains:

For molasses, candy, syrup, fruit, tea, coffee, chocolate—*water*.

For blood—*soap and water*.

For grease, tar, paint, varnish, chewing gum, and adhesive plaster—*carbon tetrachloride*.

For shellac—*alcohol*.

For grass—*alcohol and soap*.

For iodine—*sodium thiosulfate* (photographer's *hypo*).

For rust—*lemon juice or vinegar*.

For fresh ink—*water, or soap and water*. Several repetitions may be necessary if the ink has been allowed to "soak in." For old ink stains, soak in ammonium oxalate or oxalic acid.

food

With the aid of chemical analysis we are constantly extending our knowledge about the relationship between the various kinds of food and our physical health. A sufficient daily diet includes one pint of milk, one portion of meat or poultry or fish, one egg, two vegetables (one of which contains green leaves, such as lettuce), one citrus and one non-citrus fruit, cheese, butter (or oleomargarine), cereals, and bread. This diet is well rounded in fats, carbohydrates, proteins, minerals, and vitamins—the elements necessary for the maintenance and growth of the body.

The chemistry of food is closely allied to the chemistry of cooking. Here are a few simple rules that help to retain the body-building properties of food in the process of cooking:

1. Baking soda should not be used with green vegetables, for baking soda destroys the vitamins of these vegetables.

2. Air should not be stirred into food while the food is being cooked, for the oxidation of the air destroys the vitamins.

3. Foods that are rich in vitamins should not be fried.

4. Very little water should be used in cooking; and whatever water is left after the cooking should be used for soups and gravies. Otherwise the vitamins that have become dissolved in the water will be lost.

5. Hot foods should not be filtered through a sieve. The metal, especially when heated, tends to neutralize vitamin C.

fuels

Fuels are chemicals that are comparatively inexpensive, easy to kindle, and productive of sufficient energy to warrant their use for heating purposes.

Most of the solid fuels consist of vegetation—such as recently cut plants or buried plants fossilized into coal. These fuels are a combination of cellulose and sap.

The liquid fuels, such as gasoline, kerosene, and the other fuel oils, are produced by a distilling or refining process from crude oil. Gasoline is a volatile mixture of hydrocarbons; it flows easily and possesses little viscosity (stickiness). Kerosene is a mixture of hydrocarbons with heavier molecular weights; and hence it flows less easily and possesses greater viscosity. The molecules of the other fuel oils are still heavier than those of kerosene; and therefore these fuels are even less volatile and more viscous and harder to ignite. But for these very reasons the oils that are bad for fuel are good for lubrication.

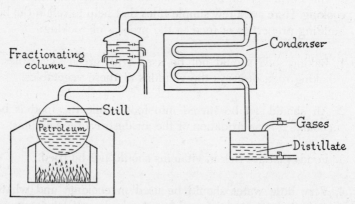

Cracking petroleum in a still to produce more efficient fuels. In this process the larger molecules are broken down by heating under pressure.

In addition to the solid and the liquid fuels we have gas fuels. The commonest of these is water gas—a mixture of hydrogen and carbon monoxide manufactured by the processing of burning coke with alternate blasts of air and steam.

A fuel that generates a tremendous amount of heat is the colorless acetylene—a gas prepared by the decomposition of water with calcium carbide. This fuel is used largely for welding and for cutting hard metals such as iron and steel.

glass

Ordinary glass is a mixture of white sand, soda ash, and limestone. Strictly speaking, it is not a solid but a cooled liquid of very high viscosity.

One of the most useful modern inventions is the so-called *pyrex*, or *borosilicate glass*—a glass toughened by a high content of silica and boric oxide. This glass is so resistant to blows and sudden changes in temperature that it is used extensively in the manufacture of cooking and baking utensils.

Equally useful among the modern improvements in glassware is the so-called *unbreakable glass*—a layer of synthetic plastic sandwiched between two slices of glass and heated and pressed into a cohesive unit. This glass is used largely for windowpanes and windshields. Somewhat similar in structure is the product known as *bulletproof* glass—a thin plate of glass at the top, another thin plate at the bottom, a thick plate in the center, and two plastic sheets between the three glass plates. All five layers are pressed together into an almost "impregnable" shield.

medicine

All life is a chemical process of growth and decay. And therefore the role of chemistry in medicine—the art of fomenting growth and preventing decay—is of paramount importance.

The chemical agents that keep the body in a healthy state of harmony are called *hormones*. They control our digestion, our growth, our physical hunger for food and reproduction, and even our emotions and thoughts. Some of the hormones secreted by the pancreas and by the adrenal and thyroid glands—such as *insulin, adrenalin,* and *thyroxin*—have proved of great benefit in the treatment of various diseases.

The service of chemistry in the maintenance of health has been further ultilized in the analysis of foods and medicines, in the testing of drinking and bathing water, and in the protection of workers against noxious fumes and gases. Chemical tests of our physical functions—such as the analysis of digested foods and liquids—chemical aids to the X-ray and fluoroscope examinations of the body, chemical researches in more effective and less harmful anesthetics, and chemical sedatives for reducing pain and producing sleep—these are but a few of the medical expedients for the better diagnosis and the safer treatment of many diseases. Practically all the medicines used nowadays are chemical compounds—either of natural herbs or of synthesized drugs. Antiseptics and germicides are the chemical agents for the prevention as well as for the cure of disease. And one of the great advances in the control of respiratory diseases, such as influenza and pneumonia, is the result of the discovery of the *sulfa* chemicals and of *penicillin,* a chemical substance found on bread and cheese molds. These latest discoveries have given impetus to the important branch of medicine known as *chemotherapy*—healing by means of chemistry.

plastics

In the manufacture of plastics the chemist has transformed his crucible into a magic wand. He has made buttons out of sour milk; automobile trimmings out of soybeans; plywood for airplanes out of phenol and formaldehyde; and safety glass windows for airplanes and automobiles, as well as electric insulators and elastic glass bands for belts, suspenders and wrist-watch bracelets out of various liquids solidified by the chemical process known as *polymerization*—the union of smaller and lighter molecules to form larger and heavier molecules. In many cases the synthetic plastics are more resistant to shock and less liable to shrinkage than some of the natural products which are used for the same purposes.

rubber

Natural rubber is made out of a sticky substance, called *latex*, found in the bark of various trees. The latex is collected in its liquid form and is then treated with dilute acetic acid which coagulates it into an elastic solid.

In this form, however, the rubber is unsatisfactory because in the summer it becomes sticky and exudes an offensive odor, and in the winter it turns hard and brittle. Therefore much of the rubber used for automobile tires and for other commercial purposes is vulcanized—that is, mixed with sulphur and then heated sufficiently to make it less sticky in the summer and less brittle in the winter.

Within recent years various attempts have been made to produce synthetic rubber. The results to date, in the opinion of some of the industrial chemists, have not been quite satisfactory. Synthetic rubber, as they point out, is less resistant to wear and tear and heat and cold, and less resilient and tensile (capable of being stretched) than natural rubber.

But, on the other hand, synthetic rubber is less susceptible than natural rubber to the action of destructive chemicals. Many industrial chemists are engaged in a series of experiments—with *butadiene* (a hydrocarbon produced from coal, petroleum, or alcohol), and with other subtances which, like butadiene, are chemically similar to *isoprene*, the basis of natural rubber. Some of them believe that in time they will be able to produce artificial rubber as good as, and perhaps even better than, natural rubber.

REVIEW QUESTIONS IN CHEMISTRY

1. What is matter?

2. What is energy?

3. What is an element? A compound?

4. How many elements do the scientists recognize today?

5. What is alchemy?

6. What is a molecule? An atom?

7. How rapidly do the electrons revolve around the protons?

8. What constitutes the difference in the elements?

9. Who discovered oxygen?

10. Who is the "father of modern chemistry"?

11. What is the color of oxygen?

12. What is an oxide?

13. What causes combustion?

14. How can you distinguish liquid hydrogen from water?

15. What is a halogen?

16. A deficiency of what chemical element may produce goiter?

17. How important is sulphur in our present-day activities?

18. Name two important, and contradictory, uses of nitroglycerine.

19. What is the pressure of the air upon a square inch of the earth's surface?

20. Why is breathing upon a high mountain difficult?

21. What is the composition of the air?

22. How does country air compare in composition with city air?

23. What chemical element is the basis of life?

24. Why is carbon monoxide so poisonous?

25. What are the seven principal "fuels" of the engine known as the human body?

26. Why is aluminum a useful metal?

27. What is duralumin?

28. Why is copper used so extensively in the manufacture of wires for electrical purposes?

29. Which is the most malleable of the metals?

30. Why is gold used as the basic metal for currency?

31. What is hematite?

32. What is the nature of steel?

33. Why does lead make a good lining for vats and tanks?

34. What causes the tarnishing of silver?

35. Are "tin cans" made out of tin?

36. Why is tungsten so valuable for the making of filaments used in electric lamps?

37. Why cannot zinc be used as a food container?

38. What is chemical analysis? Chemical synthesis?

39. Name five synthetic products.

40. What is electrolysis?

41. What is an ion?

42. How can water be made into a good conductor of electricity?

43. Name three uses of the electrolytic process.

44. What is nuclear chemistry?

45. Can the "baser" metals be changed into gold?

46. What is a cyclotron?

47. Name five things that can be done with the cyclotron.

48. Why is the military exploitation of radioactivity dangerous?

49. Is radioactivity always a menace to life?

50. What is the most encouraging feature of atomic research?

ANSWERS TO THE QUESTIONS IN CHEMISTRY

1. Anything which has mass or weight and occupies space.

2. The capacity for doing work or for producing motion.

3. A basic substance which cannot be decomposed into two or more substances by ordinary chemical means. A substance which *can* be decomposed by ordinary chemical means.

4. Ninety-six.

5. The pseudo science of transmuting one element into another.

6. A molecule is a group of two or more atoms—the smallest part of a compound capable of maintaining its identity as that particular compound. An atom is the smallest part of an element capable of maintaining its identity as that particular element.

7. About 150,000 miles a second.

8. The different number of electrons within the atoms of the various elements.

9. Joseph Priestley.

10. Antoine Lavoisier.

11. In its gaseous form, it is colorless; in its liquid form, light blue.

12. A combination of oxygen with one other element.

13. The union of oxygen with any inflammable substance.

14. By placing a cork upon the surface. The cork will sink in hydrogen, but not in water.

15. Any element which, combined with metals, produces salt.

16. Iodine.

17. It is perhaps the most important of all the chemical substances.

18. It serves as a deadly explosive and as a healing medicine.

19. Nearly fifteen pounds.

20. Because the pressure of air decreases with its height above the earth.

21. A mixture of seventy-eight per cent oxygen and twenty-one per cent nitrogen, the remaining one per cent consisting of argon, carbon dioxide, neon, helium, ozone, water vapor, and dust.

22. It contains less dust and less carbon dioxide.

23. Carbon.

24. Because it prevents the blood from carrying oxygen to the parts of the body.

25. Water, air, proteins, fats, carbohydrates, mineral salts, and vitamins.

26. Because of its lightness, strength, ductility, and resistance to tarnish.

27. A metal one third as heavy as steel but equal to it in strength. It is compounded of ninety-four per cent aluminum, three per cent copper, and small amounts of manganese, magnesium, and silicon.

28. Because it is one of the best electric conductors among the less expensive metals.

29. Gold.

30. Because it is not susceptible to injury by air.

31. The ore from which iron is extracted.

32. An alloy of iron and about one per cent carbon.

33. Because it is airproof and moistureproof.

34. Exposure to sulphureted hydrogen.

35. Not entirely. They are made out of steel and plated with tin.

36. Because it takes an extremely high temperature —3370°—to melt it.

37. Because the zinc salts are poisonous.

38. Chemical analysis is the taking apart of various compounds. Chemical synthesis is putting them together.

39. Synthetic tires, gas, copper, rayon, and nylon.

40. The decomposition of a chemical by an electric current.

41. An atom that carries an electric charge, positive or negative.

42. By dissolving sodium chloride or some other "conducive" substance in the water.

43. The extraction of various metals from their ores; the refining of metals; and the production of various alloys.

44. The chemistry that deals with the changes produced upon an atom through the bombardment of its nucleus and the consequent "splitting" of the atom.

45. Mercury can be changed into gold, but at a prohibitive price.

46. An atom-smashing instrument, or "gun."

47. The breaking up of the atom; the transmutation of the elements into one another; the making of the atomic bomb; the production of artificial radioactivity; and the conversion of substances into industrial and medicinal goods.

48. Because it releases a poison that spreads in every direction—to the attackers as well as to the defenders.

49. No.

50. The fact that, at least in the United States, it is cooperative.

BIOGRAPHICAL SKETCHES OF GREAT CHEMISTS

Bacon, Roger (c. 1214–94). English philosopher and scientist. Born in England, studied in Paris, and joined the order of the Franciscans at Oxford on his return to England. Accused of "black magic" because of his scientific studies, he was twice imprisoned —from 1257 to 1267, and from 1278 to 1292—by the leaders of the Franciscan order. During the years of his incarceration he was deprived of his books, his instruments, and his writing materials. Yet in spite of these persecutions he found in the years of his freedom the time and energy to prepare, among several other books, a voluminous encyclopedia of the sciences, covering grammar, logic, mathematics, physics, philology, and philosophy. He anticipated the methods of modern science. He is credited with the invention of gunpowder, and it is thought that he used the telescope and the microscope.

Cavendish, Henry (1731–1810). British chemist. He was a grandson of the second Duke of Devonshire. Born in Nice, Italy, he received his college education at Cambridge. He was considered an eccentric during his life. He lived in retirement, wore old-fashioned clothes, ordered his servants to keep out of his sight, spoke with hesitation. He remained a bachelor and left a huge fortune behind him. He engaged in researches in physics, delved into geology; but his fame rests on his chemical investigations. He revealed the compound character of water, obtaining water by mixing electrically the proper amounts of hydrogen and oxygen. He discovered the composition of nitric acid, experimented with arsenic, contributed data to the phenomena of vaporization and liquefaction.

Priestley, Joseph (1733–1804). English clergyman and chemist. He was born in Fieldhead, England, but found no honor in his own country. He discovered the nature of oxygen, experimented in electricity, and wrote between seventy and eighty books on the various aspects of philosophy and science. But his unorthodox independence in religious matters and his political sympathies for the underdog aroused the enmity of the reactionaries. In the summer of 1791 his house, his laboratory, and his manuscripts were burned by the mob because of his sympathy with the French Revolution. Compelled to flee for his life, he migrated to America and ended his days at Northumberland, Pennsylvania.

Lavoisier, Antoine Laurent (1743–94). "The father of modern chemistry." He prepared himself for the bar but abandoned legal litigation for scientific investigation. He joined a map-making expedition to the Vosges Mountains. Upon his return he was elected to the French Academy. This honor necessitated considerable research in, and reports upon, all sorts of scientific subjects. A practical businessman as well as a scientific student, he induced his politically influential father-in-law to secure him a job as manager of the French Arsenal. It was in this capacity that he was able to undertake the investigations which led to the establishment of chemistry upon a scientific basis. His scientific motto was "not to rely upon speculation but to build upon facts." Among his many contributions to chemistry were the naming of oxygen, the definition of the term *chemical element,* and an entire international vocabulary used by chemists to the present day. The crowning achievement of his monumental labor as a scientist was the publication of his *Elementary Treatise of Chemistry* (1789). Five years later the leaders of the French Revolution sent him to the guillotine on the trumped-up charge that he had been "plotting with the enemies of France."

Dalton, John (1766–1844). British chemist. Born in Eaglesfield, Cumberland County. With but little formal education of his own, he taught school from the age of twelve. As a young man he undertook a series of lectures on natural philosophy based on his personal observations. He was appointed instructor of natural philosophy and mathematics, "for want of a better candidate," in a newly opened school of "dissenters." In his spare time he studied meteorology—again from his personal observations rather than from books. And then he resigned from the school, moved into the house of a clergyman, and dedicated the rest of his life to the study of chemistry and physics. In the course of his protracted experiments he discovered the application of the atomic theory to chemistry. And thus he "transformed the chaos of alchemy into the order of chemistry."

Davy, Sir Humphry (1778–1829). English chemist. Born at Penzance, Cornwall, he served as an apprentice to an apothecary-druggist. While in his teens he was appointed director of the laboratory at Dr. Beddoes' Pneumatic Institute, where his experiments with nitrous oxide, "laughing gas," won Davy national fame. He entered the Royal Institution in London as assistant director and rose to a commanding position in the society. He made important contributions to the field of electrolytics, discovered potassium and sodium, magnesium, barium and calcium, iodine and chlorine. He invented a miners' safety lamp which helped to decrease the incidence of explosions in the coal pits. He was made a baronet. Toward the end of his life he served as president of the Royal Society. He died of a nervous disorder at the height of his career.

Gay-Lussac, Joseph Louis (1778–1850). French chemist and physicist. He was the first to announce that two parts of hydrogen and one part of oxygen combine to make water. In 1815 he isolated the gaseous compound, cyanogen. He devoted much of his later life to the practical applications of chemistry.

Berzelius, Baron Jöns Jakob (1779–1848). Swedish chemist. Born in East Gothland. Educated in medicine, he devoted himself largely to chemical research. For a time he taught medicine at Uppsala University and then he was elected president of the Stockholm Academy of Sciences. The Swedish king raised him to the rank of baron in recognition of his "services to learning." Of his numerous books on science the most important was *A Text Book of Chemistry* in three volumes. In this book he invented the "alphabet" of chemical compounds—that is, the system of denoting a compound by the first letters of the elements that produce the compound, with a number placed below each letter to indicate the number of atoms of the element contained in the compound; for example, H_2O.

Bunsen, Robert Wilhelm von (1811–99). German chemist. His achievements in chemistry are numerous. He developed a celebrated method of measuring the volumes of gases. He investigated photochemical measurements. He invented the carbon-zinc electric cell, the vapor and ice calorimeters, and the filter pump. He was the first to obtain magnesium in its metallic state. He made important contributions to the study of spectrum analysis, and he discovered an antidote for arsenical poisoning. During his career he was professor of chemistry at Kassel, Marburg, Breslau, and Heidelberg universities. He almost died on one occasion from arsenical poisoning. On another occasion he lost an eye in an explosion.

Mendeleyev, Dimitri Ivanovich (1834–1907). Russian chemist. Born in Tobolsk, Siberia. He was educated at the University of St. Petersburg, and was appointed professor there in 1866. He later served as director of the Bureau of Weights and Measures. Mendeleyev's great contribution to chemistry was the Periodic Table, an arrangement of chemical elements according to their atomic weight.

CAREERS IN CHEMISTRY

There are practically no limits to a career in chemistry. The phenomenal development of industrial chemistry has been responsible, within the last decade, for a hundred per cent jump in the employment of chemical workers. The study of chemistry is essential to a career in the medical sciences. It is basic for practically all branches of engineering.

The field of agricultural chemistry is especially attractive. The chemurgist converts farm products into industrial uses. It has been prophesied that a large segment of the nation's farmers will one day grow crops to build everything on wheels.

There is need for soil and plant chemists in the Department of Agriculture. The paper and pulp industry requires wood chemists to study trees and allied products. The petroleum industry needs chemists to refine the crude products into gasoline and allied lubricants. The canning industry has need of experts in the chemical processing of food. The control chemist who tests and analyzes samples of industrial products to determine their quality is absolutely vital today. Chemical engineers whose duties consist of applying the discoveries of research chemists to industry are among the highest-paid experts in the professsion.

The rapidly expanding field of plastics has developed new channels for the chemist. Plastics today are being utilized in the rubber, textile, furniture, and building industries. The synthetic rubber industry is particularly fertile for young creative specialists. Government services employ biochemists who devote their careers to combating diseases with drugs. About fifteen per cent of all chemists enter the teaching field to train the chemists of the future.

chemical engineer

EXPERIENCE REQUIRED: Graduation from accredited school of engineering. Graduate study an asset. Non-college man may attain professional status by utilizing free time for night school, working in a chemical or process industry during day.

DESCRIPTION OF JOB: Putting discoveries of chemists to use. Designing equipment for purpose. Applies science to industrial process to effect chemical, physical changes.

OPPORTUNITIES FOR ADVANCEMENT: Good opportunities. Executive, consultant jobs with government.

WHERE TO APPLY FOR JOBS: All important industries.

chemistry teacher

EXPERIENCE REQUIRED: Graduate degree for college teaching. Requirements for high school teaching vary in each state. Thorough knowledge of all branches of chemistry. Ability to teach and understand pupils essential.

DESCRIPTION OF JOB: Teaches and does laboratory demonstration work. Large proportion of time spent on laboratory work.

OPPORTUNITIES FOR ADVANCEMENT: Assistant professor, associate, and full professor. Supervisory positions in high school chemistry departments.

WHERE TO APPLY FOR JOBS: College or university placement bureaus. Boards of education.

chemurgist

EXPERIENCE REQUIRED: Degree in chemistry or chemical engineering, and graduate study in botany, biochemistry, agriculture, and agronomy. Knowledge of livestock and farm-crop production problems. Good health.

DESCRIPTION OF JOB: Breaks down waste and farm material into a basic formula and rearranges it to get a new product for industry. Develops products that are commercially useful.

OPPORTUNITIES FOR ADVANCEMENT: Research, administrative positions.

WHERE TO APPLY FOR JOBS: United States Department of Agriculture, industrial laboratories, paint and varnish companies.

control chemist

EXPERIENCE REQUIRED: College degree plus industrial experience. Training in inorganic and organic chemistry.

DESCRIPTION OF JOB: Analyzes samples. Is responsible for quality of materials entering plant and the products leaving it.

OPPORTUNITIES FOR ADVANCEMENT: Executive, functional head.

WHERE TO APPLY FOR JOBS: All important industries, government.

cotton technologist

EXPERIENCE REQUIRED: Graduation from accepted textile school. Training in textile technology, mechanical engineering, physics, and chemistry.

DESCRIPTION OF JOB: Research, assist, supervise in fields of fiber technology, textile chemistry, dyeing and finishing, etc.

OPPORTUNITIES FOR ADVANCEMENT: Civil service upgrading.

WHERE TO APPLY FOR JOBS: Government.

industrial chemist

EXPERIENCE REQUIRED: College degree and experience in industry. Thorough training in all branches of chemistry. Adequate training in mathematics and physics.

DESCRIPTION OF JOB: Performs duties related to all phases of manufacture.

OPPORTUNITIES FOR ADVANCEMENT: Assistant chemist, supervisor of production, supervisor of laboratory.

WHERE TO APPLY FOR JOBS: All important industries.

patent chemist

EXPERIENCE REQUIRED: Thorough knowledge of chemistry and patent law.

DESCRIPTION OF JOB: Studies research to locate inventive material. Prepares and prosecutes patent applications. Studies infringements and validity.

OPPORTUNITIES FOR ADVANCEMENT: Administration, consultant.

WHERE TO APPLY FOR JOBS: Corporate patent departments, United States Patent Office.

petroleum chemist

EXPERIENCE REQUIRED: College degree and experience in petroleum industry. Graduate work recommended.

DESCRIPTION OF JOB: Directs the processing of crude oil into commercial products.

OPPORTUNITIES FOR ADVANCEMENT: Executive, consultant, functional head.

WHERE TO APPLY FOR JOBS: Petroleum, chemical, and rubber companies.

plastic chemist

EXPERIENCE REQUIRED: Degree in chemistry or chemical engineering.

DESCRIPTION OF JOB: In research, discovery of new materials, improvement of materials already known. Designs, operates, supervises operation of machinery and equipment for chemical processes.

OPPORTUNITIES FOR ADVANCEMENT: Executive, functional divisional head.

WHERE TO APPLY FOR JOBS: Chemical companies.

research chemist

EXPERIENCE REQUIRED: College degree plus experience. Ph.D. desirable. Wide knowledge of industrial chemistry, mathematics, and natural sciences. Familiarity with foreign languages desirable.

DESCRIPTION OF JOB: Concerned with search for new products, development of new uses for products, the improvement of production methods, and reduction of costs. Often works with chemical engineer.

OPPORTUNITIES FOR ADVANCEMENT: Functional head, special assignments, supervisor of laboratory, executive.

WHERE TO APPLY FOR JOBS: All important industries.

soil scientist

EXPERIENCE REQUIRED: Graduation from an agricultural college with a major in soil chemistry or other soil specialization. Farm experience desirable. Graduate work an asset.

DESCRIPTION OF JOB: Concerned with applications of science to soil resources. Laboratory and field activities. Beginning job normally soil surveyor or laboratory technician.

OPPORTUNITIES FOR ADVANCEMENT: College department head, research head, management.

WHERE TO APPLY FOR JOBS: Federal and state governments, bureaus, colleges, fertilizer companies, owners of large estates or farms.

textile chemist

EXPERIENCE REQUIRED: College degree and specialized graduate study. Thorough grounding in chemistry of natural and artificial fibers.

DESCRIPTION OF JOB: Tests natural or artificial fibers and fabrics for ability to take dye, preparation of dye, testing finishing compounds.

OPPORTUNITIES FOR ADVANCEMENT: Chief chemist, administrative positions.

WHERE TO APPLY FOR JOBS: Textile manufacturers.

BIBLIOGRAPHY: BOOKS ON CHEMISTRY FOR FURTHER READING AND STUDY

Black, Newton Henry, and James Bryant Conant: *Practical Chemistry*. New York, 1928.

Brauer, Oscar Leo: *Chemistry and Its Wonders*. New York, 1938.

Brinkley, Stuart Robert: *Introductory to General Chemistry*. New York, 1945.

Brownlee, Raymond Bedell: *Chemistry in Use*. Boston, 1939.

——: *First Principles of Chemistry*. Boston, 1940.

Deming, Horace Grove: *Fundamental Chemistry*. New York, 1947.

Elder, Albert Lawrence: *Textbook of Chemistry*. New York, 1941.

Foster, William, and Hubert N. Alyea: *An Introduction to General Chemistry*. New York, 1947.

Frier, William T., and Albert C. Holler: *Introduction to Industrial Chemistry*. New York, 1945.

Glocker, George, and Ruby C. Glocker: *Chemistry in Our Time*. New York, 1947.

Hatcher, William Hooker: *An Introduction to Chemical Science*. New York and London, 1940.

Hildebrand, Joel Henry: *Principles of Chemistry*. New York, 1947.

Holmes, Harry Nicholls: *General Chemistry*. New York, 1941.

Kendall, James: *General Chemistry*. New York, 1936.

Kruh, Frank O.: *Modern-Life Chemistry*. Philadelphia, 1941.

Landis, Walter Savage: *Your Servant, the Molecule*. New York, 1944.

McPherson, William: *Chemistry at Work*. Boston, 1943.

Masson, Louis T.: *Chemistry Made Easy*. New York, 1947.

Offner, Monroe M.: *Fundamentals of Chemistry*. New York, 1944.

Strong, Ralph Kempton: *Chemistry for the Executive*. New York, 1946.

Timm, John Arrend: *General Chemistry*. New York, 1944.

Weaver, Elbert Cook, and Laurence Standley Foster: *Chemistry for Our Times*. New York, 1947.

Wendt, Gerald: *Chemistry*. New York, 1942.

Young, Leona Esther, and C. W. Porter: *General Chemistry*. New York, 1943.

physics—the science of energy

The word *physics*—from the Greek *physika, objects of nature* —was originally used to designate the study of *natural philosophy,* as distinguished from the study of *natural history.* Today it is used in a more restricted sense. Physics is the study of *energy,* as distinguished from chemistry, which is the study of *matter.* The science of natural philosophy, therefore, includes at the present time both chemistry and physics. Chemistry tries to explain how nature is constructed; physics, how nature works.

Energy, the province of physics, is *the capacity for doing work.* This capacity may be either in motion or at rest. Energy in motion is called *kinetic*—from the Greek *kinein,* to move; energy at rest is called *potential.*

We see examples of kinetic energy—or the capacity of a *moving* body to do work—in the striking of a bullet against a target, the tumbling of water over a dam, and the movement of a pendulum as it swings to and fro. And we see examples of potential energy —or the capacity of a *resting* body to do work—in a bullet before its discharge from the gun, water held in check by the walls of a container, and the pendulum in the positions it assumes at the two ends of its swing.

Thus the kinetic energy of a body may be changed into potential energy by bringing the body to rest, and its potential energy may be changed to kinetic energy by bringing it into motion. The study of physics, in brief, is the observation of these changes and the formulation of the laws that govern them.

In this chapter of our book, therefore, we shall consider the general nature of energy, its relationship to the material world, and its various manifestations in the fields of mechanics, heat, sound, light, magnetism, and electricity.

MASSES, LIQUIDS, AND GASES

Chemistry, as we have seen, deals with the combinations of atoms; physics with the transformations of energy. But the two fields are very closely intertwined—atoms and energy are but different aspects of nature. Indeed, it is sometimes difficult to draw a sharp line between the chemical and the physical investigations into the secrets of nature. In the last section of our chapter on chemistry, for example, we considered the subject of atomic energy. This subject belongs to physics as well as to chemistry, since it is a bridge that connects the two sciences. Throughout this book it is important to remember that our study of the *sciences* is merely an extended study of *science*. Nature knows no subdivisions of the world into astronomy, geology, chemistry, physics, and the like. The subdivisions known to us under the above headings are artificial. They are merely conveniences that enable our human minds to make a piecemeal study of the secrets of nature.

And these secrets of nature, examined through the medium of physics, become partially revealed to us as manifestations of energy. The world, thus regarded, is said to consist of, not atoms and molecules, but solids, liquids, and gases. For solids, liquids, and gases represent the *physical* rather than the *chemical* changes of nature—*the alteration of forces* rather than the *combination of elements.*

The forces of nature, then, are made manifest to us through their action in solids, liquids, and gases. A *solid* has a definite volume and a definite form. A *liquid* has a definite volume but no definite form. A *gas* has neither a definite volume nor a definite form.

Both liquids and gases are called *fluids,* because they *flow.*

The fluidity of gases, however, is different from that of liquids. A gas can flow—that is, expand—indefinitely and in every direction.

But all three substances can be changed into one another. A solid under high temperature can be melted into a fluid; a gas under low temperature can be condensed into a liquid; and a liquid under freezing temperature can be hardened into a solid. Indeed the state of a substance depends largely upon temperature conditions. The selfsame substance may exist, under different temperatures, in all the three states—as solid ice, liquid water, and gaseous steam.

All these substances, whether solid or liquid or gaseous, possess five properties in common. These five properties are: *mass, weight, volume, density,* and *inertia.* The *mass* of a body represents the quantity of material substance, or matter, in a body. Its *weight* is the measure of the force with which it is pulled toward the center of the earth. Its *volume* is the product of its dimensions. Its *density* is the thickness of its mass as compared to its volume. And its *inertia* is its tendency to persist in doing whatever it is doing—to remain at rest if it is at rest, or to go on moving if it is in motion.

Of these five properties, the first four may change under various conditions. Thus the mass of a body—according to the modern theory of relativity—increases with the velocity of its motion. Its weight depends upon its nearness to the center of the earth. An object weighs more at a lower than it does at a higher altitude, because the lower altitude is closer than the higher to the earth's center. The volume of a body expands under heat and contracts under cold. Its density increases when pressure is exerted upon it, and decreases when the pressure is removed.

But one of the properties of material bodies never changes. This invariable property is inertia. Inertia is the property, common to all matter, that prevents a change in a body's state of rest or motion, without the action of some force.

It was this universal and invariable property of inertia that led Sir Isaac Newton (1642–1727) to formulate his celebrated First Law of Motion: *Every body continues in its state of rest, or in its state of moving with constant velocity in a straight line, unless acted upon by some external force.* It takes *energy,* in other words, to start or to stop or to alter the motion of *matter*.

Now this energy, or force, that acts upon a body has its origin in another body; and *whenever the second body acts upon the first body, the first body reacts upon the second body with an equal force.* Thus every force is a double phenomenon—an energy of action and of reaction. When a book lies on a table, there is a force pressing down upon the table and another force pushing up against the book. When a weight is held up by a string, at every point in the string there is a downward pull toward the weight, and an equal upward pull away from the weight. When a piece of iron is attracted by a magnet, there is a force pulling the iron to the magnet and an equal force pulling the magnet to the iron. This relationship between opposing forces has been formulated into another of Newton's laws: *To every action there is an equal and opposite reaction.*

Thus, when a ball is hit by a bat, the force of the impact upon the bat is equal to the force of the impact upon the ball. This equal force compels them both to recoil in opposite directions. The *distance* of the recoil depends upon the weights of the two objects, their elasticity, and so forth.

When the forces that act upon a body are so related that they neutralize each other, the body is said to be in *equilibrium.* That is, the body either remains at rest, or it continues at a constant speed in a straight line or—like a well-balanced wheel—in a circle.

There are, however, three kinds of equilibrium: *stable, unstable,* and *neutral.* A body is in stable equilibrium, like a cone resting on its base, when considerable work is necessary in order to overturn or to displace it. It is in unstable equilibrium, like a cone balanced upon its apex, when only a slight force will displace it. It is in neutral equilibrium, like a ball on a flat table, when a force exerted upon it can set it in motion without, however, raising or lowering its center of gravity.

The center of gravity—in every material object, whether regular or irregular in shape—is the point at which its entire weight is concentrated. It is the spot about which all the parts of the object come to an exact balance with one another, so that when this spot is supported, the entire object is supported. The center of gravity is also called the *center of mass,* or the *center of inertia*

—that is, the concentration point of a body's resistance to change.

The center of gravity, however, must not be confused with specific gravity. The specific gravity of a substance is the ratio of its density to the density of water. The density of water, which is used as a general standard, consists of one gram per cubic centimeter. The specific gravity of gold is 19.3—since a cubic centimeter of gold has a density of 19.3 grams, or 19.3 times the density of water. The specific gravity of ice is .9—which means that ice is only nine tenths as heavy as water. This is a fortunate thing, for if ice were heavier than water it would not float on the surface but would sink to the bottom. The water on top would then be frozen in turn; and it, too, would sink to the bottom, until finally the entire body of water would be turned into a single mass of ice and all the living matter contained therein would be destroyed.

UNITS OF MEASUREMENT

In our brief survey of physical substances and their properties we have had occasion to refer to various measurements—such as centimeters, grams, and the like. All physical substances can be measured in units of length, mass and time. And these units, as generally adopted in scientific circles, are based upon the metric system.

This metric system has the merit of being internationally understood. Its standard of length is the meter—an arbitrary distance between two points on a rod constructed of an alloy of platinum and iridium, and kept at the International Bureau of Weights and Measures in Paris. This measure was intended to be one ten-millionth part of the distance between the equator and the North Pole along the meridian of Paris. But the survey was inaccurate, so that the meter is a convenient standard of science rather than an actual measure of the earth.

Like the metric standard of length, the scientific standard of mass is based upon an arbitrary unit. This unit, the kilogram, is the mass of a piece of platinum which is also kept at the Bureau of Weights and Measures in Paris.

The metric system is used almost exclusively in physics. But occasionally an American or a British scientist prefers to use the English system. The following tables, therefore, will serve as a guide to the metric units and to some of their more familiar English equivalents:

units of length

10 millimeters (mm.)	= 1 centimeter (cm.)	= about $\frac{2}{5}$ inch
10 centimeters	= 1 decimeter (dm.)	= about 4 inches
10 decimeters	= 1 meter (m.)	= about $1\frac{1}{10}$ yards
10 meters	= 1 dekameter (Dm.)	
10 dekameters	= 1 hectometer (Hm.)	
10 hectometers	= 1 kilometer (Km.)	= about $\frac{5}{8}$ mile

units of mass

10 milligrams (mgm.)	= 1 centigram (cg.)	
10 centigrams	= 1 decigram (dg.)	
10 decigrams	= 1 gram (gm.)	= about $\frac{1}{30}$ ounce
10 grams	= 1 dekagram (Dkg.)	
10 dekagrams	= 1 hectogram (Hg.)	
10 hectograms	= 1 kilogram (Kg.)	= $2\frac{1}{5}$ pounds

In addition to the above there are two other measures that are frequently used in physics:

The *liter*, which is a unit of capacity measuring 1000 cubic centimeters or 1 cubic decimeter, and which equals about 1 quart.

The *second*, which is common both to the metric and to the English system, and which is $\frac{1}{86400}$ of the average solar day.

The above metric system is known, in physics, as the *c.g.s. system*—that is, the computation based upon the *centimeter*, the *gram*, and the *second*.

By means of these units of measure—which may be called the *alphabet of physics*—it is possible to explain the various complicated relationships between matter and energy. This is the starting point for the study of physics—the story of the world in motion.

MOTION—THE COSMIC DANCE OF LIFE

We commonly say that a body may be at rest or in motion. Actually there is no such thing as rest. You and I are sitting on a chair. But neither you nor I nor the chair can be said to be absolutely without motion. All of us keep constantly moving, together with the earth, over its axis and around the sun. Moreover, every atom in the universe—as we have seen in our chapter on chemistry—is a continual motion of streams of energy.

But there are different *kinds* of motion; and it is the province of physics to notice these differences, to study their relationships, and to regulate their power for the benefit of man.

But before we consider the different *kinds* of motion, let us glance at the meaning of motion in general. As defined in Webster's Dictionary, motion is "the act, the process, or the fact of changing place . . . the passing from one place to or toward another; opposed to rest."

And since there is no point of absolute rest—that is, no point that can be used as an absolute reference for various movements —all motion is relative. Thus, for example, a plane that passes over a city possesses motion relative to the city; a passenger walking through the plane possesses motion relative both to the city and to the plane; the hands of a watch on the passenger's wrist possess motion relative to the city, the plane, and the passenger; and the city, with all its various activities, possesses a multitudinous motion related to the plane, the passenger, and the watch on his wrist.

To take a simpler and—from the standpoint of physics—more interesting example, let us suppose a train traveling fifty miles an hour and a passenger in the forward end of one of the coaches throwing a ball to the rear end with an equal speed of fifty miles an hour. The ball in this case would have motion relative to the coach. But it would have no motion relative to the ground, for the backward speed of the ball would be neutralized by the forward speed of the train. And thus the two equal motions in opposite directions would—from the standpoint of the earth—be no motion at all.

All motions, therefore, are the changes of position in one object as related to the changes of position in other objects. There are several kinds of such changes of position, or motion:

1. If an object moves in a single direction—that is, in a straight line—its motion is called *rectilinear*.

2. If an object moves in a path whose direction is constantly changing, its motion is called *curvilinear*.

3. If an object moves over equal distances in equal and successive intervals of time, its motion is called *uniform*. An example of uniform motion is that of a plane traveling three thousand miles at three hundred miles per hour. Another example is that of a watch hand covering an equal segment of the dial at every second.

4. If an object travels over unequal distances in equal and successive intervals of time, its motion is called *variable*, or *accelerated*. An object falling to the ground has accelerated motion, for the force of gravity compels it to keep increasing its speed as it approaches the earth.

Now all these motions, as we have seen, are relative. That is, they have actually no fixed point of reference. In dealing with everyday problems, however, the physicists generally regard motion as related to a (theoretically) fixed earth.

All motions—that is, all changes of position—involve three factors: time, space, and direction. The rate of motion as related to time is called *speed*. Thus we say that a train travels at a speed of fifty miles an hour. The rate of motion as related to time and direction is called *velocity*. A train traveling from New York to Boston—a distance of about 225 miles—in four and a half hours is said to have a velocity of fifty miles an hour north.

If the velocity of a moving object is uniform, it is equal to the distance divided by the time. And, by the same token, the distance is equal to the velocity multiplied by the time. Put into the formula of physical equations, the above may be expressed as follows:

$$V \text{ (velocity)} = \frac{S \text{ (distance)}}{t \text{ (time)}} \text{ ; and } S = V \times t$$

If the speed of a moving object is *not* uniform, the velocity (V) represents the *average* speed.

EXAMPLES:

1. If a plane travels eastward 900 miles in 3 hours, what is its velocity, or average speed?

$$V = \frac{S}{t}$$

$$V = \frac{900 \text{ miles}}{3 \text{ hours}} = 300 \text{ miles an hour east}$$

2. If a plane travels 6 hours at an average speed of 225 miles an hour, what distance does it cover?

$$S = V \times t$$

$$S = 225 \text{ miles per hour} \times 6 \text{ hours} = 1350 \text{ miles}$$

When the velocity of a moving object keeps increasing or decreasing, it is called variable, or *accelerated*. If the increase or the decrease in the velocity is uniform, the motion is said to be *uniformly accelerated*. Thus a ball dropped from a height to the ground gains, through the force of gravity, a uniform acceleration of about 32.16 feet per second.

Likewise, a ball thrown vertically into the air loses, through the same force of gravity, a velocity of about 32.16 feet per second. This *loss* of acceleration is sometimes called *deceleration*.

the formula for uniform acceleration

V_0 represents the initial speed of a moving object;
V_1 represents the speed at the end of t seconds;
a represents the acceleration.

The formula may then be expressed in the following equations:

$$a = \frac{V_1 - V_0}{t}; \text{ and } V_1 = V_0 + (a \times t)$$

To express this in words, the acceleration (a) is equal to the difference between the final speed (V_1) and the initial speed (V_0) divided by the number of seconds (t) during which the acceleration has taken place. And, likewise, the final speed (V_1) is equal to the sum of the initial speed (V_0) and the speed gained.

TO TAKE SOME SPECIFIC EXAMPLES:

1. If the initial speed of a moving object is 20 feet per second, and its final speed at the end of 12 seconds is 116 feet per second, what is its acceleration?

$$a = \frac{V_1 - V_0}{t}$$

$$a = \frac{116 - 20}{12} = 8 \text{ feet per second}$$

2. If the initial speed is 15 feet per second, and its acceleration is 10 feet per second, what will be its final speed at the end of 20 seconds?

$$V_1 = V_0 + (a \times t)$$

$$V_1 = 15 + (10 \times 20) = 215 \text{ feet per second}$$

MECHANICS—THE GADGETS OF THE UNIVERSE

Mechanics is the department of physics which deals with the motions of masses and with the effect of forces that cause or modify these motions. Mechanics may thus be divided into two sections: *kinematics* (from the Greek *kinema*, movement), which treats of motion regardless of force; and *dynamics* (from the Greek *dynamis,* power), which deals with the science of forces.

Thus far, in our treatment of motion, we have confined ourselves largely to *kinematics.* We have referred to motion as though it had an independent existence of its own. But actually motion is closely related to force. In order to understand a moving body we must understand the forces that move it.

It is necessary for the physicist, therefore, to consider not only the kinematics of the mechanical world but its dynamics as well.

Briefly defined, a force is either a push or a pull. This definition is sufficient for the understanding of many problems in the field of dynamics.

In order to determine the strength of a push or a pull, the physicists use either a metric or an English unit of measurement.

The unit of force in the metric system is the *dyne*. A dyne is the force required to move one gram of mass one centimeter in one second.

The unit of force in the English system is the *poundal*. A poundal is the force required to move one pound of mass one foot in one second.

All masses on earth are subject to a gravitational force, or pull. This force, measured in the metric system, is 980 centimeters per second. That is, the attraction of the earth imparts to one gram of mass, when falling, an acceleration of 980 centimeters per second. And since a dyne imparts to one gram of mass an acceleration of one centimeter per second, it follows that one *gram of force* is 980 times as strong as one *dyne*.

Similarly, the gravitational force of the earth imparts to one pound of mass, when falling, an acceleration of (approximately) 32.16 feet per second. And since a poundal imparts to one pound of mass an acceleration of one foot per second, one *pound of force* is 32.16 times as strong as one *poundal*.

And therefore

$$1 \text{ gram of force} = 980 \text{ dynes}$$
$$1 \text{ pound of force} = 32.16 \text{ poundals}$$

The law of gravitation as formulated by Newton assumes a pulling force not only between the earth and objects upon its surface, but between all bodies everywhere in the universe. Thus, Newton asserted, the same kind of force that causes the apple to fall from the tree *toward* the earth causes the moon to revolve in its orbit *around* the earth.

Moreover, the force of attraction between two bodies—or their gravitational pull—is *mutual*. That is, the apple and the moon pull the earth just as definitely as the earth pulls the apple and the moon. But the superior mass of the earth is sufficiently strong to keep the moon from drawing away into outer space, and yet not strong enough to pull the moon into itself. The result is a balance which carries the moon in a perpetual orbit around the earth.

This principle of mutual attraction has been formulated by Newton into the following formula: *The gravitational attraction between two bodies is directly proportional to the product of their masses and inversely proportional to the square of the distance between them.*

work

Why is it harder to climb a mile on a steep mountain than to walk a mile on a level road? The answer is that in climbing a mountain we are pulling our weight *upward* in direct opposition to the *downward* pull of the earth's gravity. This motion—*any motion against an opposing force*—means an expenditure of effort. In physics this expenditure of effort against force is called *work*.

It is important to remember that (scientifically speaking) work is accomplished only when it results in motion. Thus, when you hold a heavy weight at arm's length, you do no work. You begin the work when you *lift* the weight.

In computing the amount of work done on any object, we must consider two factors: the *force* applied and the *distance* the object is moved. A unit of work represents the movement of an object over a certain distance as the result of a certain force. There are three such units in common use:

1. The *erg* (from the Greek word for *work*) measures *the work done when a force of one dyne acts through a distance of one centimeter.*

2. The *foot-pound* measures *the work done when a force of one pound acts through a distance of one foot.*

3. The *kilogram-meter* measures *the work done when a force of one kilogram acts through a distance of one meter.*

Since the first unit, the *erg*, is far too small for practical measurements, a multiple of this unit is generally used. This multiple—called *joule*—is equal to 10,000,000 ergs. Briefly expressed,

$$1 \text{ joule} = 10^7 \text{ ergs (that is, 10 multiplied by itself}$$
$$7 \text{ times, or } 10,000,000).$$

EXAMPLE:

How much work is done when a force of 400 dynes causes a body to move 5 meters (a) in ergs? (b) in joules?

(a) Let W = work
          F = force
          L = distance
        W = F × L
        W = 400 dynes × 5 meters
        W = 400 dynes × 500 centimeters
           = 200,000 dynes-cm. = 200,000 ergs

(b) Since 1 joule = 10^7 ergs,

$$\frac{200,000 \text{ ergs}}{10^7} = .02 \text{ joules}$$

ANSWER $\begin{cases} 200,000 \text{ ergs} \\ .02 \text{ joules} \end{cases}$

power

When work is exerted over a period of time, the amount of work done in that period is measured in units of power. And thus power (P) represents the *time-rate* of work. One unit of power equals the amount of work done in one unit of time.

The units of power generally used in physics are:

1. *Horsepower* (H.P.)—the power representing a moving force of 33,000 foot-pounds (ft.-lbs.) per minute, or 550 ft.-lbs. per second.

2. *Watt*—the power representing a moving force of one joule per second. 1000 watts equal 1 *kilowatt* (kw).

If we change 550 ft.-lbs. per second (H.P.) to joules per second (watts), we find that 1 H.P. is equal to 746 watts.

The H.P. unit is commonly used by mechanical engineers; the watt by electrical engineers.

In order to compute the power of an engine, the following formula is used:

$$P \text{ (the work done in 1 unit of time)} = \frac{W \text{ (the total work done)}}{t \text{ (the time spent)}}$$

EXAMPLE: An engine raises 11,000 lbs. 600 feet in 10 minutes. What is its power in H.P. and kw.?

$$P = \frac{W}{t} = \frac{F \times L}{t} = \frac{11{,}000 \text{ lbs.} \times 600 \text{ ft.}}{10 \text{ min.}}$$

$$= \frac{6{,}600{,}000 \text{ ft.-lbs.}}{600 \text{ sec.}} = 11{,}000 \ \frac{\text{ft.-lbs.}}{\text{sec.}}$$

$$= (11{,}000 \text{ ft.-lbs. per second}) = \frac{11000}{550} \text{ H.P.} = 20 \text{ H.P.}$$

$$= 20 \times 746 \text{ watts} = 14{,}920 \text{ watts} = 14.92 \text{ kw.}$$

$$\text{ANSWER} \begin{cases} 20 \text{ H.P.} \\ 14.92 \text{ kw.} \end{cases}$$

machines

A machine is a contrivance for doing work by the transfer of energy from one object to another. There are two types of machines:

1. The simple type, such as the *lever, rope and pulley, wheel and axle, inclined plane, wedge,* and *screw.*

2. The complex type, or the elaborate machines that are combinations of the simple machines.

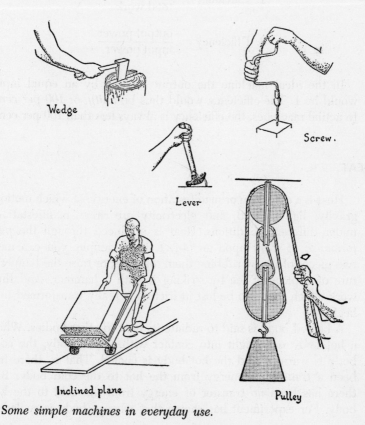

Some simple machines in everyday use.

In the ideal machine the *output* of energy would be equal to the *input* of energy. That is, the work done *by* the machine would be equal to the work done *on* the machine. But such an ideal machine does not exist in nature. In all actual machines, part of the work put in is wasted in *useless* energy—such as the overcoming of friction, the generation of noise, and so forth. The ratio of the *useful output* of energy to the *total input* of energy is called the efficiency of the machine—or *the work output divided by the work input.*

This ratio may be expressed in either of the two following equations:

$$1. \text{ Efficiency} = \frac{\text{useful work}}{\text{total work}}$$

$$2. \text{ Efficiency} = \frac{\text{output power}}{\text{input power}}$$

In the ideal machine the output divided by an equal input would be 1. The efficiency would thus be *unity,* or *100 per cent.* In actual machines, the efficiency is always less than 100 per cent.

HEAT

Heat is a condition or manifestation of energy, of which motion, gravity, light, sound, and electricity are other manifestations under different conditions. Heat is produced through the *performance of work* upon an object. For example, you can melt two pieces of ice by rubbing them together, or raise the temperature of a piece of ice by striking it with a hammer. And thus work which seems to be lost in friction is really transformed into heat.

A heated body is said to radiate its heat to other bodies. When a hot body is brought into contact with a cold body, the cold body is warmed and the hot body is cooled. That is, there has been a transfer of energy from the hot to the cold body. But there has been *no* transfer of energy from the cold to the hot body. For experiment has shown that when a body is cooled it *loses* something. It has given away some of its ability to do work. But when a body is heated it *gains* something. It has received additional ability to do work.

The addition of heat increases not only the *energy* but—in many instances—the *size* of an object. Gases, liquids, and even solids expand under increased heat. Other changes, too, take place. Gas or vapor, when heated, exerts a greater pressure. If sufficiently heated in an enclosed vessel, it may blow off the lid. A great amount of heat will melt a solid into a liquid; a smaller amount of heat will melt a liquid into vapor.

And that which measures the amount of heat in a body—*the degree of its hotness or its coldness*—is called its *temperature.*

Our sense of temperature comes to us from our sense of touch. But our sense of touch is a very unreliable measure of temperature. Suppose, for example, you hold your right hand in a vessel of hot water and your left hand in a vessel of cold water. And then, after a few seconds, suppose you withdraw the two hands and put them into a vessel of tepid water. The tepid water will feel cool to your right hand and warm to your left hand. Likewise, if you go into a warm bedroom after a hot shower, the air in the bedroom feels cool. Or if you step out of a cold night into a cool room, the temperature of the room seems warm.

And thus our sense of temperature is too inaccurate a measurement of heat. An instrument such as the *thermometer* is necessary for this measurement.

the thermometer

The thermometer—from the Greek *therme,* heat + *metron,* measure—is an instrument based upon the "expansion-under-heat" property of physical bodies. Among the liquids commonly used for the registration of the degrees of heat in a thermometer are mercury and alcohol. Mercury can register a wide range of temperature, since it boils at 674° Fahrenheit and freezes at −37.8° Fahrenheit. And alcohol can measure temperatures as low as −173° Fahrenheit.

In the measuring of temperature upon a thermometer, two scales are commonly used. These scales are the *Fahrenheit* and the *Centigrade* (or *Celsius*).

The Fahrenheit scale, named after its German inventor, Gabriel D. Fahrenheit (1686–1736), places the freezing point of water at 32° above zero and the boiling point of water at 212° above zero. As for the zero on this scale, it is an arbitrary point determined by the temperature of a certain cold day at Danzig, where Fahrenheit resided in the winter of 1709. This scale—indicated by the letter F—is regarded as the standard in the United States and Great Britain.

The Centigrade scale, invented by the Swedish astronomer, Anders Celsius (1701–44), is based on the metric system. The zero on this scale marks the freezing point of water, and the 100 marks the boiling point. Thus one degree on the Centigrade scale represents one hundredth part of the difference in temperature between the two "fixed points"—the freezing and the boiling point of water. This scale—indicated by the letter C—is generally used in scientific laboratories.

In laboratory experiments it is often necessary to convert Fahrenheit readings to Centigrade, and vice versa. The method for such conversion is as follows:

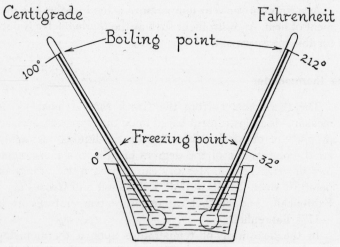

Centigrade and Fahrenheit thermometers measuring the same amount of heat on their respective scales.

Since the freezing point of the Fahrenheit scale is 32° and the boiling point is 212°, the number of Fahrenheit degrees between freezing and boiling is 212° — 32°, or 180°.

And since the freezing point of the Centigrade scale is zero and the boiling point is 100°, the number of Centigrade degrees between freezing and boiling is 100°.

Hence the ratio of the magnitude of a Centigrade degree to that of a Fahrenheit degree is 180 to 100, or $\frac{9}{5}$. In other words, one Centigrade degree is $\frac{9}{5}$ as big as one Fahrenheit degree. And consequently one Fahrenheit degree is $\frac{5}{9}$ as big as one Centigrade degree.

But, in converting a reading from one scale to another, we must remember that there is a difference of 32° between the freezing point of the Fahrenheit thermometer and that of the Centigrade thermometer. This difference between their freezing points, and the ratio of the magnitude of their degrees, will give us all the necessary data for our conversions.

And now let us see how it works out. Suppose we want to change a Centigrade reading of 45° (above zero) to a Fahrenheit reading. We multiply the 45° by $\frac{9}{5}$, which gives us a reading of 81° Fahrenheit *above freezing point*. We now add 32° to the 81°, and we get 113°—the corresponding Fahrenheit reading above zero.

In changing the Fahrenheit reading to the Centigrade reading, we reverse the process. We *subtract* the 32° from the 113°, and then we *divide* the 81° by $\frac{9}{5}$ (which is the same as multiplying it by $\frac{5}{9}$). And thus we get 45° Centigrade above zero.

These two processes may be expressed in the following two formulas:

$$(\frac{9}{5} \times C) + 32° = F \qquad\qquad \frac{5}{9} \times (F - 32°) = C$$

EXAMPLES:

1. Change 15° C. to F.

$$(\frac{9}{5} \times 15) + 32 = 59° F$$

2. Change 95° F. to C.

$$\frac{5}{9} \times (95-32) = 35° C$$

measurement of heat

This is not to be confused with the reading of temperature. The measurement of heat is known as *calorimetry*. And the unit quantity of heat in general use is known as a *calorie*.

A *calorie* (cal.) is the *amount of heat necessary to raise the temperature of one gram of water one degree Centigrade.*

There are other units of heat that are used occasionally. For example:

The *large calorie,* which is equal to 1000 (small) calories, and which represents the amount of heat necessary to raise the temperature of one kilogram of water one degree Centigrade.

The *British thermal unit* (B.T.U.), which is the amount of heat necessary to raise the temperature of one pound of water one degree Fahrenheit.

The British thermal unit can be reduced to calories as follows:

$$1 \text{ pound} = 453.6 \text{ grams}$$
$$1 \text{ degree F} = \frac{5}{9} \text{ degree C}$$

Therefore, $1 \text{ B.T.U.} = \frac{5}{9} \times 453.6 = 252$ calories.

how heat is produced

There are three methods for producing heat: through *chemical action, electric currents,* and *mechanical work.*

1. *Chemical action.* When two or more substances combine, the process is generally accompanied by the generation of heat. Thus the phenomenon known to us as combustion, or burning, is the rapid combination of the burning substance with the oxygen of the air. Sometimes there is combustion without the presence of oxygen, as in the burning of copper in chlorine gas. As a general rule it takes an *application of heat* to start the combustion—that is, the *production of heat.* But once started, the heat of the combination is sufficient to maintain the combustion. In the case of explosives such as gunpowder, all the elements necessary for the combustion are already present, so that the mere application of a spark or a jar is enough to precipitate the change.

It is interesting to note the various amounts of heat given off by the combustion of the following fuels which are commonly used in the heating of our office buildings, factories, and homes:

Wood	4000	calories	per	gram
Anthracite coal	7800	"	"	"
Charcoal	8000	"	"	"
Gasoline	12000	"	"	"

2. *Electric currents.* This method of generating heat is used extensively in incandescent and arc lights, and in many industrial processes. It must be pointed out, however, that an electric current is in itself the product either of chemical action or of mechanical work. And thus the heat produced by electric currents belongs either to the first method or to the third.

3. *Mechanical work.* Heat is produced from work either through friction, such as the rubbing of a brake against a wheel; through rotation, such as the twirling of a stick in a socket; or through compression. In 1850 the British physicist, Dr. James P. Joule, concluded a series of experiments in which he demonstrated that

energy may be converted into heat, and vice versa. Furthermore he showed that there is an exact equivalence between heat and work. That is to say, when a certain amount of work is apparently lost through friction, it produces a precisely equivalent amount of heat. This discovery led to the formulation of the *first law of thermodynamics:*

A *definite amount of work can produce a definite amount of heat, and vice versa.*

And this brings us to one of the most interesting subjects in physics—the conversion of heat into the energy that propels the engines of the world.

translating heat into work

The earth is rich with potential deposits of heat that can be converted into work. These deposits of heat—gas, petroleum, and coal—are storehouses of the sun's energy which fell upon the earth many thousands of years ago and which are ready to be changed into energy again at the touch of a flaming spark. For *every* form of energy can be transformed into *heat* energy. This process is very simple. It is, scientifically speaking, a *downhill* process. Indeed, heat is said to be the *lowest form* of energy.

But the reverse process—the transformation of heat into energy —is not so simple. For this is an *uphill* task. The best that engineers can do is to convert only a fraction of the heat of combustion into mechanical energy. The rest is called "unusable" or "wasted" heat.

And the fraction that represents an engine's ability to convert heat into energy is called the *efficiency* of the engine. Following is a table of the approximate efficiency of the various types of engines in use today:

Small steam engine	about	15 per cent
Gasoline motorcar engine	"	20 per cent
Large steam engine	"	25 per cent
Large steam turbine	"	30 per cent
Large diesel engine	"	40 per cent

the melting power of heat

One of the most important properties of heat is its capacity for *changing the states* of physical bodies. It can change solids into liquids, and liquids into gases. In thus transforming the physical state of an object, the energy of the heat overcomes the power of cohesion (sticking together) and increases the motion of the molecules.

The point at which a body changes from a solid to a liquid is called its *melting* point. This melting point is definite in the case of *crystalline* substances—such as gold, silver, ice, copper, and lead. But it is not definite in the so-called *amorphous* (formless) substances—such as glass, paraffin, wrought iron, and wax. These amorphous substances become gradually—that is, "indefinitely"—soft and plastic before melting, so that they may be easily bent or shaped or rolled into sheets.

The melting points of some of the *crystalline* substances are given in the following table:

SUBSTANCE	DEGREES C	SUBSTANCE	DEGREES C
Mercury	—39	Silver	960
Ice	0	Gold	1063
Sulphur	114	Copper	1083
Tin	232	Nickel	1452
Bismuth	271	Iron	1530
Lead	327	Platinum	1755
Zinc	419	Tungsten	3400

The freezing point at which a liquid turns into a solid is, of course, the same as the melting point at which the solid turns into the liquid. A number of liquids—such as salt dissolved in water, alcohol, and glycerine—have lower freezing points than water. And hence their solution in water results in a liquid with a lower freezing point than that of water. A 25 per cent solution of denatured alcohol in water makes a good "anti-freeze" in the radiators of motor vehicles, since such a solution has a freezing point of about —13° C.

how heat is transmitted

Heat may be carried from one body to another body, or from one part of a body to another part of a body, in three ways—*conduction*, *convection*, and *radiation*.

1. *Conduction* is the transfer of heat, through molecular activity, from one portion of matter to another portion of matter. Thus, when one end of an iron rod is heated, the other end becomes warm. The heat is *conducted* through the transmission of energy from more active molecules at the one end to less active molecules at the other end. An outdoor laborer wears woolen underclothes to prevent the escape of heat from his body, since the motionless air in the kinky fibers of the wool—even though he is unaware of the scientific principle—is a non-conductor of heat.

2. *Convection* is the conveying of heat from place to place by means of carriers. A *carrier* is a heat-containing portion of matter which conveys its heat just as a bucket is a water-containing portion of matter which conveys its water. Hot water and hot air in circulation are examples of the convection of heat. Thus the Gulf Stream, which flows northward along the eastern coast of the United States, is a convection current. Becoming heated at the tropics, the water rises to the top because of its decreased density, and then flows on the surface toward the Pole to replace the cold water that flows underneath the surface toward the equator to replace the heated water at the top. And thus the Gulf Stream is a heat-convecting current of continuous circular motion. Another example of the convection current is the ventilation of a room when you open the windows both at the top and at the bottom. The warmer and staler air escapes at the top, and the cooler and fresher air comes in at the bottom.

3. *Radiation* is the transmission of heat energy by means of waves. This type of heat transmission is different from conduction or convection. For, unlike those other two types, radiation requires no material agency either as a conductor or as a carrier.

The sun radiates its heat to the earth. Without this radiation we couldn't live. Yet we know that the interstellar spaces are empty of matter. These spaces do not conduct or convey the sun's heat. Yet the heat radiates across these extremely cold spaces—without warming them to the slightest degree—and reaches us here on earth to warm us and to give us life.

We may see another—and perhaps more convincing—example of heat radiation in the burning of a campfire during a snowstorm. If you sit close to the fire you feel the radiation of its heat. Yet if you take the temperature of the air between you and the fire you will find that it is several degrees below freezing point. The intervening air neither conducts, nor carries, nor is warmed by, the heat of the fire.

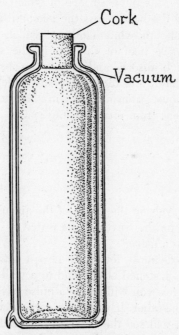

Cross section of a thermos bottle. The vacuum prevents the exchange of heat between the contents of the bottle and the outside air, and so maintains the contents at a stable temperature.

Radiation thus can be transmitted through space—even across a vacuum. Just how the heat waves travel through empty space is—at the present state of scientific knowledge—a mystery. But there is no mystery about the action of this heat upon the objects that it reaches with its radiation.

When the heat waves fall upon a substance they may be either reflected (by a polished surface), or absorbed, or transmitted. Thus water absorbs the heat radiation from the sun, and rock salt transmits it. Some substances, however, may absorb one radiation and transmit another. Glass, for example, absorbs the radiation from the cool earth and transmits the radiation from the hot sun. Thus a glass window or the glass covering of a greenhouse allows the heat of the sun to pierce inward, or to enter, but does not allow the heat of the earth to pierce outward, or to escape.

Among other interesting examples of heat radiation are the thermos bottle, the outer surface of which is silvered to prevent the escape of the heat across the vacuum between the walls of the bottle; smooth white clothing, which reflects and throws off the excessive heat of the sun in the summer; rough dark clothing, which absorbs and retains the insufficient heat of the sun in the winter; and the atmosphere which, like the glass roof of the greenhouse, transmits the sun's heat to the earth but keeps the earth's heat from escaping into space.

SOUND

A sound travels on the waves of the air just as a piece of driftwood travels on the waves of the water.

But what is a *wave?*

Before we define it, let us see how it acts. If you hold tightly a rope that is fastened at one end to a wall and strike the other end with a stick, you will notice a pulse passing from one end of the rope to the other. If you put a cork upon an oscillating body of water you will see the cork rise and fall with the motion of the water. But when the disturbance has passed, you will observe that the cork has come to rest in its original position.

What you have seen in the pulse of the rope and the oscillation of the water is a disturbance or motion of energy passing through a medium. This disturbance is familiarly known as a *wave*.

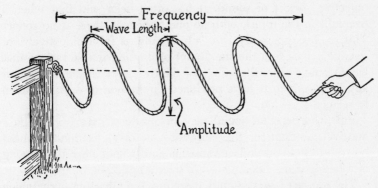

The motion of sound is much like the wave motion of this rope. The main terms used in connection with wave motion are shown here.

And you have noted that the wave in the rope or in the water does not carry any part of the rope or of the water along with it. It merely passes the motion and the energy along from one part of the body to the next by the interaction of the adjoining parts.

A *wave*, then, is *energy transmitted through a medium without causing the medium itself to be moved*. In other words, a wave is a means by which a certain amount of energy is transmitted through a medium. This energy remains with the wave as it moves along its oscillating path.

And one of the familiar types of energy carried along by the oscillation of waves is *sound*.

the transmission of sound

The term *sound* may mean one of two things:

1. The sensation which is produced in living creatures by means of the ear.

2. The vibrations that are capable of transmitting this sensation to the ear.

In physics we are concerned primarily with the second, or objective, aspect of sound. It has often been said that when a tree falls in the forest, with no one to hear it, there is no sound. This, while apparently true subjectively, is false objectively, or scientifically. From the standpoint of physics, the vibrations that have resulted from the falling of the tree, even in the absence of any living creature, have produced the motion of energy known to science as sound.

But, in order that sound may be produced, there must be a material medium for the vibrations to travel in. Sound cannot be transmitted through a vacuum. You cannot hear the ringing of a bell that has been placed in a jar emptied of its air.

The source of every sound, therefore, is a vibrating body which is capable of producing air vibrations—or air waves. A tuning fork is set in vibration by being struck; a harp string by being plucked; a violin string by being rubbed with a bow. These vibrations are often evident to the eye; they can always be felt when the string is touched with a piece of paper. Thomas Edison, after he had become stone-deaf, said that he could hear through his skull and his teeth. "Ordinarily," he said, "I place my head against the phonograph. If there is some faint sound that I don't quite catch this way, I bite into the wood and I get it good and strong."

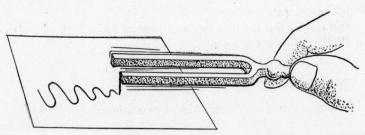

The vibrations of this tuning fork are being recorded by a pencil attached to one prong of the fork.

And thus the transmission of sound may be recorded not only by the ear, but by any device which can receive vibrations and convert them into some other form of energy. For example, the vibrations of sound can be transcribed on the moving disk of a phonograph record, or impressed upon the electric current of a telephone transmitter. In either case the sound vibrations are translated into a motion—or energy—which is no longer sound, but which can be *retranslated* into sound at an other time (through the phonograph needle) or in another place (through the telephone receiver).

the velocity of sound

In a thunderstorm we can see the electric disturbances in the form of lightning before we can hear them in the form of thunder. This is due to the fact that light travels much faster than sound.

The velocity of sound depends upon various factors—such as the medium through which it is transmitted, the temperature, the humidity, and the wind. For example, sound travels more speedily through water at 13° C. than it does through air at 0° C. And it travels even more speedily through some of the solids than it does either through the water or over the air.

TABLE OF SOUND VELOCITIES

MEDIUM	METERS PER SECOND	FEET PER SECOND
Carbon dioxide at 0° C.	261	856
Air at 0° C.	331.45	1087.8
Hydrogen at 0° C.	1286	4219
Water at 13° C.	1441	4728
Pine wood rod	3300	10,830
Brass rod	3600	11,800
Iron rod	4950	16,240
Steel rod	5000	16,410

By the use of velocity as a measure, it is possible to estimate the approximate distance to the source of a sound such as a thunderbolt. Suppose you hear the sound three seconds after you see the flash. Since the velocity of light is 186,000 miles a second, the time of its journey from the point of disturbance to your eye is negligible. And therefore the sound has reached your ear three seconds after the disturbance. Multiplying the three seconds by one fifth of a mile, the (approximate) velocity of sound through the air, you find that the starting point of the thunderbolt is (approximately) three fifths of a mile away.

In like manner it is possible to estimate the distance to a cliff by shouting and by noting the time elapsed between the shout and the return of the echo.

musical sounds and noises

When sound waves are regular and sustained, they produce *music;* when they are irregular and abrupt, they produce *noise.*

All musical sounds have three characteristics—*intensity, pitch,* and *quality.* And each of these characteristics depends upon the physical nature of the sound waves.

1. The *intensity,* or *loudness,* of a sound depends upon (a) the energy of the vibrations, and (b) the distance between the source of the sound and the ear of the listener.

2. The *pitch* of a sound depends upon the frequency of the vibrations—that is, the number of vibrations that reach the ear per second. The notes on the high scale, for example, vibrate through the air much more rapidly than the notes on the lower scales.

3. The *quality,* or *timbre,* of a sound, depends upon the shape of the sound wave. Thus the note A on the piano may have the same intensity and pitch as its equivalent note A on the violin. Yet the two notes are easily distinguished because of the difference of their *timbre.* For they are carried to the ear by waves of different shapes.

Thus, while music is an art, it has a scientific basis in the physical properties of sound. A combination of sounds will produce a pleasurable sensation if it possesses a harmonious union of intensity, pitch, and timbre. All other combinations are discords, noises, "painful blows" upon the listener's ear.

But there are some sounds—audible to other living creatures—that are inaudible to the human ear. The limits of tonal vibrations that can be intercepted by the average ear range from a frequency of 20 to a frequency of 20,000 per second. The lowest note on a piano has a frequency of about 27; and the highest note, a frequency of about 4100. The tones of the human voice range from a frequency of about 65 to a frequency of about 1000. Yet vibrations as high as 35,000, and even higher, have been measured in the laboratory. And thus there are many sounds—and much music—apprehended by science but unrecorded on our musical instruments and unperceived by our limited sound receptors.

LIGHT

The term *light*, like the term *sound*, may be used either subjectively or objectively. It may indicate the sensation produced in the eye or the waves that produce it. Physics deals primarily with the objective meaning of light. Thus defined, *light is radiant energy that is capable of producing sight.* X rays and radio waves are other forms of radiant energy. At one time it was believed that such waves traveled through a theoretical medium, permeating all space, called the "ether." However, today the idea of an "ether" has been definitely discarded. Light waves and the other forms of radiant energy are transmitted in a vacuum at the rate of 186,000 miles a second. They are simple, periodic variations which set up electrical forces in their paths. This force is of alternating character, increasing to a definite value, then decreasing and becoming reversed in direction many times a second. The length of one complete variation, or the distance between two points for which the electrical force of the wave is a maximum is called the *wave length.*

If light waves fall within certain lengths, they produce light that can be seen by the eye. If they are too short or too long, they become invisible to the eye.

And this brings us to a consideration of the spectrum—or the rainbow.

the colors of the rainbow

When a beam of white light passes through a rain cloud or a glass prism, it spreads out in a ribbon of colors that shade from red to violet. This shows that white is a combination of the various colors—you can prove this to yourself if you watch the spinning of a rainbow-colored top—and that the prism separates these colors and arranges them side by side in the order of their wave lengths.

The position of these colors in the spectrum is from red to orange, to yellow, to green, to blue, to violet. The red waves are the longest; the violet the shortest.

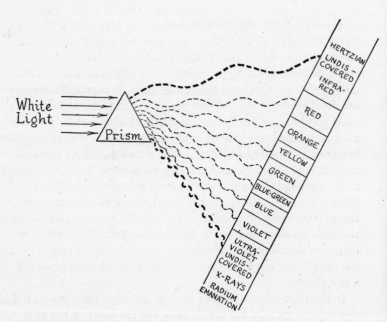

White light broken up by a prism into rays of various wave lengths.

The colors between the two ends of the rainbow are the only colors visible to the human eye. Yet a photographic plate can register light waves that are longer than the red waves at the one end of the spectrum and shorter than the violet rays at the other end. The light waves longer than the red waves are called *infrared;* those that are shorter than the violet waves are called *ultraviolet.*

So far as science has been able to conclude—and there is no reason to doubt this conclusion—the invisible infrared and ultraviolet rays are no different from the visible rays except in their wave lengths. All the wave lengths, visible as well as invisible, possess energy. That is, all of them can radiate heat. When they come within the *visible spectrum* they can radiate light as well as heat. When they fall outside this spectrum they can radiate heat but no light—so far, of course, as the human eye is concerned.

As we advance farther into the field of ultraviolet rays—that is, rays of *very short* waves—we come to the X ray, a radiation which can penetrate some substances, such as flesh, wood, or pasteboard, that are opaque to ordinary light. Other examples of energy that lie within the ultraviolet field are the penetrating *gamma rays* from radioactive substances and the so-called *cosmic rays*—a mysterious and extremely powerful radiation that seems to travel to the earth from spaces beyond the sun.

It is interesting at this point to note the effect of the light waves, both visible and invisible, upon human life. The *infrared waves* are capable of producing heat; but beyond that they have little effect on living tissue. The *waves of the spectrum* are of the utmost benefit to life; indeed, without the light and the energy of the sun—a combination of all the wave lengths of the spectrum— no form of life is conceivable. The *ultraviolet waves* are dangerous if we expose ourselves to them for too long a period. It is some of the ultraviolet rays that are largely responsible for sunburn. Moderate exposure to these rays, however, is beneficial. Ordinary glass cuts off most of the ultraviolet rays. Hence you cannot get their benefit if your windows are closed in the winter. Some hospital windows have been provided with a type of glass that allows the passage of these rays into the patient's room. The ultraviolet rays also possess the property of killing germs, and are therefore valuable in the sterilization of milk. But if handled without care—in the misuse of the electric arc, for example—they can produce serious burns on all living tissue. And therefore the body, especially the eyes, must be carefully protected when a person is exposed to ultraviolet rays.

complementary colors

A white light, as we have noted, is the sum of all the colors. But white may also be produced by the combination of only two colors. Such colors are called *complementary*, because each of them, when added to the other, *completes* the unit of white light. There are many combinations of colors that will produce white. For, if we take several colors of the spectrum and combine them, we get one resultant color. And if we take the remaining colors and combine them, we get another resultant color. The addition of *these two resultant colors* will produce the same white light as the addition of *all the colors* of the spectrum. Hence the color produced by the combination of any part of the spectrum is complementary to the color produced by the rest of the spectrum. And since there are many such combinations, there are many complementary colors.

Among the most important complementary colors are green and purple, red and blue-green, orange and blue. These colors are popular in decoration wherever an effect of violent contrasts is desired. On the other hand, when the effect desired is soft and unexciting, the colors used are those that lie next to each other— such as red and orange, green and yellow, or green and blue.

the velocity of light

For a long time it was believed that a ray of light passes *instantaneously* from the source to the observer—that we *see* the sun this instant as it *is* this instant. Experiments conducted by Galileo and by other scientists seemed to show no perceptible lapse of time in the passage of light over considerable earth distances. The trouble with these experiments was that the distances were not big enough. In 1675 the Danish astronomer, Ole Römer, took the distance between the earth and the sun—about 93,000,000 miles—as the field for his measurement of the velocity of light. And he proved, by observing the delay between the *expected* and the *actual* time of certain eclipses, that it takes a ray of light eight minutes and twenty seconds to travel from the sun to the earth. Thus he showed that light is not instantaneous but has a finite velocity of about 186,000 miles a second.

We see, then, the sun at this instant as it was about eight minutes and twenty seconds ago. In the case of some of the stars, we see them today as they were thousands of years ago. Many stars that have been long extinct can still be seen at the present time.

Römer's estimate of the velocity of light has since been confirmed by various scientists. One interesting experiment to prove the speed of light was that performed by Albert A. Michelson, American physicist and Nobel Prize winner, between 1878 and 1882. The setup for the experiment is shown in the illustration. A beam of light passes from a light source through a slit and is directed onto one facet of a revolving mirror which has eight facets. From here it is reflected by mirrors A and B to a concave

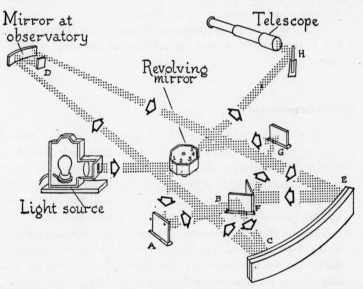

An ingenious experiment to measure the velocity of light. For explanation, see text.

mirror at C. From point C it is directed to another concave mirror at an observatory twenty-two miles distant. A small mirror D reflects it back to the observatory's concave mirror, from which point it is directed to the first concave mirror, at E. Here, through mirrors F and G, it returns to the revolving mirror, and then, through mirror H, to a small telescope. The observer sees the beam as a bright line on a graduated scale marked in the eye-piece. The speed of the revolving mirror must be set at about 525 revolutions per second for the beam to be seen in the telescope. At this speed the light beam returning to the revolving mirror will do so on facet 5, rather than on facet 4; thus the mirror has made one eighth of a revolution. One eighth of a revolution takes $\dfrac{1}{8 \times 525}$, or $\frac{1}{4200}$ of a second to travel forty-four miles, or approximately 186,000 miles a second.

The velocity of light is the greatest speed known to science. Indeed, science assumes that there is no greater speed in the universe. It is the one outstanding measure not only in terrestrial physics (the physics of the earth) but in astrophysics (the physics of astronomy, or of the stars).

And this light speed, whether it carries the white rays of the sun or the colored rays of the rainbow or the stars, is always the same.

light measurement

Light measurement, called *photometry,* is that branch of physics which evaluates light as a form of energy. The standard unit of light is the *candle.* The intensity of a source of light—that is, the amount of its energy—is called its *candle power.* The candle power of a source of light is the ratio of the energy emitted by that source to the energy emitted by a candle.

The illumination produced by one candle power at a distance of one foot is called one *foot-candle.* And the illumination produced by one candle power at a distance of one meter is called one *lux* (or one *meter-candle*).

The amount of illumination necessary for various purposes is, on the average, as follows:

Street lighting	0.02 to 0.05 foot-candles
Halls and theaters	2 to 5 " "
Offices and lobbies	4 to 7 " "
Reading and sewing	10 to 15 " "

The number of foot-candles necessary for individual use and comfort depends, of course, upon the individual's eyesight. The eye can stand a great deal of punishment in its adaptability to various intensities of light. Yet the illumination in every case must be adapted to the eye, rather than the eye to the illumination, if injury and discomfort are to be avoided.

our human perception of light

The development of our human perception of light, like the general development of our human understanding, has been very slow. It seems probable that early man saw the world as a panorama of white and black. He had no conception of colors, just as many of us today have no conception of colors in our dreams. And this world of white lights and dark shadows seemed just as natural to him as a black and white movie seems to us. The primitive Indo-Europeans had no words to indicate colors. They probably had no idea of blue skies, sunset-tinted clouds, red or yellow flowers, green trees, and brown earth.

The conception of color was primitive even at the height of Greek civilization. The Greeks, who made a religion of beauty, could see it only in a few colors. The philosopher Xenophanes, according to Professor Max Mueller, recognized only red, yellow, and purple in the colors of the rainbow. Even Aristotle spoke of the "tricolored rainbow."

And if this seems strange to us, let us remember that even today there are many people who are color-blind. That is, they are unable to detect certain colors—especially red and green. Such people have no way of distinguishing between "stop" and "go" lights at street intersections. Indeed, all of us are color-blind to *some* extent. And—here is an interesting point—no two of us ever see the same colors. For example, magenta (a red-and-green color) appears completely green to some and completely red to others, depending on the nature of their color blindness.

Hence the eye has always been a poor detector of color. The only real detector is the mechanical instrument which measures the wave lengths of the spectrum.

The human eye is inaccurate not only in detecting color but in judging distance. Fortunately, however, we have *binocular* vision to help us in correcting our judgment of distance. *Our two eyes give us two different pictures of the external world.* From where I am now sitting I can see a tall chimney in the foreground outlined against a hilltop in the distance. When I look at the chimney with my right eye alone, I can see it to the left of the summit. When I look at it with my left eye alone, I can see to the right of the summit. And now, looking at it with both eyes, I can get a fairly good—though even now far from accurate—idea of the relative positions and distances of the chimney and the hilltop.

And now, as I look once more through the window, I see a horizontal bar on a roof across the street. But this bar is of no great help to me in my judgment of distance. For my eyes, like the bar, are placed horizontally. In order to judge the distance

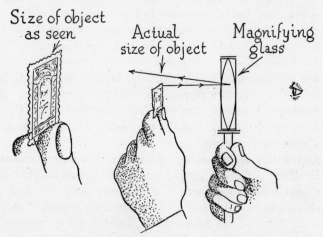

How a simple magnifying glass enlarges an image. Rays of light coming from the object are refracted by the lens and to the observer seem to come from a point behind the actual object.

of the bar—or of a wire stretched across my field of vision—I should have to tilt my head so that one of my eyes would see the bar from above and the other from below.

It is this binocular—or two-eyed—vision that enables us to get the sense of "depth" in a landscape. A familiar device for creating the illusion of depth in a picture is the *stereoscope*. Through this device you see two photographs placed side by side, like the two images ordinarily seen through the naked eyes. The two photographs merge into one, and thus the various objects in the photographs fall into their proper perspective. Compared to the pictures as seen through the prisms of the stereoscope, an ordi-

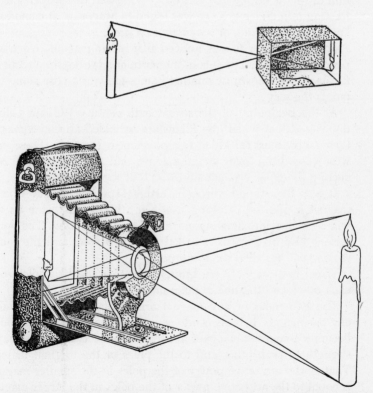

A pinhole camera (above) *and a camera with a lens* (below) *both transmit an upside-down image.*

nary photograph looks flat and unalive. For it is a *one-eyed* picture—a scene recorded upon a single screen. A single-screen picture is like a landscape observed through one eye. The only illusion of depth is due to *chiaroscuro*—the lights and the shadows of the various parts.

But in the *accurate* measurement of light, the human eye must always give way to the scientific instrument.

MAGNETISM AND ELECTRICITY

As early as 600 B.C. it was noticed that certain specimens of iron ore—now designated as Fe_3O_4—possessed the property of attracting iron. Since this ore was found in Magnesia, it came to be known as *magnetite,* or *magnetic iron ore.*

Somewhat later it was noticed that a bar magnet, when suspended by a thread, points to the north and the south. And hence it came to be known by another name—*lodestone* (the stone that points the way).

At the beginning of the seventeenth century William Gilbert discovered that when iron filings are sprinkled around a magnet they collect most thickly at two points near the ends. These ends were named the *poles* of the magnet, and the straight line connecting the poles was named the *axis* of the magnet.

It was then found, through further experiment, that when a magnet is allowed to swing freely in a horizontal plane its axis will seek an approximately north and south direction. The north-seeking end of the axis is called the *north pole;* and the south-seeking end is called the *south pole.*

When two magnets are brought together the *like* poles *repel* each other and the *unlike* poles *attract* each other.

The two poles of any magnet are of equal strength. And if any bar magnet is broken into several pieces, each of the pieces becomes a complete magnet in itself, with the two poles equal in strength to each other and to the poles of the original magnet. That is, the attractive power of the poles in the smaller magnets is equal to the attractive power of the poles in the larger magnet.

Any substance attracted by a magnet is called a *magnetic substance*. Many substances are magnetic, but in different degrees.

Thus hard steel is more magnetic than soft iron; soft iron is more magnetic than nickel, cobalt, manganese, and chromium. Diamagnetic substances, such as bismuth, copper, tin, wood, paper, aluminum, and glass, are examples of substances that are not magnetic.

A piece of metal can be magnetized by being stroked with a magnet a number of times in the same direction. Such a magnetized piece of metal is called an *artificial* magnet. Soft iron is easily magnetized, but quickly loses its magnetism. Steel is harder to magnetize, but retains its magnetism much longer than iron.

The region which surrounds a magnet and within which its magnetic force is exercised is known as its *magnetic field.* All of us, therefore, live in a magnetic field. For the earth is a magnet, with its northern magnetic pole situated west of Baffin Bay and almost due north of Omaha, Nebraska.

The magnetic field of the earth is rather more complicated than that of a simple magnet, and local irregularities have been found in many regions. Yet in general the magnetism exerted by the earth over its entire field is such as would be exerted by a huge steel magnet situated at the earth's center with its poles pointing approximately north and south.

The earth, like any other magnet, can induce magnetism in various substances. For example, a strip of tin-coated iron will

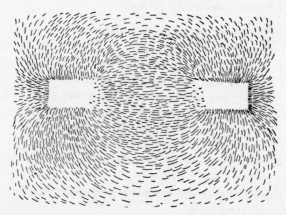

A bar magnet and the magnetic field around it shown by iron filings.

become magnetized if it is vigorously bent and twisted while it is being pointed toward the north magnetic pole. An iron pipe held for some time in a north and south direction will be converted into a *temporary* magnet. If struck with a hammer while it is held in this position, it will become a *permanent* magnet. Iron rails that stretch north and south frequently acquire magnetism from the magnetism of the earth.

The magnetic attraction of the earth has enabled mariners to chart their course by means of the compass—an instrument with a magnetic needle that points to the north. But this method for navigation is not always reliable. For the direction of the earth's magnetism is subject to changes—some of them seasonal, but others very sudden and unpredictable. These sudden changes are due to magnetic storms, disturbances that occur at periods of great solar activity. As a result of these violent "sun storms" the magnetic field of the earth may become disarranged, the compass needle may swerve materially away from the north, and shipwreck may thus follow in the wake of a tempest ninety-three million miles away.

The *exact* causes of these magnetic disturbances upon the earth are still in the realm of theory. But it seems probable that the electric particles—or "bullets"—shot out from the sun produce a profound effect upon the magnetic condition of the earth.

magnetic fields and electric currents

Every electric current is surrounded by a magnetic field and reacts upon it. And the magnetic field in return reacts upon the electric current. Suppose you hang a wire vertically near a horizontal magnet, and then send an electric current through the wire. You will see the wire swing in a somewhat circular path (over the magnetic field) until it comes to rest against one of the sides of the magnet. And now, if you reverse the current, you will see the wire retrace its path. It will now swing around from its position against one of the sides of the magnet until it comes to rest against the opposite side.

Obviously, then, there is some sort of connection between magnetism and electricity.

The existence of electricity was recognized by the ancients.

About 600 B.C. the Greeks observed that a piece of amber, when rubbed with a cloth, acquires a "mysterious power" to attract light bodies just as magnetite attracts iron. Since the Greek word for amber is *electron,* its mysterious power of attraction came to be known as *electricity.*

It was not until 1600, however, that electricity was found to exist in substances other than amber. Today it is an established fact that *any two substances,* when rubbed together and then separated, acquire the property of attracting other bodies. If you rub a piece of glass with a piece of silk, you will find that the two substances will attract not only each other but small bits of paper, pith balls, and the like. If you stroke a cat in the dark, you will notice the emission of sparks from the fur. And if you rub your shoes against a dry rug on a clear, cold day, you will be able to light an open gas jet by touching it with your finger.

Similar examples may be multiplied indefinitely. All substances that acquire this property of attraction through friction are said to be *electrically charged.*

But there are two kinds of electrical charge. If you rub a rod of glass with silk and a rod of hard rubber with cat's fur, both rods become electrified—but in different ways. The glass rod is said to be *positively* charged, and the rubber rod is said to be *negatively* charged.

And now, if you suspend a light pith ball near the positively charged glass rod, you will find an interesting bit of action and reaction. At first the pith ball will be *attracted to,* and then suddenly it will be *repelled from,* the glass rod. The same activity— first attraction and then repulsion—will result if you suspend the pith ball near the negatively charged rubber rod. But now, if you take the pith ball that is being repelled by the rubber rod and place it near the glass rod, you will find an attraction instead of a repulsion, and vice versa. Furthermore, if you place the glass rod near the rubber rod, you will also find an attraction instead of a repulsion.

All these and many similar experiments have demonstrated what is known as the *first law of electrostatics: When two bodies are similarly electrified—that is, both positive or both negative— they repel each other; but when they are dissimilarly electrified— that is, one positive and the other negative—they attract each other*. Put into everyday language, this law means that—electrically speaking—like bodies repel each other and unlike bodies attract each other.

But what is electricity?

the nature of electricity

The real nature of electricity is as much of a mystery today as it was among the ancient Greeks. So far as science can tell at the present time, electricity is the underlying basis of all matter. If we understood the nature of *matter* we could probably understand the nature of *electricity*.

Let us, however, attempt a groping approach toward the solution of the mystery—a brief consideration of some of the "clues" that point the way.

Matter, it appears, is built up of electrically positive and negative particles—or charges. The basic positive charge is called the *proton*, and the basic negative charge is called the *electron*. According to this theory, every atom consists of a nucleus of protons surrounded by a revolving ring of electrons; and the atom is held together by the *attraction of the negative electrons to the positive protons*.

Now this theory, though it doesn't explain the *nature* of electricity, helps to account for much of its *action*. A *positive* charge of electricity means a *deficit* of electrons; a *negative* charge means a *surplus* of electrons; and an *electric current* means a *motion* of electrons.

All matter, therefore, is made up of two kinds of electricity—positive and negative. (These names were first applied by Benjamin Franklin.) And an electric current results from the circulation of electrons between two bodies. Thus, if A, a more active body, is rubbed against B, a less active body, the following phenomenon takes place: the "free" electrons from A move readily into B, while the "restrained" electrons from B do not move readily into A. Hence A acquires a positive charge through the *loss* of negative electrons, and B acquires a negative charge through the *gain* of negative electrons.

Electricity, therefore, may be defined as *the energy which constitutes the basis of all matter*. And the entire field of electricty may be divided into two sections: *electrostatics* and *electrodynamics*.

static electricity

Static electricity—or electrostatics—deals with electric energy at rest, or resident upon physical objects that are at rest. This type of electricity is produced by friction, pressure, heating, or induction. It is the only form in which electricity was known until comparatively recent times.

This form of electricity acquires power in a body when the body is *charged*—that is, when electrons have been either added to it or taken away from it. When electrons have been *added* to it, the body is *negatively* charged; when they have been *taken away* from it, the body is *positively* charged. When the body has the *same amounts* of positive and negative electricity, it is *uncharged,* or *neutral.* Ordinarily physical bodies exist in this state of neutrality—the positive and the negative amounts of electricity balance each other and therefore remain static.

When an object becomes charged, the free charge can reside only on the *outside surface* of the object. This phenomenon received a spectacular demonstration in 1837, when Michael Faraday shut himself up in a metal box which was electrically charged. Although spectators on the outside of the box were able to draw sparks from the surface, Faraday detected no trace of electricity in the interior.

Another important property of electricity is its capacity for flowing through some substances but not through others. Your electric lamp is connected to the outlet of your electric supply by means of a metal wire. But the wire is covered with a protection of rubber as a precaution against your receiving an electric shock. You cannot safely touch the wire when the electricity is on, but you *can* touch the rubber. This is because electricity flows through the wire but not through the rubber. In other words, the wire is a *conductor,* but the rubber is an *insulator.*

Among the best conductors—substances which allow the free flow of electricity—are metals such as gold, platinum, copper, and silver. Somewhat less effective as conductors are acids and solutions of metallic salts called *electrolytes.* Among the best insulators are rubber, paraffin, amber, mica, wood, sulphur, paper, and glass. Dry air is a very good insulator, but moist air is not nearly so good.

A conductor—such as a metal wire, for example—may be compared to a vein of gravel in the earth through which a stream of water is able to flow. An insulator is like a vein of clay through which a stream of water is unable to flow.

The terms *conductor* and *insulator,* however, are only relative. Electricity flows, to some extent, through *all* substances. The conductivity of a substance depends upon the ease with which the electrons can be dislodged from the atoms. A conductor is a body of "free" electrons; an insulator, a body of "restricted" electrons. And the flow of free electrons in a conductor constitutes its electric current.

One of the most useful electric conductors, so far as human safety is concerned, is the lightning rod. To be completely protected from lightning, a house would have to be put inside of a hollow conductor—just as Faraday put himself inside of a metal box. Since this sort of protection is impossible, the next best thing is a number of rods, projecting above the roof and grounded in the damp earth. These form a partial and generally safe screening. In cities the houses are pretty adequately protected by the large number of telephone and electric light wires.

electricity in motion

Thus far we have considered electricity either at rest or moving in a current so transitory as to remain for the greater part quiescent. We now come to that phase of electricity which can be produced to last for a considerable time and to exercise considerable power. This branch of electricity is called *electrodynamics,* or *electricity in a state of motion.*

Durable and powerful currents of electricity in motion can be produced in the *storage battery*—literally, a storehouse of electric energy. This type of battery contains a plurality of cells so connected as to produce a constant flow of electricity.

When a storage cell is fully *charged,* its voltage is about 2.6 volts. When it is *discharged,* its voltage has come down to about 1.8 volts.

When a battery is completely discharged, it becomes *sulphated.* That is, the plates are covered with lead sulphate—a substance deposited on the metal by the discharge, and a charging current can no longer flow through in order to "revive" the battery. The battery, in other words, is *dead.*

In order to keep a storage battery alive, it is necessary to refill it with distilled water every few weeks. A well-treated battery can last several years, and will be in better condition when used than when it is left idle.

electric measurements

An electric current, as we have noted, is a flow of electrons. But this current of electrons is like a relay race. For each electron does not flow through the entire circuit, but moves only a short distance before it collides with an atom and dislodges—that is, sets in motion—another electron, which continues the relay until it, in turn, collides with another atom. And so on, until the circuit is completed.

And thus the current has an average "racing" power, or working strength. This average of current strength is measured by a unit called the *ampere.*

An *ampere*—named after the French physicist, André Ampère (1775–1836)—is a *current which, when passed through a solution of silver nitrate in water, will deposit .001118 grams of silver in one second.*

And for every *unit of strength* in an *electric current* there must be a *unit of quantity* in the *electricity used.* This unit of quantity is called a *coulomb.*

A *coulomb*—this term is also named after a French physicist, Charles A. de Coulomb (1736–1806)—is the *amount of electricity conveyed by a current of one ampere in one second.*

Now every electric current, like water flowing through a pipe, is the result of pressure. That is, the electricity flows from a point of higher pressure to a point of lower pressure. These higher and lower pressures in a current are called the *electric potential,* and the difference between these two pressures is called the *difference of potential,* or *voltage.* And the standard measure of this potential difference, or voltage, is called a *volt.*

A *volt*—named after the Italian physicist, Alessandro Volta (1745–1827)—is the *unit of electromotive power in an electric current*. The pressure of the Weston cell, accepted by an act of Congress as the standard measurement of electric power, is 1.0183 volts.

The electromotive power of a current is thus pumped into an object by means of a battery. The most powerful of these electric pumping machines is the *dynamo,* or *generator.* A dynamo that supplies electric power to trolley lines exerts a pressure of about 550 volts. The pressure that illumines an electric house lamp is about 115 volts. And the pressure that lights an automobile lamp is only about 10 volts.

The electric power used in industry and in the home is measured in *watt-hours* or in *kilowatt-hours*. A *watt* is a *volt-ampere*—that is, the product of the two. A *kilowatt* is *1000 watts*. And a *kilowatt-hour is the amount of electricity supplied by one kilowatt of electric force in one hour.*

EXAMPLE: If a 550-volt current supplies 10 amperes for 200 hours, how many kilowatt-hours are used?

$$550 \text{ volts} \times 10 \text{ amperes} = 5500 \text{ watts}$$

$$\frac{5500}{1000} \text{ kilowatts} \times 200 \text{ hours} = 1100 \text{ kw.-hrs.}$$

electromagnetism

It was the Danish physicist, H. C. Oersted, who first discovered (in 1819) the relationship between magnetism and electricity. In a series of experiments with a magnetic needle placed near an electrically charged wire, he showed that electricity produces a magnetic field around its current. As a result of this discovery, it is now possible to make extremely powerful *electromagnets.*

An *electromagnet* is a mass of iron or steel magnetized by the passage of an electric current through a wire coiled about it. The power of an electromagnet increases with the current that is passed through it. A small current making many turns will produce the same power as a larger current making fewer turns. Some electromagnets are so powerful that they are capable of lifting many tons.

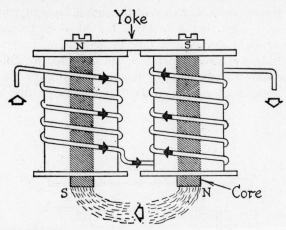

An electromagnet can be simply made by winding an electric wire (with current supplied by a battery) around a soft iron core.

uses of electric power

The most important uses of electromagnets are in the "field coils" of dynamos and motors. But their general application covers the entire range of electrical engineering. The telegraph, the telephone, and the doorbell are but a few examples of the common use of electromagnets. In every one of these—and of similar—instruments, the action of electromagnetism is roughly that of a piece of metal moved over a magnetic field and energized to rise and fall—or to vibrate—like a hammer over an anvil as the operator "makes" the circuit by striking a key or talking into a receiver or pushing a button, and then "breaks" the circuit by withdrawing his action. When the circuit is made, the striking of the "hammer" produces the sound; when the circuit is broken, the sound stops.

Electric energy can be transformed not only into sound but into heat. Among the practical applications of electric heating are *electric cautery*—the performance of surgical operations by an electrically heated platinum wire; *electric welding*—the cementing of iron rods by pressing them firmly together and passing an electric current through them; *incandescent lighting*

—the transmission of a current through a filament whose resistance is so high that it becomes heated to incandescence and
produces light; and electric *fusion*—the melting of metals in electric furnaces whose temperature can be raised to 3500°C. Since
all the known elements have melting points below this temperature, there is no substance thus far discovered that cannot be
melted by electricity.

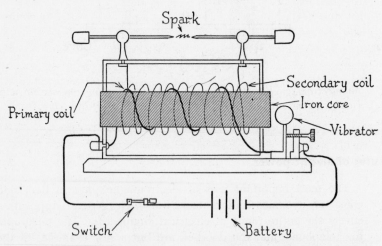

*In this induction coil, the primary coil magnetizes the iron core, thus
attracting the vibrator. But when the vibrator moves to the left, the
current is broken; the iron core then loses its magnetism and the
vibrator springs back to the position shown in the figure. This is repeated, so that the vibrator actually vibrates. Meanwhile, when current flows through the primary coil, the magnetized iron core induces
a current in the secondary coil, causing a spark to jump the gap.*

MODERN PHYSICS—RELATIVITY

In 1905 Albert Einstein made a startling assertion that revolutionized the entire picture of physics. Newton had declared that
everything tends naturally to remain at rest. But Einstein main-

tained that everything is actually in a state of motion. Moreover —he said—the motions of the various bodies of the universe are relative and hence there are no absolute measures of things. The measure of a thing depends upon the position of the person or of the instrument that measures it.

For example, suppose there are two men inside a moving train and two men outside, and the four men are trying to measure its length. The two men who are riding inside will stretch a tape from one end of the train to the other, and thus they will get the distance in the manner of the classical physicists. The two men who are standing outside will hold the tape between them; and, upon a prearranged signal, each of them will mark the position of his end of the train upon the tape. And then they will get the length of the train by measuring the distance between their two marks on the tape.

Will the measures of the two pairs of men coincide? No, declared Einstein. For the men on the outside, according to the theory of relativity, cannot arrange a signal that both of them will receive at the same instant. Hence they cannot get an accurate measure of the train. In other words, the length of an object as measured by observers who move *together with* the object is different from the length of the same object as measured by observers who are *on the outside*. Moreover, to an outside observer the length of an object depends upon the velocity of its motion.

All motions and measures, therefore, are *relative* to one another —with one important exception. In this universe, declared Einstein, there is one *absolute* measure. This absolute measure is the velocity of light. However fast and in whatever direction an observer may travel, his measure of light—the maximum speed that we know—will always be the same. This is the one unchanging factor in all our equations about the relative speeds of moving bodies.

But the law of relativity, asserted Einstein, applies not only to the *speed* of a moving body, but also to its *size*. All bodies contract in their motion. To the two men who measure the train from the outside, the train is shorter than it is to the two men who measure it from the inside. The faster it travels, the shorter it looks. And thus, *the rate of the contraction of a moving object increases with its increasing speed.* A train a mile long in a state of so-called rest *would shrink to zero* if it were set in motion at the speed of light.

All motion and all size, therefore, are relative. All *space* is relative. And so, too—declared Einstein—is all *time.* The past, the present, and the future are merely three related points in what we call *time,* just as Washington, New York, and Boston are three related points in what we call *space.* Points of time, like points of space, are events with intervals between them. Regarded in one way, they represent a *time element;* regarded in another way, they represent a *space element.* But these events, to be properly understood, must be studied in their *relation to one another.* Space is a planetary map, and time is a planetary clock; and both of them are *measures of motion.* Every moving planet has its own system of local direction and local time. And the system of every planet differs from that of every other planet. Our own terrestrial system of space and time is not to be taken as an *absolute measurement* for the entire universe. It is merely a *local schedule* of the earth's journey over its orbit. A year is a relative unit that measures a single revolution of the earth around the sun. Our own point in *time,* therefore, depends upon our own position in *space.*

Time, in other words, is a physical part of space. The physical universe, maintains Einstein, consists of a *space-time continuity;* and every object within this continuity moves at a speed which is relative to the speeds of all the other objects. Time and space are the human "laboratory" which contains the measuring rods for the motions of the heavenly bodies *as they appear to the observers upon the earth.*

But the *one standard measure for the entire universe* is the velocity of light. A ray of light covers 186,000 miles of *space* in one second of *time.*

Space and time, then, are dependent upon each other. Neither can be understood as a separate entity. Both must be considered as *co-ordinate aspects of motion* in our physical approach to reality. The world of physics, as regarded today, is not three-dimensional. It consists of three dimensions of space and of an additional fourth dimension—time.

THE USES OF PHYSICS IN EVERYDAY LIFE

Our modern life is dependent, to a great degree, upon the practical applications of physics. We shall here touch upon just a few of the contributions of this science to the promotion of a happier and more comfortable human existence.

airplanes

The lifting power of an airplane is based upon a simple principle in physics: when the plane travels through the air, the velocity of the air *above* the wings is greater than the velocity of the air *underneath* the wings. Hence the pressure of the air on top is less than the pressure of the air on the bottom. And it is this difference in pressure that enables the plane to rise *into* and to travel *through* the air.

But in order to get its upward and forward impetus, or push, the plane has a propeller which, in its whirling motion, "cuts a passage" through the air.

When the propeller starts the movement of the plane along the ground, the lifting power of the wings lessens the weight of the plane upon the wheels. And the weight upon the wheels keeps on *decreasing,* as the speed and the lifting power of the wings keep on *increasing*—until finally the lift is greater than the weight and the plane rises from the ground.

automobiles

The self-moving power of the automobile is based upon the fact that gases expand when they are heated. In the automobile a mixture of gasoline and air is introduced into the cylinder through the carburetor. This mixture is then ignited through the action of the spark plug in the cylinder; the ignition produces a rapid expansion, or explosion, of the mixture; and the pressure of this explosion within the cylinder propels the piston which, in turn, communicates the motion to the axles of the vehicle.

electronics

Electronics is that branch of physics which deals with the application and the control of electric currents through a vacuum or gas or vapor. The tool which translates the principle of electronics into practical service is the *electron*—or *vacuum—tube*.

The control of an electric current through a vacuum tube has become the basis of radio transmission and reception, long-distance telephone and telegraph communication, the generation of fluorescent lighting, the purification of the air through the killing of bacteria, the operation of mechanical devices through the emission of electrons by means of the glass tube known as the photoelectric cell, and the transmission of light through television over great distances. The future industrial and medicinal possibilities of this branch of electricity are almost unlimited.

The modern study of electronics is the result of Edison's discovery that electrons can be made to "migrate" from metal to

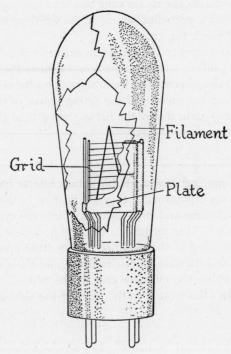

The inside of a radio vacuum tube.

metal by the application of heat. He made an evacuated glass bulb containing a metal plate and a filament. As long as the filament remained cold, there was no current between the filament and the plate. But when the filament was heated, a current began to flow—*provided the plate was positive with respect to the filament*. This observation was the beginning of the great "electronic revolution" in physical mechanics. And all the applied uses of electronics are founded upon the principle that a current of electricity is a stream of electrons, and that it is possible to harness this flow of electrons to our human needs.

medical instruments

Among the more important instruments which medicine has acquired from physics are the *electrocardiograph,* the *encephalograph,* and the *X-ray machine.*

The *electrocardiograph* is a mechanism which produces an *electrocardiogram,* or printed record of the strength and the intervals of the heartbeats. The heart, as it pumps the blood through the body, produces electric currents which follow a regular pattern when the heart is healthy. But when the heart is diseased, the pattern becomes irregular; and the nature of the disease can generally be ascertained from the pattern recorded upon the cardiogram.

The records of the heartbeat pattern are made through metal electrodes that are attached to the two arms and the left leg of the patient. The electronic circuit that passes between the electrodes and the patient's body not only intercepts the electric currents of the heart but magnifies them for permanent transcription upon a strip of paper.

The *encephalograph,* an instrument similar in operation to the cardiograph, records the electric currents of the brain. In this way the physician can ascertain whether the "brain waves" are normal and therefore healthy, or abnormal and therefore diseased. Physicians have found this instrument of great service in the detection and the location of brain tumors.

The *X-ray machine* is based upon the principle that when electrons in rapid motion are made to strike a metal surface X rays are produced. These rays are able to "pierce through" a number of substances that are opaque to ordinary light. Thus an X ray will penetrate the flesh, but not the bones, of the human body. Nor will it penetrate the opaque areas of certain diseases. This selective penetration of the X ray enables the physician to diagnose the location of bone fractures, lung lesions, ulcers, and other internal disturbances of the normal functioning of the body.

Furthermore the X ray possesses the property of destroying diseased tissue more rapidly than healthy tissue. This property has enabled the physician to use the X ray in the treatment of ulcers—with the greatest precaution, however, since an over-exposure to the X ray may destroy the healthy as well as the unhealthy tissue.

the photoelectric cell

In 1888 Heinrich Rudolph Hertz discovered that a ray of light, falling upon a metal surface, gives off negative charges of electricity. These charges were later identified as electrons; and the discovery led to the invention of the *photoelectric cell,* or *magic eye*—an evacuated glass bulb provided with two electrodes, or metal plates. The first plate transmits the light to the second plate, which is coated with sodium or potassium or some other light-sensitive chemical.

The power of the released electrons, which are collected and concentrated upon the sensitized plate, has been harnessed to serve as an exposure regulator for cameras, a recorder of the number of automobiles passing a certain point, a self-regulating manipulator for the faucets of drinking fountains, an automatic opener for swinging doors, and various similar uses. In a number of cities the photoelectric cell is used for turning on the street lights at dusk and for turning them off at dawn.

radio

The principle of the radio is founded upon the discovery of James Clerk Maxwell in 1862 that an electric vibration can set off another electric vibration, and that the resultant chain of vibrations produces a type of wave motion previously unknown. These waves, or *electromagnetic oscillations,* move with the speed of light, and carry our wireless messages around the world and our radio programs from the broadcasting stations to our homes.

Our reception of the radio broadcasts has, within recent years, become revolutionized through the introduction of the *vacuum tube*. This tube (see p. 240) enables the electromagnetic current to move across space without the aid of a conductor. The signal from the transmitter, as it travels through the air, is picked up by the antenna, or aerial—a "feeler" sensitive to the electromagnetic waves. The aerial in turn brings the energy down to the receiving set, where the signal is caught up and amplified in its passage through the vacuum tube and into the listener's ear.

television

One of the most interesting applications of electronics—or the properties of free electrons—is in the field of television. Briefly summarized, a television tube is constructed as follows: the narrow end of the tube contains an "electric gun"—consisting of (1) a heated cathode, or exit, covered with an oxide to facilitate the discharge of the electrons, and (2) electrically charged metal plates which guide the electrons so that they "shoot out" from the gun in a straight and narrow beam. The other end of the tube

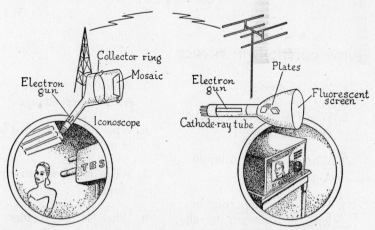

Schematic representation of television transmission and reception.

contains a screen which serves as the "target" for the discharged electrons. This screen is covered with a substance which, upon being hit by the electrons, reflects a brilliant spotlight. The time that it takes for the electrons to travel from the deflecting plates to the screen is about one hundred-millionth of a second. In other words the current of a television transmitter changes its direction a hundred million times in a single second.

This tremendous speed of the electrons depends upon the shooting power, or the voltage, of the electric gun which starts them upon their journey. The potential necessary for this acceleration is from 2500 to 3000 volts.

The light that falls upon the screen from the discharge of the electrons is not emitted by the electrons themselves. It is produced by luminous gas molecules which are hit by the electrons as they travel through the tube from the gun to the screen.

And thus the "eye"—or *iconoscope*—of the television apparatus takes the light waves that fall upon it and converts them into electric waves. It then transmits them by radio until they strike the *kinescope,* or receiving set, which converts the electric waves back again into light waves. And these reconverted light waves reproduce the original scene within a fraction of a second after it has been televised by the iconoscope.

Television, therefore, is a process of transformation from light to electricity, and back again into light.

REVIEW QUESTIONS IN PHYSICS

1. Define physics.

2. What is kinetic energy? Potential energy?

3. What is a solid? A liquid? A gas?

4. What five properties belong in common to all substances?

5. Which one of these properties never changes?

6. What is Newton's first law of motion?

7. When is a body in equilibrium?

8. What is the center of gravity? Specific gravity?

9. What is the c.g.s. system?

10. When is a body at rest?

11. What is accelerated motion?

12. State the formula for, and give the answer to, the following question: If a plane travels 900 miles in 3 hours, what is its velocity?

13. State the formula for, and give the answer to, the following question: If the initial speed of a moving object is 15 feet per second, and its acceleration is 10 feet per second, what will be its final speed at the end of 20 seconds?

14. One gram of force is equal to how many dynes? One pound of force is equal to how many poundals?

15. Why is it harder to climb upon a steep mountain than to walk on a level road?

16. How much work is done when a force of 400 dynes causes a body to move 5 meters, in ergs? In joules?

17. State the formula for the computation of the power of an engine.

18. State the F. equivalent of 15° C.

19. State the three methods for producing heat.

20. State the three ways in which heat may be transmitted from one body to another body, or from one part of a body to another part of that body.

21. What is a heat transmitter?

22. How far away is the starting point of a thunderbolt, when you hear the sound three seconds after you see the flash?

23. What are the three characteristics of all musical sounds?

24. Are humans able to hear all the sounds audible to other living creatures?

25. Are humans able to see all the colors of the world?

26. What causes sunburn?

27. What are complementary colors?

28. Name three groups of complementary colors.

29. If you look at a star tonight, do you see it as it actually *is* tonight?

30. What property of sight gives us our perception of "depth" in a landscape?

31. State the law of attraction and repulsion when two magnets are brought together.

32. How can you convert an iron pipe into a permanent magnet?

33. What are the two kinds of electrical charges?

34. State the first law of electrostatics.

35. What produces an electric current?

36. What is static electricity?

37. Name three of the best conductors for an electric current.

38. Name five of the best insulators.

39. What is current electricity?

40. What is the voltage of a storage battery that is fully charged?

41. What is a sulphated battery?

42. What is an ampere?

43. A coulomb?

44. A volt?

45. A kilowatt?

46. A kilowatt-hour?

47. If a 550-volt current supplies 10 amperes for 200 hours, how many kilowatt-hours are used?

48. What is an electromagnet?

49. Does the size of a body change when the body is in motion?

50. What is the one standard measure of motion for the entire universe?

ANSWERS TO THE QUESTIONS IN PHYSICS

1. Physics is the study of energy; it explains how nature works, rather than what it is.

2. Kinetic energy is energy in motion. Potential energy is energy at rest.

3. A solid is a substance which has a definite volume and a definite form. A liquid is a substance which has a definite volume but no definite form. A gas is a substance which has neither a definite volume nor a definite form.

4. Mass, weight, volume, density, and inertia.

5. Inertia.

6. Every body continues in its state of rest, or in its state of moving with constant velocity in a straight line, unless acted upon by some external force.

7. When the forces that act upon it are so balanced that they neutralize each other.

8. The center of gravity of a material object is the point at which its entire weight is concentrated. The specific gravity of a substance is the ratio of its density to the density of water.

9. The system of computation based upon the centimeter, the gram, and the second.

10. Never.

11. The motion of a body over unequal distances in equal and successive intervals of time.

12. $V = \frac{S}{t}$. 300 miles an hour.

13. $V_1 = V_o + (a \times t)$. 215 feet per second.

14. 980 dynes. 32.16 poundals.

15. Because, in climbing a mountain, we pull our weight upward against the downward pull of the earth's gravity.

16. 200,000 ergs. .02 joules.

17. $P = \frac{W}{t}$; or $P = \frac{F \times L}{t}$

18. 59° F.

19. Chemical action, electric currents, and mechanical work.

20. Conduction, convection, and radiation.

21. An object that allows heat waves to pass through.

22. Three fifths of a mile, approximately.

23. They have intensity, pitch, and quality.

24. No.

25. No.

26. Exposure to the (invisible) ultraviolet rays of light.

27. Any two colors or groups of colors which, added together, produce a white light.

28. Green and purple, red and blue-green, orange and blue.

29. No.

30. Our binocular, or two-eyed vision.

31. The like poles repel each other, and the unlike poles attract each other.

32. By holding it for some time in a north and south direction and striking it, while thus held, with a hammer.

33. Positive and negative.

34. When two bodies are similarly electrified—both positive or both negative —they repel each other; when they are dissimilarly electrified—one positive and the other negative— they attract each other.

35. The movement of electrons between two bodies.

36. Electricity in a state of rest.

37. Gold, platinum, and copper.

38. Rubber, wood, sulphur, paper, and glass.

39. Electricity in a state of motion.

40. About 2.6 volts.

41. A discharged battery whose plates are covered with a coating of lead sulphate.

42. A current which, when passed through a solution of silver nitrate in water, will deposit .001118 grams of silver in one second.

43. The amount of electricity conveyed by a current of one ampere in one second.

44. The unit of electromotive power in an electric current.

45. 1000 watts.

46. The amount of electricity supplied by one kilowatt of electric force in one hour.

47. 1100 kw.-hrs.

48. A mass of iron or steel magnetized by the pas-

sage of an electric current through a wire coiled about it.

49. According to the theory of relativity, yes.

50. The velocity of light, covering 186,000 miles of space in one second of time.

BIOGRAPHICAL SKETCHES OF GREAT PHYSICISTS

Archimedes (287–212 B.C.). Greek mathematician and engineer. He composed important works on arithmetic, plane and solid geometry, and mechanics. He discovered the principle of the lever, invented the spiral pump for raising water from a lower to a higher level, discovered the law of hydrostatics known as the principle of Archimedes. There is a legend to the effect that he was taking a bath when he discovered this principle of the buoyancy relationship between a body placed in a fluid and the fluid displaced by the body. He was so excited by this discovery that he rushed unclothed into the street and shouted, "Eureka [I have found it]!" His mechanical devices were used at the siege of Syracuse. He was killed during the capture of the city, remarking to his assailant, "Please do not disturb my diagrams."

Gilbert, William (1540–1603). English physician and physicist. He was born at Colchester. At eighteen he entered Cambridge University. He received a degree in medicine, and in 1601 he was elected president of the Royal College of Physicians. Shortly afterward he was appointed chief physician to Queen Elizabeth. He devoted his spare hours to physics, making epochal discoveries in electricity and magnetism. His prime discovery was that the earth is a magnet with axis, equator, magnetic poles. He was a champion of the Copernican theory, and he enlisted his genius to substantiate it.

Pascal, Blaise (1623–62). French philosopher and physicist. Though better known as a philosopher, Pascal made important contributions to many fields of science. A precocious youth, at seventeen he had written on conic sections, anticipating the treatment of

modern mathematicians. At the age of eighteen he invented a
calculating machine. His great contribution to physics was his
formulation of the law of pressure, which states that in any enclosed body of liquid a pressure exerted on any area is transmitted undiminished throughout the entire volume of the liquid.
This is known as Pascal's law.

Boyle, Robert (1627–91). English natural philosopher. The seventh
son of the Earl of Cork, he was born in Ireland. At eight he was
sent to Eton. Afterward he traveled abroad to continue his education. He joined a group of scientific researchers who called their
society the Philosophical College. Eventually it became known
as the Royal Society. Following the principles set forth in Bacon's
Novum Organum, Boyle undertook investigations which led to
important discoveries in physics and chemistry. He enunciated
the famous law that the volume of a gas varies inversely with the
pressure. In addition, he contributed significant data on specific
gravities and refractions, on color and electricity, on the function
of air in the projection of sound.

Newton, Sir Isaac (1642–1727). English mathematician and physicist. Educated at Trinity College, Cambridge. He was only
twenty-four when the fall of an apple, as he worked in his garden
at Woolsthorpe, suggested to him the now famous theory of
gravitation. He investigated the nature of light and made several
major discoveries about the refraction of light rays of various
colors in the spectrum. In 1671 he became a member of the Royal
Society. He wrote a number of books that still serve as bases for
important scientific investigations. The greatest of these books
is the *Principia Mathematica* (published in 1687), in which he
expounds the Newtonian laws of motion—the starting point for
all modern physics. He was the codiscoverer, with Leibnitz, of
calculus. From 1703 to 1727 he served as president of the Royal
Society, and in 1705 he was knighted.

Fahrenheit, Gabriel Daniel (1686–1736). German physicist. Born
in Danzig. He started life as a merchant but soon gave up his
business prospects for scientific research. He settled in Holland
and began to experiment with the thermometer. He substituted

mercury for alcohol, thus improving the accuracy of the instrument, and devised the "Fahrenheit" method for graduating the scale of the thermometer. He discovered the boiling point of liquids other than water, and the fact that this boiling point varied with the changes of pressure in the atmosphere. In 1724 he was elected to the Royal Society of London.

Celsius, Anders (1701–44). Swedish physicist and astronomer. Born at Uppsala and educated at its university. In 1730 he was appointed professor of astronomy at Uppsala. In 1733 he published a collection of observations on the aurora borealis (northern lights). In 1737 he joined a group of French scientists in an expedition to measure one degree of meridian in the Arctic. In 1740 he became the director of the observatory at Uppsala. Two years later he published the Centigrade method for the measurement of heat on the thermometer.

Coulomb, Charles Augustin de (1736–1806). French physicist. Born at Angoulême. In 1777 he won a prize from the French Academy for his work on magnetic needles; and in 1779 another prize for his *Theory of Simple Mechanisms.* During the French Revolution he lived in retirement, taking part neither in scientific research nor in political agitation. Later on, however, he offered his services to the new government. As a result of his contributions to the science of electricity, his name has been given to an electric unit of measurement. A coulomb is the quantity transferred by a current of one ampere in one second.

Galvani, Luigi (1737–98). Italian physician and physicist. Born at Bologna, he studied at first for the Church but later decided upon a medical rather than a clerical career. He joined the medical faculty of Bologna and entered, as an avocation, upon a series of experiments in electricity. His initial interest in electricity was due to a casual incident. One day his wife happened to notice the convulsive movements of a skinned frog when the nerve of its leg was accidentally touched by a scalpel which lay on the table and which had become charged by contact with an electrical machine. She mentioned this phenomenon to her husband; and it was this casual observation that led him to undertake his prolonged series of researches into the "secrets" of electricity. Like his compatriot, Volta, Galvani is honored through the perpetuation of his name in a number of scientific terms—such as galvanism, galvanic battery, galvanometer, etc.

Volta, Count Alessandro (1745–1827). Italian natural philosopher. Born in Como. He was successively professor of physics at the Como Gymnasium and at the University of Pavia. He invented, among other instruments, the electrophorus, the electroscope, the electrical condenser, the electrical pistol, and the voltaic battery. It was he who first advanced the theory that electricity is generated by the contact of dissimilar metals. In 1801 Napoleon invited him to France, where a medal was struck in his honor. In 1810 he was raised to the Italian nobility; and in 1815 he was made director of the philosophical faculty of Padua. His name has been perpetuated in a number of electrical terms.

Ampère, André Marie (1775–1836). French physicist and mathematician. Born at Lyons. At eighteen he plunged into his studies in an effort at "forgetfulness" when his father died on the guillotine, a victim of the French Revolution. His researches in electricity led him to the invention of the astatic needle—the basis of the modern astatic galvanometer; to the discovery of the mutual attraction of two parallel conductors carrying currents in the same direction, and of their mutual repulsion when carrying the currents in opposite directions; and to the formulation of the theory that the earth possesses electric currents which attract the magnetic needle. The standard unit of electric-current strength, the ampere, has been named after him.

Faraday, Michael (1791–1867). English chemist and physicist. Born near London, the son of a blacksmith; apprenticed at an early age to a bookbinder. In his spare moments he experimented with chemical elements and compounds, and with an electrical machine of his own construction. Before long, his experiments led to a number of important discoveries in chemistry and in physics. In 1824 he was elected to the Royal Society; and in 1825 he was put in charge of the laboratory at the Royal Institution. Among his outstanding contributions to science were his discoveries of a number of new chemical compounds, of the operations of magnetoelectricity, of the secrets of electrolysis—it was he who gave us the terms *anode* and *cathode*—of the action of polarized light under a magnetic field, and of the "lines of force," or the curvatures along which both electrostatic and electromagnetic induction takes place. Offered the presidency of the Royal Society, he declined with the modest observation that this honor belonged to "a man better educated than myself."

Helmholtz, Hermann Ludwig Ferdinand von (1821–94). German physiologist and physicist. Born at Potsdam, he commenced his active career in medicine, assuming the profession of military surgeon in Potsdam and teaching anatomy in Berlin. Appointed professor of physiology at Heidelberg, he returned to Berlin to assume the chair of physics. In addition he served as director of the physicotechnical institute at Charlottenburg near Berlin. He accomplished outstanding work in the entire field of science. In physics his investigations in optics and the conservation of force are especially noteworthy. He invented the ophthalmoscope, delved into physiological acoustics, explored the electromagnetic theory of light. His pupil, Hertz, revealed the existence of electromagnetic waves under his inspiration. In addition Helmholtz made original contributions to the fields of meteorology and hydrodynamics.

Thomson, William (Lord Kelvin) (1824–1907). British physicist and inventor. His father was a professor of natural philosophy at Glasgow University. At eighteen he wrote an original paper on the dynamics of heat. At twenty-two he was appointed professor at Glasgow, and established the first modern laboratory in Great Britain. He conducted experiments in the measurement of the atom, refrigeration, heat, electricity, the "dynamics of the nebulae," the "nature of the dewfall," etc. And he invented, among other things, a galvanometer, a syphon recorder, and a new type of compass. He wrote important treatises on *Natural Philosophy, Electricity and Magnetism, The Wave Theory of Light, The Dynamic Theory of Heat,* and three volumes of *Popular Lectures* on all sorts of scientific subjects. He was raised to a peerage and was further honored through the naming of various scientific instruments and processes after him.

Roentgen, Wilhelm Konrad (1845–1923). German physicist. Born at Lennep-on-the-Rhine. He received his education at the University of Zurich. In 1895 he read a paper on his discovery of the Roentgen or X rays. In 1900 he received the Barnard medal from Columbia University for "the greatest discovery in science during the preceding five years." In 1901 he was awarded the Nobel Prize for physics.

Edison, Thomas Alva (1847–1931). American inventor born in Milan, Ohio. In 1859 he got a job as a newsboy on the train running between Port Huron and Detroit. At sixteen he became a telegraph operator; and at seventeen he entered upon his career as an inventor. Among the long list of his inventions are the automatic telegraph repeater, the kinetoscope (moving picture machine), the phonograph, and the system of electric lighting. All in all, he took out more than a thousand patents for his inventions. In 1876 he moved his laboratory to Menlo Park, New Jersey, and in 1887 from Menlo Park to West Orange, New Jersey, where he worked at his inventions for the remainder of his life. He died at his home in Llewellyn Park, West Orange.

Planck, Max (1858–1947). German physicist. Born in Kiel, he studied at the universities of Munich and Berlin. He later taught at the University of Kiel and also in Berlin. As a result of his investigations into radiation from black bodies, he originated and developed his famous quantum theory which states that energy must be radiated or absorbed in certain definite "energy packets" called quanta. Planck also made contributions to thermodynamics and mechanics. He was awarded the Nobel Prize in physics in 1918. In 1930 he was named president of the Kaiser Wilhelm Society for the Advancement of Science.

Curie, Marie Sklodovska (1867–1934). Polish physicist and chemist. Born in Warsaw, she came to study in Paris and remained there for the rest of her life. Together with her husband, Pierre Curie, she discovered radium—for which they jointly received the Nobel Prize for physics in 1903. Upon the death of her husband, in 1906, she succeeded him as professor of physics and director of the physical laboratory at the Sorbonne. There she continued her researches in radium, polonium, and radioactivity. In 1911 she received the Nobel Prize for chemistry.

Einstein, Albert (1879–   ). German-American physicist, author of the theory of relativity. Born in Ulm, Germany, he studied at the University of Zurich, taught for a time at the Technische Hochschule, and then became examiner of patents in Berne. It was during his clerkship at the patent office that he published his first paper on relativity. He left the patent office to become (in 1912) professor of physics at the Technische Hochschule in Zurich. In 1914 he was appointed to the chair in physics at the Kaiser Wilhelm Institute. In May 1919 an eclipse of the sun corroborated his theory rather than the earlier theories of Newton. Einstein was now generally recognized as the greatest physicist since Newton. In 1920 he became professor of the sciences at Leyden University. In 1921 he received the Nobel Prize for physics. From that time on distinctions were heaped upon him from every part of the world. But the anti-Semitic wave that followed the Nazi revolution made him *persona non grata* in Germany. He was exiled from Germany and came to live in America, receiving an appointment as head of the School of Mathematics at Princeton University. Here he taught from 1933 until his resignation in 1945.

CAREERS IN PHYSICS

Industry today is based on scientific research. The demand for the physicist is commensurate with the giant needs of industry. Electronics, the core of radio, television, photoelectric devices, and X rays, has an ever-increasing need for specialists. And the field is still in its infancy. Every phase of engineering requires trained physicists. Radar, optics, aviation, metallurgy, and meteorology are some additional specialties.

The physicist may become an acoustical engineer, specializing in soundproofing buildings, hospitals, radio stations, and motion picture establishments. As a biophysicist he may devise electronic weapons to fight against disease. Specializing in the field of optics, he may manufacture lenses, design cameras, conduct research in the field of photographic equipment. He may specialize in glass making or carry out investigations in polarized light. As a metallurgist he would find a job with all industries that employ metals, supervising the operations of smelting and refining.

The airplane industry has an almost limitless demand for physicists. Training in physics is essential for all phases of aviation research. Aeronautical engineering is an especially dynamic field. Experts in aircraft design, devising new models for higher altitudes and greater speeds, are at a premium today.

acoustical engineer

EXPERIENCE REQUIRED: Graduation from accredited school of engineering. Training in engineering physics, mechanical and electrical engineering.

DESCRIPTION OF JOB: Job control of sound reverberations in a building; noise quieting, sound insulation, reduction of sound passing through windows, walls, floor, ceiling of room.

OPPORTUNITIES FOR ADVANCEMENT: Can rise to sales engineer, manager, executive.

WHERE TO APPLY FOR JOBS: All contracting engineers, architectural firms, telephone and motion picture companies, acoustic-material manufacturers.

airline engineer

EXPERIENCE REQUIRED: Graduation from accredited school of engineering or recognized commercial school. Knowledge of research techniques, drafting, operating economics, production engineering vital.

DESCRIPTION OF JOB: Adapts equipment, selects planes to meet traffic demand, supervises maintenance and inspection, utilizes navigation aids. Instructs maintenance and flying personnel in principles involved in design or characteristics.

OPPORTUNITIES FOR ADVANCEMENT: Operations manager, divisional engineer, supervisor, superintendent.

WHERE TO APPLY FOR JOBS: Airlines, Civil Aeronautics Adminstration.

architectural engineer

EXPERIENCE REQUIRED: Graduation from school of engineering, specialization in structural engineering.

DESCRIPTION OF JOB: Works in architectural office, drafting, designing, etc. May work for a contractor. Works on all phases of structural design.

OPPORTUNITIES FOR ADVANCEMENT: Superintendent, sales manager, executive.

WHERE TO APPLY FOR JOBS: Construction companies, architectural firms, state building inspection department.

electronics engineer

EXPERIENCE REQUIRED: College degree with specialization in electronics.

DESCRIPTION OF JOB: Designs and develops electronics equipment and devices.

OPPORTUNITIES FOR ADVANCEMENT: Executive, specialist, division head.

WHERE TO APPLY FOR JOBS: Radio and telephone equipment manufacturers. Electronic equipment manufacturers.

civil engineer

EXPERIENCE REQUIRED: Graduation from accredited school of engineering plus practical experience surveying, plotting maps, etc. (High degree of knowledge in physics and mathematics.)

DESCRIPTION OF JOB: Design, construction, maintenance, operation, testing of bridges, water supply and irrigation systems, dams, reservoirs, transportation systems, buildings, etc.

OPPORTUNITIES FOR ADVANCEMENT: Executive, consultant.

WHERE TO APPLY FOR JOBS: Government agencies, contracting, engineering, railroad, mining, public utility, steel, power, etc.

metallurgical engineer

EXPERIENCE REQUIRED: Graduation from accredited school of engineering. Aptitude for physics and chemistry.

DESCRIPTION OF JOB: Supervises reduction or separation of metals from ores, the refining of metals, etc. Develops methods for examining and heat-treating metals and alloys.

OPPORTUNITIES FOR ADVANCEMENT: Consultant, executive, functional division head.

WHERE TO APPLY FOR JOBS: Smelting plants, manufacturers of automobile and electrical equipment, government.

physicist

EXPERIENCE REQUIRED: Graduation from accredited school of science. Graduate work desirable. Broad fundamental knowledge. Familiarity with instruments.

DESCRIPTION OF JOB: May begin as a technician tester or research aide in industry, e.g., electronics and radio. Continues in research, development or process control work.

OPPORTUNITIES FOR ADVANCEMENT: Executive, functional head.

WHERE TO APPLY FOR JOBS: Government, electrical manufacturing companies, public service corporations, etc.

physics teacher (college or high school)

EXPERIENCE REQUIRED: For college teaching, graduate work required. Ability in teaching. Research aptitude.

DESCRIPTION OF JOB: Teach classes combined with experimental work, laboratory sessions, often combined with pure research activities.

OPPORTUNITIES FOR ADVANCEMENT: Instructor, assistant professor, associate professor, full professor, department head.

WHERE TO APPLY FOR JOBS: University placement bureaus, commercial placement bureaus, boards of education.

public health engineer

EXPERIENCE REQUIRED: Graduation from accredited school of engineering, and graduate work in public health. Thorough training in chemistry, biology, mathematics, and physics.

DESCRIPTION OF JOB: Deals with water supply and treatment, sewage disposal, stream-pollution correction, sanitation of rural and recreational areas, sanitary control of floods, insect and rodent control.

OPPORTUNITIES FOR ADVANCEMENT: Design engineer, sales engineer for manufacture of sanitary equipment, chief engineer, consultant.

WHERE TO APPLY FOR JOBS: Public health departments, sanitary equipment manufacturers, engineering offices, government.

radio and television operating engineer

EXPERIENCE REQUIRED: Graduation from accredited school of electrical engineering.

DESCRIPTION OF JOB: Monitors high-fidelity telephone equipment, transmits radio programs over telephone circuits. Co-ordinates the activities of many radio stations, listening to several programs at a time.

OPPORTUNITIES FOR ADVANCEMENT: Chief operating engineer.

WHERE TO APPLY FOR JOBS: Radio stations.

radio inspector

EXPERIENCE REQUIRED: College degree, major in physics or graduate from accredited school of electrical engineering. Graduate study or experience in radio engineering desirable for advanced work.

DESCRIPTION OF JOB: Inspects radio equipment at land installations, in aircraft, on ships.

OPPORTUNITIES FOR ADVANCEMENT: Civil service upgrading.

WHERE TO APPLY FOR JOBS: Government.

research engineer

EXPERIENCE REQUIRED: Graduation from accredited school of engineering and practical engineering experience.

DESCRIPTION OF JOB: Deals with industrial engineering problems. Discovers and improves new machinery for production purposes. Improves present products, discovers new products.

OPPORTUNITIES FOR ADVANCEMENT: Department head, executive.

WHERE TO APPLY FOR JOBS: Large manufacturing companies, research institutes, government bureaus.

BIBLIOGRAPHY: BOOKS ON PHYSICS FOR FURTHER READING AND STUDY

Anderson, William Ballantyne: *Physics for Technical Students.* New York, 1937.

Avery, Madalyn: *Household Physics.* New York, 1938.

Black, Newton Henry, and J. N. Davis: *Elementary Practical Physics.* New York, 1938.

Born, Max: *The Restless Universe,* tr. by Winifred M. Deans. New York, 1936.

Bridgman, Percy Williams: *The Nature of Physical Theory.* Princeton, 1936.

Brown, Thomas Benjamin: *Foundations of Modern Physics.* New York, 1940.

Caswell, Albert Edward: *An Outline of Physics.* New York, 1938.

Crew, Henry: *The Rise of Modern Physics.* Baltimore, 1935.

Dees, Bowen Causey: *Fundamentals of Physics.* Philadelphia, 1945.

Dull, Charles Elwood: *Modern Physics.* New York, 1943.

Dunning, John Ray, and H. C. Paxton: *Matter, Energy, and Radiation.* New York, 1941.

Eddington, Sir Arthur Stanley: *The Nature of the Physical World.* New York, 1929.

Einstein, Albert, and Leopold Infeld: *The Evolution of Physics.* New York, 1938.

Eldridge, John Adams: *College Physics.* New York, 1947.

Frisch, O. R.: *Meet the Atoms,* New York, 1947.

Fuller, Robert Warren: *First Principles of Physics.* Boston and New York, 1937.

Harrison, George Russell: *Atoms in Action.* New York, 1941.

Howe, Harley Earl: *Introduction to Physics.* New York, 1942.

Kimball, Arthur Lalanne: *A College Text-Book of Physics.* New York, 1939.

Lemon, Harvey Brace: *From Galileo to the Nuclear Age.* Chicago, 1946.

McNiff, William Thomas: *College Physics.* New York, 1942.

Masson, Louis T.: *Physics Made Easy.* New York, 1941.

Meyer, Jerome Sydney: *The A B C of Physics.* New York, 1944.

Millikan, Robert Andrews: *New Elementary Physics.* Boston, 1941.

Osborn, Frederick Arthur: *Physics of the Home.* New York, 1935.

Perkins, Henry Augustus: *College Physics.* New York, 1943.

Richtmeyer, Floyd Karker: *Introduction to Modern Physics.* New York, 1942.

Robeson, Frank Leigh: *Physics.* New York, 1942.

Rusk, Rogers D.: *Forward with Science.* New York, 1943.

Semat, Henry: *Fundamentals of Physics.* New York, 1945.

Small, Sidney Aylmer: *Simplified Physics.* New York, 1943.

Taylor, Lloyd William: *Physics, the Pioneer Science.* Boston, 1941.

White, Marsh William: *Practical Physics.* New York, 1943.

mathematics—the measuring rod of the sciences

THE MEANING OF MATHEMATICS

Mathematics—derived from the Greek word *mathema*, meaning the result of learning, or universal knowledge—is the science which lies at the foundation of all the other sciences, for it deals with the *measure of magnitude*—that is, the computation of quantities that are capable of increase and of decrease. And thus mathematics embraces the mensuration of the heavens, or *astronomy;* the evolution of our planet, or *geology;* the inventory of the earth's various features and resources, or *geography;* the calculation of the forces of nature, or *physics;* the composition of the elements into compounds, or *chemistry;* and so on, throughout the entire field of the sciences. In all our scientific thinking we use numbers. All our exact knowledge about the universe is reducible to mathematical processes—additions, subtractions, multiplications, divisions—interrelations and combinations of intricate parts into simple and comprehensive units.

Mathematics, therefore, is the "science of relationships." It relates the various departments of the separate sciences, and all the sciences together, into a logical pattern of understanding. To quote the excellent definition of Professor Benjamin Pierce, mathematics is *"the science which draws necessary conclusions."* It is through mathematics—the computations based upon the necessary conclusion that one plus one always equals two—that we can obtain our concrete and statistical knowledge of the world. Hence mathematics is not only the *foundation* of the other sciences; it is the *most exact* of the sciences. Mathematics is the language that brings order into the human mind through the exposition of a logical order in the universe.

THE STORY OF MATHEMATICS

Mathematics is the oldest of the sciences. It arose out of man's universal need for numbers and measures. When the first human creature began to distinguish between *himself* and *others,* he arrived at a conception of numbers. This early conception, however, included only three figures—*one, two,* and *many.*

Later, when our ancestors had learned to count on their fingers, they acquired a system of enumeration by *ten.* Yet thus far they were able merely to *count*—that is, to *observe*—numbers. They had not as yet acquired the ability to *combine* these numbers and to *prove the accuracy* of their combinations.

It was not until the seventh century B.C. that mathematics became a logical science.

The first scientific mathematician known to history was the Greek philosopher, Thales (640–546 B.C.). His interests, however, were not so much in arithmetic as in geometry. For mankind had now emerged from the hunting to the agricultural stage of its development, and hence there was need for a scientific method for the parceling out of the land.

The interest in geometry reached its climax in Euclid (about 300 B.C.). But the general study of mathematics as "the noblest of the arts" had become the focal point in the philosophy of Pythagoras (572–501 B.C.). And, in the philosophy of Plato (427–347 B.C.), the "mathematical harmony of the universe and of the human soul" was regarded as the basis of all existence.

Yet the ancients, including even the Greeks and the Romans, had no numerical system like our own. It was not until about A.D. 1000 that our present "mathematical alphabet" of ten digits —from 0 to 9—was introduced into Europe from Arabia. During the next five centuries the development of mathematics was confined largely to the Arabian scientists. But in the two centuries that followed—from 1500 to 1700—mathematics became gradually enthroned in Europe as "the science of the sciences." Copernicus (1520) accepted it as the basis for his calculations in astronomy. Tartaglia (1556) widened its scope through the development of algebra (a branch of mathematics first discovered in the Orient). Spinoza (1632–77) developed his famous system of ethics in the form of geometric theorems. Napier (1550–1617) invented "arithmetical ratios," or logarithms. And Newton (1642–1727) organized a new method—the calculus—for computing mathematical problems. While the "old mathematics" deals with *fixed* quantities, the calculus computes *variable* quantities. And since the objects of nature are not fixed, but keep constantly changing, the invention of the calculus has been of the utmost importance in the application of mathematics to the solution of all sorts of scientific problems.

Mathematics as a basis for all the sciences has made tremendous strides during the last two hundred and fifty years. And the general line of its development has been in the direction of our new scientific knowledge about the nature of the universe. Thus Lobatchevsky (1826) and Riemann (1866) developed a non-Euclidian system of geometry based upon a spatial universe which is far more complicated than the simple universe of Euclid's conception. And Einstein adopted mathematics to demonstrate his theory about a variable universe of relative, rather than absolute, values in space and time. Today mathematics is used not only as a basic touchstone for scientific theories but as a vital instrument for mechanical inventions. Practically all of the world of our human achievement is constructed upon the formulas and the figures of mathematics.

ARITHMETIC

we read numbers backward

Very few of us realize that we read numbers not from left to right, but from right to left. This is because we derive our numerical system—as we have observed—from the Arabians; and the

Arabians, like the Hebrews, do all their writing from right to left.

Try to read the number 47936328964 just as you read these words, from left to right. Pretty difficult, isn't it?

Now try it from right to left. See how easy it becomes? Four units, six tens, nine hundreds, eight thousands, two ten-thousands, three hundred-thousands, and so on.

And now, as a further help in your reading of this number, you mark off the figures, by commas, into groups of three. This you do again, like the Arabians, *from right to left:*

$$47,936,328,964$$

And thus at last you are ready to translate your *Arabic* number into an *English* number and to read it as forty-seven billion, nine hundred thirty-six million, three hundred twenty-eight thousand, nine hundred sixty-four.

We not only *read* numbers, but *add* and *subtract* and *multiply* them, as we shall see later on, after the Arabic fashion—from right to left.

digits, integers, and decimals

A *digit,* so called from the ancient custom of counting on the fingers, is *any one of the ten Arabic numerals*—0, 1, 2, 3, 4, 5, 6, 7, 8, 9—whose combinations express all the possible numbers. An *integer,* from the Latin word which means untouched or entire, is a *whole number.* A *decimal*—from the Latin *decimus,* a tenth— is a *fraction* computed in tenths, hundredths, thousandths, and so on.

The value of a digit in an integer is *multiplied by ten* as we move from *right to left.* Thus 26 means six units and two tens; 326 means six units, two tens, and three hundreds. But the value of a fraction in a decimal number is *divided by ten* as we move from *left to right.* For example:

.3 equals three tenths of one unit.
.23 equals twenty-three hundredths of one unit.
.423 equals four hundred twenty-three thousandths of one unit.

Furthermore, a cipher (0) placed *before* a digit in an integer does *not* change its value, but a cipher placed *after* a digit *does* change its value. For example:

3 is read as three
03 is read as three
003 is read as three
30 is read as thirty
300 is read as three hundred
3000 is read as three thousand

But in decimals it is just the other way around. A cipher placed *before* a decimal digit *does* change its value, but a cipher placed *after* it does *not* change its value. Thus:

.3 is read as three tenths
.03 is read as three hundredths
.003 is read as three thousandths
.30 is read as three tenths
.300 is read as three tenths
.3000 is read as three tenths

addition

When you add a column of figures, get into the habit of *grouping* the figures instead of adding them singly. Add the *short* rather than the *long* way. Observe the following column, for example:

4
3
7
9
4
3
2
5
4
6

The *long* way to add this column is to take up each figure separately, thus: 4 + 3 are 7, + 7 are 14, + 9 are 23, and so on. Total, 47. The *short* way, however, is to *group* the figures—in your mind if not on paper—as follows:

$$
\left.\begin{array}{c} 4 \\ 3 \\ 7 \end{array}\right\} \text{group one} = 14
$$

$$
+
$$

$$
\left.\begin{array}{c} 9 \\ 4 \\ 3 \end{array}\right\} \text{group two} = 30
$$

$$
+
$$

$$
\left.\begin{array}{c} 2 \\ 5 \end{array}\right\} \text{group three} = 37
$$

$$
+
$$

$$
\left.\begin{array}{c} 4 \\ 6 \end{array}\right\} \text{group four} = 47
$$

HOW TO PROVE AN ADDITION

An addition can be proved by either of the following simple methods:

1. Add the columns in the opposite direction. If you have added (as is usually done) from top to bottom, now reverse the process and add from bottom to top. And vice versa.

2. Add each column separately, arrange the totals as illustrated below, and then add the totals:

$$
\begin{array}{r}
3,648 \\
5,927 \\
7,584 \\
9,635 \\
\hline
26,794
\end{array}
$$

The first (right-hand) column totals   24
The second column totals   17
The third column totals   26
The fourth (left-hand) column totals   24
$$\overline{\qquad\quad 26{,}794}$$

subtraction

SUBTRACTION—AUSTRIAN METHOD

This method is generally used in giving change to a customer. Instead of *subtracting* the amount of the purchase from the amount of the coin or bill given in payment, you *add* from the amount of the purchase up to the amount of the coin or bill given in payment. The process is as follows:

Suppose the amount of the purchase is $3.08, and the bill given in payment is $10. You give the customer the following money units for his change: 2 cents, to make the sum $3.10; 5 cents, to make the sum $3.15; 10 cents, to make the sum $3.25; 25 cents, to make the sum $3.50; 50 cents, to make the sum $4.00; a dollar, to make the sum $5.00; and $5.00, to bring the sum up to $10.

SHORT CUTS IN SUBTRACTION

1. *Subtraction by ciphers*

$$\frac{\begin{array}{r} 73842 \\ -\,49973 \end{array}}{23869} = \frac{\begin{array}{r} 73842 + 27 \\ -\,49973 + 27 \end{array}}{} = \frac{\begin{array}{r} 73869 \\ -\,50000 \end{array}}{23869}$$

Add to the *minuend* (the quantity from which the subtraction is made) and to the *subtrahend* (the quantity to be subtracted) a number which, by this addition, will make the subtrahend end in ciphers. The subtraction is thus greatly simplified.

2. *Subtraction in couples*

$$\begin{array}{r} 926375 \\ -\ 342746 \\ \hline 583629 \end{array} = \begin{array}{rrr} 98 & 66 & 79 \\ -\ 40 & 30 & 50 \\ \hline 58 & 36 & 29 \end{array}$$

Add to the couples of the minuend and the subtrahend such numbers as will make the couples of the subtrahend end in ciphers. Thus, in the above examples, you add 6 to the left-hand couple, 3 to the middle couple, and 4 to the right-hand couple.

multiplication

Multiplication is *simplified addition*. It is the abbreviated process of adding any given quantity a certain number of times. Thus, 389 × 7 = 389+389+389+389+389+389+389 (389 added 7 times).

The following terms are most frequently used in multiplication:

The *multiplicand* is the number which is to be multiplied.
The *multiplier* is the number which does the multiplying.
The *product* is the result of the multiplication.

HOW TO PROVE A MULTIPLICATION

A multiplication can be proved by either of the following methods:

1. Reverse the multiplicand and the multiplier, as in the following example:

$$\begin{array}{r} 4735 \\ 537 \\ \hline 33145 \\ 14205 \\ 23675 \\ \hline 2,542,695 \end{array} \qquad \begin{array}{r} 537 \\ 4735 \\ \hline 2685 \\ 1611 \\ 3759 \\ 2148 \\ \hline 2,542,695 \end{array}$$

2. Divide the product either by the multiplicand or by the multiplier, as follows:

$$4735$$
$$537 \overline{\smash{)}2542695}$$
$$2148$$
$$\overline{3946}$$
$$3759$$
$$\overline{1879}$$
$$1611$$
$$\overline{2685}$$
$$2685$$

SHORT CUTS IN MULTIPLICATION

1. To multiply a number by 5, add one zero and divide by 2.

$$372 \times 5 = 3720 \div 2 = 1860$$

2. To multiply a number by 25, add two zeros and divide by 4.

$$127 \times 25 = 12{,}700 \div 4 = 3175$$

3. To multiply a number by 125, add three zeros and divide by 8.

$$254 \times 125 = 254{,}000 \div 8 = 31{,}750$$

4. To multiply a number by 10, 100, 1000, etc., add as many zeros as there are in the multiplier.

$$157 \times 10 = 1570$$
$$157 \times 100 = 15{,}700$$
$$157 \times 1000 = 157{,}000$$

5. To multiply a number of two digits by 11, add the digits and place the sum between them.

$$63 \times 11 = 693$$

If the sum of the two digits is more than 10, follow the plan as above and then add 1 to the digit on the left.

$$67 \times 11 = 737$$
$$(6 + 7 = 13. \text{ You place 3 in the middle,}$$
$$\text{and add 1 to the 6.})$$

6. To multiply a number of more than two digits by 11, multiply the number by 10, and add the multiplicand to the product.

$$673 \times 11 = 6730 + 673 = 7403$$

7. To multiply a number by 101, 1001, etc., multiply the number by 100, 1000, etc., and add the multiplicand to the product.

$$673 \times 101 = 67,300 + 673 = 67,973$$
$$673 \times 1001 = 673,000 + 673 = 673,673$$

8. To multiply a number by 9, 99, 999, etc., multiply the number by 10, 100, 1000, etc., and substract the multiplicand from the product.

$$347 \times 9 = 3470 - 347 = 3123$$
$$347 \times 99 = 34,700 - 347 = 34,353$$
$$347 \times 999 = 347,000 - 347 = 346,653$$

division

The following terms are most frequently used in division:

The *dividend* is the number which is to be divided.
The *divisor* is the number by which the dividend is divided.
The *quotient* is the result of the division.
The *remainder* is the number that is left over when the divisor does not evenly divide the dividend.

HOW TO PROVE A DIVISION

To prove a division, multiply the quotient by the divisor, and add the remainder, if any.

EXAMPLE:

$$
\begin{array}{r}
412 \\
84\,\overline{)34673} \\
336 \\
\hline
107 \\
84 \\
\hline
233 \\
168 \\
\hline
65
\end{array}
$$

ANSWER, $412\frac{65}{84}$

PROOF:

$$
\begin{array}{r}
412 \\
\times 84 \\
\hline
1648 \\
3296 \\
\hline
34608 \\
+65 \\
\hline
34,673
\end{array}
$$

SHORT CUTS IN DIVISION

1. To divide a number by 10, 100, 1000, etc., start counting from the right and point off as many figures in the dividend as there are zeros in the divisor.

$$658 \div 10 = 65.8$$
$$658 \div 100 = 6.58$$
$$658 \div 1000 = .658$$

2. To divide a number by 20, divide by 10 and then by 2; by 30, divide by 10 and then by 3. Follow the same process up to 90.

3. To divide a number by 200, divide by 100 and then by 2; and so on, up to 900.

4. To divide a number by 2000, divide by 1000 and then by 2; and so on.

5. To divide by 5, multiply by 2 and divide by 10.

$$44,565 \div 5$$
$$44,565 \times 2 = 89,130$$
$$89,130 \div 10 = 8913$$

6. To divide by 25, multiply by 4 and divide by 100.

7. To divide by 125, multiply by 8 and divide by 1000.

DIVISIBILITY OF NUMBERS

Any number is divisible by 1.

Any even number is divisible by 2.

Any number is divisible by 3 if the sum of its digits is divisible by 3.

Any number is divisible by 4 if its last two digits are divisible by 4.

Any number is divisible by 5 if it ends in 5 or in zero.

Any even number, if divisible by 3, is divisible by 6.

Any number is divisible by 8 if its last three digits are divisible by 8.

Any number is divisible by 9 if the sum of its digits is divisible by 9.

Any number ending in zero is divisible by 10.

Any number is divisible by 11, if the sum of its digits in the even places is equal to the sum of its digits in the odd places. Thus, 267,894 is divisible by 11, because the sum of its digits in the even places, 6+8+4, is equal to the sum of its digits in the odd places, 2+7+9.

A number is also divisible by 11 if the difference between the sum of the odd and the even digits is divisible by 11. Thus,

1,607,364 is divisible by 11, because 19 (6+7+6)—8 (1+0+ 3+4)=11.

fractions

The word *fraction* is derived from the Latin word *fractus,* which means broken. A *fraction* is a *broken* number, or part of a number.

The *terms* of a fraction are the *numerator,* which is written *above* the line, and the *denominator,* which is written *below* the line.

A fraction may be raised to a higher term, or reduced to a lower term, without changing the value of the fraction.

To raise a fraction to higher terms, *multiply* both the numerator and the denominator by the same number.

EXAMPLE: Raise $\frac{3}{7}$ to seventieths.

$$\frac{3 \times 10}{7 \times 10} = \frac{30}{70}$$

To reduce a fraction to lower terms, *divide* both the numerator and the denominator by the same number.

EXAMPLE: Reduce $\frac{24}{64}$ to thirty-seconds.

$$\frac{24 \div 2}{64 \div 2} = \frac{12}{32}$$

The above fraction, you will note, can be reduced to still lower terms. To reduce a fraction to the *lowest* terms, keep on dividing both the numerator and the denominator, each time by the same number, until you can no longer divide them in this way. For example:

$$\frac{72 \div 2}{120 \div 2} = \frac{36}{60}$$

$$\frac{36 \div 2}{60 \div 2} = \frac{18}{30}$$

$$\frac{18 \div 2}{30 \div 2} = \frac{9}{15}$$

$$\frac{9 \div 3}{15 \div 3} = \frac{3}{5}$$

This process of reducing a fraction to its lowest terms is called *cancellation*.

THE LOWEST COMMON DENOMINATOR

Two or more fractions that have the same denominator are said to have a *common denominator*. Such fractions are called *similar fractions*.

To reduce two or more fractions to *similar fractions*, reduce them to fractions that have the *lowest common denominator*—that is, the *lowest possible figure* that can serve as a denominator for all the fractions.

EXAMPLE: Reduce ½, ⅔, and ¾ to similar fractions.

The lowest common denominator of 2, 3, and 4—that is, the lowest possible figure into which 2, 3, and 4 can be divided—is 12. HENCE

$$\tfrac{1}{2} = \tfrac{6}{12}$$

$$\tfrac{2}{3} = \tfrac{8}{12}$$

$$\tfrac{3}{4} = \tfrac{9}{12}$$

ADDITION OF FRACTIONS

To add fractions, proceed as follows:

1. Reduce the fractions to similar fractions having a lowest common denominator.

2. Write the sum of the numerators over the lowest common denominator.

3. Reduce the resulting fraction to the lowest terms.

ADD: $\frac{1}{2}$, $\frac{2}{3}$, $\frac{3}{4}$, $\frac{5}{6}$

$$\frac{1}{2} = \frac{6}{12}$$

$$\frac{2}{3} = \frac{8}{12}$$

$$\frac{3}{4} = \frac{9}{12}$$

$$\frac{5}{6} = \frac{10}{12}$$

$$\frac{6}{12} + \frac{8}{12} + \frac{9}{12} + \frac{10}{12} = \frac{33}{12} = 2\frac{9}{12} = 2\frac{3}{4}$$

SUBTRACTION OF FRACTIONS

To subtract one fraction from another, reduce them both to simple fractions having a lowest common denominator, write the difference between the two numerators over the common denominator, and reduce the result to the lowest terms.

EXAMPLES:

1. Subtract $\frac{7}{30}$ from $\frac{11}{18}$

$$\frac{11}{18} = \frac{55}{90}$$

$$\frac{7}{30} = \frac{21}{90}$$

$$\frac{55}{90} - \frac{21}{90} = \frac{34}{90} = \frac{17}{45}$$

2. Subtract $\frac{5}{6}$ from $1\frac{1}{12}$

$$1\frac{1}{12} = \frac{13}{12}$$

$$\frac{5}{6} = \frac{10}{12}$$

$$13\tfrac{3}{12}-10\tfrac{1}{12}=3\tfrac{3}{12}=\tfrac{1}{4}$$

MULTIPLICATION OF FRACTIONS

To multiply fractions, proceed as follows:

1. Change all the numbers to fractions. Whole numbers are to be regarded as having 1 for the denominator. Thus, $7=\tfrac{7}{1}$.

2. Cancel as much as possible.

3. Find the product of the canceled numerators and the canceled denominators.

EXAMPLE: Multiply $6\times\tfrac{3}{4}\times1\tfrac{3}{5}$

Reduce to fractions: $\tfrac{6}{1}\times\tfrac{3}{4}\times\tfrac{8}{5}$

Cancel: $\tfrac{6}{1}\times\tfrac{3}{4}\times\tfrac{\overset{2}{\cancel{8}}}{5}$

Multiply: $\tfrac{36}{5}=7\tfrac{1}{5}$

DIVISION OF FRACTIONS

To divide fractions, *invert* the numerator and the denominator of the *divisor,* and then multiply the fractions. Note: To *invert* a fraction means to *put it upside down*—that is, to put the denominator *above* the line and the numerator *below* the line.

EXAMPLE: Divide $6\tfrac{3}{4}\div1\tfrac{7}{8}$

$27\tfrac{7}{4}\div15\tfrac{5}{8}$

$27\tfrac{7}{4}\times\tfrac{8}{15}$

$$\frac{\overset{9}{\cancel{27}}\times\overset{2}{\cancel{8}}}{\underset{1}{\cancel{4}}\times\underset{5}{\cancel{15}}}=18\tfrac{3}{5}=3\tfrac{3}{5}$$

decimals

A *decimal* is a fraction whose denominator is 10, or a power of 10. The denominator is not written under a line, but is indicated by the position of the decimal point as follows:

$$3.4 \quad = 3\frac{4}{10}$$

$$3.45 = 3\frac{45}{100}$$

$$3.457 = 3\frac{457}{1000}$$

ADDITION AND SUBTRACTION OF DECIMALS

To add or to subtract decimals, write the numbers so that the decimal points are lined up directly one under the other. If necessary in subtraction, add zeros at the end of the decimals—since zeros at the *end* do not change the value of a decimal fraction.

ADD: $57.6 + 4.76 + 3.053$

$$
\begin{array}{r}
57.6 \\
4.76 \\
3.053 \\
\hline
65.413
\end{array}
$$

SUBTRACT: 6.7594 from 64.3

$$
\begin{array}{r}
64.3000 \\
6.7594 \\
\hline
57.5406
\end{array}
$$

MULTIPLICATION OF DECIMALS

To multiply by a decimal, multiply as if by a whole number, and count off—from right to left—as many decimal places as there are in the multiplicand and the multiplier together.

MULTIPLY: $52.6 \times .043$

$$
\begin{array}{r}
52.6 \\
.043 \\
\hline
1578 \\
2104 \\
\hline
2.2618
\end{array}
$$

ANSWER, 2.2618

DIVISION OF DECIMALS

1. To divide a decimal by a whole number, divide as if both the dividend and the divisor were whole numbers, and write the decimal point in the quotient as soon as the decimal point in the dividend is reached.

DIVIDE: $41.4 \div 23$

$$
\begin{array}{r}
1.8 \\
23\overline{)41.4} \\
23 \\
\hline
18\,4 \\
18\,4 \\
\hline
\end{array}
$$

ANSWER, 1.8

2. To divide by a decimal, multiply both the dividend and the divisor by such a power of 10 as shall make the divisor a whole number. Then divide as in the first method.

DIVIDE: $9.12 \div .38$

$$
9.12 \times 100 = 912
$$
$$
.38 \times 100 = 38
$$

$$
\begin{array}{r}
24 \\
38\overline{)912} \\
76 \\
\hline
152 \\
152 \\
\hline
\end{array}
$$

ANSWER, 24

percentage

Per cent—derived from the Latin *per centum*—means *by the hundred*. In dealing with percentage, we are dealing with decimals whose denominator is 100.

Thus 34 per cent (written 34%)=$^{34}/_{100}$, or .34.

The following terms are commonly used in percentage:

The *base* (B) is the number of which the per cent is taken. In the example, 16 is 25% of 64, the number 64 is the *base*.

The *rate* (R) is the number of hundredths of the base. In the above example, 25%—or the decimal .25—is the *rate*.

The percentage (P) *is the product of the base and the rate.* P=B×R.

FIND 32% of $124

$$P=B\times R=\$124\times .32$$

$$\begin{array}{r} \$124 \\ .32 \\ \hline 248 \\ 372 \\ \hline \$39.68 \end{array}$$

ANSWER, $39.68

The rate equals the percentage divided by the base. R=P÷B. What per cent of $194 is $13.58?

$$\begin{array}{r} .07 \\ 194\overline{)13.58} \\ 1358 \\ \hline \end{array}$$

ANSWER, .07, or 7%

FIGURING THE PERCENTAGE OF YOUR BANK BALANCE

1. Suppose at the beginning of the year your bank balance is $6000 and at the end of the year $5400. By what per cent has your balance decreased?

$6000—$5400=$600
$600 is what per cent of $6000?

Using our formula, we divide the percentage by the base to get the rate $(P \div B = R)$.

$$600 \div 6000 = .10, \text{ or } 10\%$$

ANSWER, decrease of 10%

2. Suppose at the beginning of the year your bank balance is $10,000 and at the end of the year $11,200. By what per cent has your balance increased?

$$\$11,200 - \$10,000 = \$1200$$
$1200 is what per cent of $10,000?
$$1200 \div 10,000 = 12, \text{ or } 12\%$$

ANSWER, increase of 12%

ALGEBRA

The word *algebra*, from the Arabic *al-jabr*, means the reunion of broken parts. Algebra is the study of reunions—the *completion* of arithmetic.

Algebra not only *completes* but *simplifies* arithmetic. Many a problem that takes considerable figuring in arithmetic can be done in a few computations by the algebraic method.

There are three important differences between algebra and arithmetic:

1. In arithmetic we add, subtract, multiply, and divide *numbers*. In algebra we apply these operations not only to *numbers* but to *letters* as well.

Thus in algebra we may say that a man walked 15 miles or *a* miles, that he sold a hat for $5 or *b* dollars, that he is 50 years old or *x* years old.

Again, in algebra we may say that 15 miles is equal to a miles times b miles, or that 50 years is equal to 5 times x years. We write these expressions as follows:

$$15 = ab$$
$$50 = 5x$$

When you multiply letters by letters, or numbers by letters, you omit the multiplication sign.

Letters in algebra always represent numbers. The first letters of the alphabet (a, b, c, etc.) generally represent *known* quantities. The last letters (x, y, and z) generally represent *unknown* quantities. Algebra is the process of discovering the *unknown* quantities with the help of the *known* quantities.

2. The second important difference between algebra and arithmetic is this: in arithmetic there are *four* fundamental processes—addition, subtraction, multiplication, and division. In algebra there are *six* fundamental processes—addition, subtraction, multiplication, division, raising to powers, and extracting roots.

Raising to powers. When a number is multiplied by itself, one or more times, it is raised to a power. If multiplied by itself once, it is *squared*, or raised to the second power. If multiplied by itself twice, it is *cubed*, or raised to the third power. And so on. The power to which a number is raised is expressed as follows:

$$3 \times 3 = 3^2 = 9$$
$$3 \times 3 \times 3 = 3^3 = 27$$
$$3 \times 3 \times 3 \times 3 = 3^4 = 81$$
$$a \times a = a^2$$
$$a \times a \times a = a^3$$

Extracting roots. The extraction of roots is the reverse of raising to powers. The *square root* of a given number is a number which, when multiplied by itself, will equal that given number. The *cube root* of a given number is a number which, if multiplied by itself twice, will equal that given number. And so on.

Square roots, cube roots, etc., are expressed as follows:

$$\sqrt{4} \text{ (the square root of } 4) = 2$$
$$\sqrt[3]{27} \text{ (the cube root of } 27) = 3$$
$$\sqrt[4]{16} \text{ (the fourth root of } 16) = 2$$
$$\sqrt[5]{243} \text{ (the fifth root of } 243) = 3$$

3. The third important difference between algebra and arithmetic is this: in arithmetic we deal with numbers which are
greater than zero. In algebra we deal not only with numbers
which are *greater* than zero, but also with numbers which are
less than zero.

A number that is *greater* than zero is a *positive* number. A
number that is *less* than zero is a *negative* number.

At first it may seem absurd to talk about a number that is less
than zero. How can *anything* be less than *nothing?* But look at
the matter from the following angle: Suppose you have spent all
your money. Your wealth in that case is zero—a very bad fix to be
in. But you might have been in an even worse fix if you had
borrowed—let us say—$500 and *spent* it. Your wealth in *that* case
would have been *$500 less than zero*, or *minus* $500. To bring
yourself *back* to zero, you would have been obliged *to earn $500
and to repay your debt.*

And thus a *negative* number in algebra means that something
is *lacking.* It shows that the computation is *in the red*—that something must be added to bring it *out of the red.*

Negative numbers in algebra are written with a minus sign, as
follows:

$$-5, \quad -73, \quad -2b, \quad -4x.$$

addition of algebraic numbers

1. Add 6 shirts, 4 ties, 5 hats; 3 shirts, 6 ties, 4 hats, 9 dresses;
2 ties, 3 dresses; 3 hats, 7 dresses.

$$6 \text{ sh.} + 4 \text{ t.} + 5 \text{ h.}$$
$$3 \text{ sh.} + 6 \text{ t.} + 4 \text{ h.} + 9 \text{ dr.}$$
$$2 \text{ t.} \qquad + 3 \text{ dr.}$$
$$3 \text{ h.} + 7 \text{ dr.}$$
$$\overline{9 \text{ sh.} + 12 \text{ t.} + 12 \text{ h.} + 19 \text{ dr.}}$$

2. Add $3a$, $4bc$, $2a^2d$; $4a$, $2bc$, $2a^2d$, $4bcd$; $3a$, $5a^2d$, $2bcd$.

$$3a+4bc+2a^2d$$
$$4a+2bc+2a^2d+4bcd$$
$$3a \qquad +5a^2d+2bcd$$
$$\overline{10a+6bc+9a^2d+6bcd}$$

3. Add $5a-6b+2c$ and $3a+4b-5c+7d$

$$5a-6b+2c$$
$$3a+4b-5c+7d$$
$$\overline{8a-2b-3c+7d}$$

In adding algebraic numbers, separate them into similar terms and then add the terms separately.

subtraction of algebraic numbers

In subtracting algebraic numbers, remember the following simple rule: *Change the signs in the subtrahend—from plus to minus and from minus to plus—and then proceed as in addition.*

1. From $15ab$ subtract $9ab$

$$15ab$$
$$-\ 9ab$$
$$\overline{6ab}$$

2. From $15ab$ subtract $-9ab$

$$\begin{array}{r} 15ab \\ + \ 9ab \\ \hline 24ab \end{array}$$

3. From $-15ab$ subtract $-9ab$

$$\begin{array}{r} -15ab \\ + \ 9ab \\ \hline - \ 6ab \end{array}$$

4. From $-15ab$ subtract $9ab$

$$\begin{array}{r} -15ab \\ - \ 9ab \\ \hline -24ab \end{array}$$

5. From $8a-4b+6c$ subtract $3a+6b-2d$

$$\begin{array}{r} 8a- \ 4b+6c \\ -3a- \ 6b \quad \ +2d \\ \hline 5a-10b+6c+2d \end{array}$$

multiplication of algebraic numbers

1. Multiply 3 by 3

$$3\times3=9, \text{ or } 3^2$$

2. Multiply 3 by 3 by 3

$$3\times3\times3=27, \text{ or } 3^3$$

3. Multiply 3^2 by 3^3

$$(3\times3)\times(3\times3\times3)=243, \text{ or } 3^5$$

The small number in the upper right-hand corner is called the *exponent*, from the Latin *exponere*, meaning to set forth. It sets forth, or points out, the number of times a figure or a letter is multiplied by itself. Thus, 3^5 means that 3 is multiplied by itself 4 times—$3 \times 3 \times 3 \times 3 \times 3$. In like manner, a^5 means $a \times a \times a \times a \times a$.

When a letter appears without any exponent, the exponent (understood) is 1. Thus, $a = a^1$; $a \times a = a^1 \times a^1$, or a^2; $a \times a \times a = a^1 \times a^1 \times a^1 = a^3$.

From the above we see that when we multiply a letter or a number by itself, we *add* the exponents.

THUS:

$$a^3 \times a^4 = a^{3+4} = a^7$$

$$(x+y)^2 \times (x+y)^6 = (x+y)^{2+6} = (x+y)^8$$

EXAMPLES:

1. Multiply $3a^3b^4$ by $4a^2b^5$

$$3 \times 4 \times a^{3+2} \times b^{4+5} = 12a^5b^9$$

2. Multiply $5a^{2b+3}$ by $4a^{b-2}$

$$5 \times 4 \times a^{2b+b+3-2} = 20a^{3b+1}$$

In multiplying algebraic numbers, note the following facts:
1. A positive times a positive (like the friend of a friend) is positive. *Plus times plus equals plus.*
2. A negative times a negative (like the enemy of an enemy) is positive. *Minus times minus equals plus.*
3. A positive times a negative (like the friend of an enemy) is negative. *Plus times minus equals minus.*
4. A negative times a positive (like the enemy of a friend) is negative. *Minus times plus equals minus.*

Expressed in another way, the above four rules mean that the multiplication of two *like* signs produces a positive result, while the multiplication of two *unlike* signs produces a negative result.

$$(+)\times(+), \text{ or } (-)\times(-)=+$$
$$(+)\times(-), \text{ or } (-)\times(+)=-$$

EXAMPLES:

1. Multiply $2(a+b)^3$ by $-5(a+b)^2$

$$+2\times-5\times(a+b)^{3+2}$$
$$-10(a+b)^5$$

2. Multiply $-6(b-c)^4$ by $-4(b-c)$

$$-6\times-4\times(b-c)^{4+1}$$
$$24(b-c)^5$$

multiplication of polynomials

A *polynomial*—from the Greek *poly*, many, and *onoma*, name—is a quantity consisting of two or more terms (or names) connected by plus or minus signs. For example:

$$5x+3y$$
$$2a^2b-3bc+4cd$$

In order to understand the multiplication of algebraic polynomials, let us do the following arithmetic multiplications by the algebraic method:

1. 8×25

$$8\times(15+10)$$
$$15+10$$
$$8$$
$$\overline{120+80}=200$$

2. 20×30

$$(10+10)\times(12+18)$$

The above may also be expressed without the multiplication sign:

$$(10+10)(12+18)$$
$$10+10$$
$$\underline{12+18}$$
$$120+120$$
$$\underline{+180+180}$$
$$120+300+180=600$$

3. 15×12

$$(20-5)\ (9+3)$$
$$20-5$$
$$\underline{9+3}$$
$$180-45$$
$$\underline{+60-15}$$
$$180+15-15=180$$

And now we are ready to multiply the following algebraic polynomials:

1. $3a \times (a+2b)$

$$a+2b$$
$$\underline{3a}$$
$$3a^2+6ab$$

2. $(4a^2+3b) \times (3a+4b^2)$

$$4a^2+3b$$
$$\underline{3a\ +4b^2}$$
$$12a^3+9ab$$
$$\underline{+16a^2b^2+12b^3}$$
$$12a^3+9ab+16a^2b^2+12b^3$$

3. $(3a+2b)\times(2a-5b)$

$$
\begin{array}{l}
3a + 2b \\
\underline{2a - 5b} \\
6a^2 + 4ab \\
 -15ab - 10b^2 \\
\hline
6a^2 - 11ab - 10b^2
\end{array}
$$

Consider now the following three examples which illustrate three algebraic rules:

A. Multiply $(a+b)$ $(a+b)$, or $a+b$ squared

$$
\begin{array}{l}
a + b \\
\underline{a + b} \\
a^2 + ab \\
 + ab + b^2 \\
\hline
a^2 + 2ab + b^2
\end{array}
$$

The square of the sum of two terms is equal to the square of the first term, plus twice the product of the first term and the second term, plus the square of the second term.

B. Multiply $(a-b)$ $(a-b)$

$$
\begin{array}{l}
a - b \\
\underline{a - b} \\
a^2 - ab \\
 - ab + b^2 \\
\hline
a^2 - 2ab + b^2
\end{array}
$$

The square of the difference of two terms is equal to the square of the first term, minus twice the product of the first term by the second term, plus the square of the second term.

C. Multiply $(a+b)$ $(a-b)$

$$
\begin{array}{r}
a + b \\
a - b \\
\hline
a^2+ab \\
-ab-b^2 \\
\hline
a^2 \qquad -b^2
\end{array}
$$

The product of the sum and the difference of two terms is equal to the difference of their squares.

division of algebraic numbers

1. Divide 32 by 8

$$32=2^5;\ 8=2^3$$

$$\frac{2^5}{2^3} = \frac{2\times2\times2\times2\times2}{2\times2\times2} = 4 = 2^2$$

That is, $\dfrac{2^5}{2^3} = 2^{5-3} = 2^2$

2. Divide a^7 by a^3

$$\frac{a^7}{a^3} = \frac{a\times a\times a\times a\times a\times a\times a}{a\times a\times a} = a^4$$

That is, $\dfrac{a^7}{a^3} = a^{7-3} = a^4$

In multiplication, as we have seen, we *add* the exponents. In division, on the other hand, we *subtract* the exponents.

The rule for signs in division is the same as in multiplication:

$$(+)\div(+),\ \text{or}\ (-)\div(-)=+$$
$$(+)\div(-),\ \text{or}\ (-)\div(+)=-$$

division of polynomials

1. Divide $15a^3 - 20a^2 + 10a$ by $5a$

$$\frac{15a^3 - 20a^2 + 10a}{5a} = 3a^2 - 4a + 2$$

$$\frac{15a^3}{5a} = 3a^2$$

$$\frac{-20a^2}{5a} = -4a$$

$$\frac{10a}{5a} = 2$$

When you divide a polynomial by a single term, you divide each term in the polynomial by that single term.

2. Divide $a^2 + 3a - 28$ by $a - 4$

When you divide a polynomial by a polynomial, you proceed as in long division in arithmetic as follows:

$$
\begin{array}{r}
a + 7 \\
a - 4 \,\overline{\big)\, a^2 + 3a - 28} \\
a^2 - 4a \\
\hline
7a - 28 \\
7a - 28 \\
\hline
0
\end{array}
$$

ANSWER, $a + 7$

EXPLANATION:

$$a^2 \div a = a$$
$$a \times a = a^2$$
$$a \times -4 = -4a$$
$$a^2 - a^2 = 0$$
$$3a - (-4a) = 7a$$

Bring down the -28, and you get $7a - 28$

$$7a \div a = 7$$
$$7 \times a = 7a$$
$$7 \times -4 = -28$$

This leaves no remainder.

simple equations

The equation is the basis of algebra. Practically all the engineering constructions and scientific inventions are founded upon equations.

A *simple algebraic equation* is a proposition asserting the equality of two quantities—one known and the other unknown. The unknown quantity is generally expressed by x.

In order to understand the solution of algebraic equations, let us look at the following arithmetic equations:

1. $$9-5=4$$
    $$9=5+4$$

2. $$9=6+3$$
    $$9-6=3$$
    $$9-3=6$$

3. $$6+ 4=10$$
    $$6=10- 4$$
    $$4=10- 6$$

From the above examples you will note that when you move a term from one side of an equation to the other side, you must change the sign of the term thus moved—from *plus* to *minus,* or from *minus* to *plus.*

And now let us look at the following algebraic equations:

1. $$x- 4=6$$
    $$x= 4+6$$
    $$x=10$$

2.
$$x+\ 6=11$$
$$x=11-6$$
$$x=\ 5$$

3.
$$x-5=0$$
$$x=5+0$$
$$x=5$$

4.
$$x+4+4x-2=3x+10$$

In order to solve for x, we bring all the x terms on one side of the equation and all the numbers on the other side.

$$x+4x-3x=-4+2+10$$
$$2x=8$$
$$x=4$$

A great many problems, as we have noted at the beginning of this chapter, can be solved much more easily by the algebraic than by the arithmetic method. For example:

1. Tom, Dick, and Harry together have saved up $9000 for their college education. Dick has saved up $400 more than Tom, and Harry has saved up $700 more than Dick. How much has each one of them saved?

Let $x=$ Tom's savings
Then $x+400=$ Dick's savings
And $x+400+700=$ Harry's savings

$$x+x+400+x+400+700= \text{their combined savings}$$
$$3x+1500=9000$$
$$3x=9000-1500$$
$$3x=7500$$
$$x=2500$$
$$x+400=2900$$
$$x+400+700=3600$$

ANSWER,   Tom, $2500; Dick, $2900; Harry, $3600

2. A, B, and C have $70. A has $10 less than twice the sum that B has, and B has $1 more than twice the sum that C has. How much has each?

Sounds complicated, doesn't it? Yet see how simple it is:

Let $x=$ the sum that C has
$2x+1=$ the sum that B has
$2(2x+1)-10=$ the sum that A has

$$x+2x+1+4x+2-10=70$$
$$7x=70-1-2+10$$
$$7x=77$$
$$x=11, \text{ the sum that C has}$$
$$22+1=23, \text{ the sum that B has}$$
$$46-10=36, \text{ the sum that A has}$$

ANSWER,   A, $36; B, $23; C, $11

simultaneous equations

Simultaneous equations are sets of equations that contain more than one unknown quantity. We shall here consider sets of two equations with two unknown quantities—x and y. Such equations can be solved in two ways:

A. By addition or subtraction.
B. By substitution.

A. Solve for x and y, eliminating by addition or subtraction:

1. $$x+y=12$$
$$x-y=2$$

Adding the two equations, we get

$$x+y+x-y=12+2$$
$$2x=14$$
$$x=7$$
$$7+y=12$$
$$y=12-7$$
$$y=5$$

ANSWER, $x=7$; $y=5$

2.
$$3x+2y=17$$
$$x+4y=19$$

In order to eliminate the y's, we multiply the first equation by 2. This gives us

$$6x+4y=34$$
$$x+4y=19$$

Since the y's have the same sign, we now *subtract* the second equation *from* the first (by changing the signs of all the terms in the second equation and then proceeding as in addition). This gives us

$$5x=15$$
$$x=3$$
$$3+4y=19$$
$$4y=19-3=16$$
$$y=4$$

ANSWER, $x=3$; $y=4$

B. Solve for x and y, eliminating by substitution:

1.
$$x+2y=16$$
$$2x+3y=26$$

In the first equation, $x=16-2y$
Substituting this value for x in the second equation, we get

$$2\ (16-2y)+3y=26$$
$$32\quad -4y\ +3y=26$$
$$-\ y=-32+26$$
$$-\ y=-6$$
$$y=\ 6$$
$$x+12=\ 16$$
$$x=\ 16-12=4$$

ANSWER, $x=4$; $y=6$

It is often necessary to use simultaneous equations—that is, two unknown quantities—in order to solve an algebraic problem. The following are sample problems of this type:

1. The sum of two numbers is 34; their difference is 6. Find the two numbers.

$$x+y=34$$
$$x-y=\ 6$$
$$2x=40$$
$$x=20$$
$$20+y=34$$
$$y=14$$

ANSWER, 20 and 14

2. A grocer has two grades of coffee, worth 80 cents and 50 cents per pound. How many pounds of each must he use to make a mixture of 100 pounds worth 62 cents a pound?

Let $x=$ the number of pounds worth $80¢$ a pound
" $y=$ " " " " " $50¢$ " "

$$x+y=100$$
$$80x+50y=62\times100=6200$$

Multiply the first equation by 80;

$$80x+80y=8000$$
$$80x+50y=6200$$
$$30y=1800$$
$$y=60$$
$$x+60=100$$
$$x=40$$

ANSWER, 40 pounds worth $80¢$ a pound
60 " " $50¢$ " "

GEOMETRY

Geometry means literally the *measure of land*. *Plane geometry* is the measure, or study, of land surfaces. It deals with lines, angles, triangles, quadrilaterals, squares, polygons, and circles.

A *triangle* is a figure having *three angles*—

A *quadrilateral* is a figure having *four sides*—

A *polygon* is a figure of any number of sides.

A figure of *five sides* is a *pentagon*—

A figure of *six sides* is a *hexagon*—and so forth.

Points and lines. All geometry begins with a point. Geometrically speaking, a point has no size. We represent a point by a dot.
A *line* is the *path of a moving point*.
A *straight line* is the *shortest path between two points*.

Angles. An *angle* is a *corner* produced by the meeting of two straight lines—
The *vertex* of an angle is the point at which the two lines meet.
A *straight angle* is an angle whose two sides form one straight line.
An angle may be designated by three capital letters, as follows:

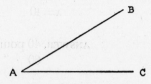

It is then read as *BAC* or as *CAB*. The vertex letter is always read in the middle.

Sometimes an angle is designated by a single small letter or number, as follows:

These angles are called *angle a,* and *angle 1.*

All angles are parts of a circle, as indicated below:

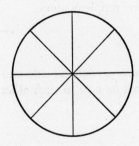

A *circle* is divided into 360 equal parts, or degrees. A half circle —or a straight angle—contains 180 degrees (written 180°). A quarter circle contains 90 degrees.

An angle that marks off a quarter circle is a *90° angle,* or a *right angle—*

An angle that contains *less than 90°* is an *acute angle—*

An angle that contains *more than 90°* and less than 180° is an *obtuse angle—*

Two angles are *complementary* if their sum is equal to 90°:

Angles *a* and *b* are complementary.

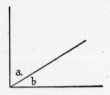

Two angles are *supplementary* if their sum is equal to 180°:

Angles 1 and 2 are supplementary.

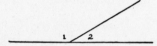

Two angles that have a common side and a common vertex—that is, two angles that *lie next to each other*—are *adjacent angles:*

Angles *ABD* and *DBC* are adjacent.

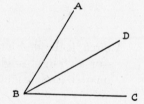

Two angles formed by intersecting straight lines are *vertical angles:*

Angles *a* and *b* are vertical.
Also, angles *c* and *d* are vertical.

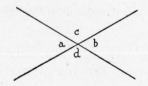

When an angle equals 90°—that is, when it is a right angle, the sides are *perpendicular* to each other.

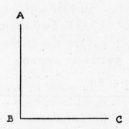

AB is perpendicular to *BC*.

general definitions

A *proposition* is a geometric statement which has to be demonstrated, or proved.

A *theorem* is another name for a proposition.

The *hypothesis* is the part of a theorem that is given in order to help the solution of the rest of the theorem.

An *axiom* is a fact that requires no proof. A knowledge of the following geometric axioms will save considerable trouble in the solution of various geometric problems:

1. Things equal to the same thing are equal to each other.

2. If equals are added to equals, the sums are equal.

3. If equals are substracted from equals, the remainders are equal.

4. If equals are multiplied by equals, the products are equal.

5. If equals are divided by equals, the quotients are equal.

6. The whole is equal to the sum of its parts.

7. The whole is greater than any of its parts.

8. One quantity may be substituted for another equal quantity in an equation.

9. One straight line, and only one, can be drawn between two points.

10. A straight line is the shortest distance between two points.

11. All right angles are equal.

12. Two intersecting straight lines cannot both be parallel to a third straight line.

13. A geometric figure may be moved from one position to another without change of shape or size.

14. Two straight lines can intersect at only one point.

geometric symbols

In order to save time, we use symbols and abbreviations instead of writing out the geometric terms in full. The following list includes some of the more common symbols used in the solution of geometric problems:

$\triangle$ stands for *triangle.*
$\angle$ "   " *angle.*
$\odot$ "   " *circle.*
$\perp$ stands for the term *is perpendicular to.*
$\parallel$ "   "   "   " *is parallel to.*
$\therefore$ "   "   "   " *therefore.*
rt. $\angle$ "   "   *right angle.*

triangles

There are several kinds of triangles:

1. *Scalene*—a triangle whose three sides are all of different lengths.

2. *Isosceles*—a triangle which has two equal sides.

3. *Equilateral*—a triangle whose three sides are all equal.

4. *Obtuse*—a triangle which has one obtuse angle.

5. *Acute*—a triangle whose three angles are all acute.

6. *Right*—a triangle which has one right angle.

7. *Equiangular*—a triangle whose three angles are all equal.

The *base* of a triangle is the *bottom* side.

The *arms* of a triangle are the two other sides.

The *hypotenuse* is the side opposite the *right angle* in a right triangle.

The *vertex* angle is the angle opposite the base.

The *altitude* of a triangle is the length of a line drawn perpendicularly from the vertex angle to the base.

The *sum of the angles* of any triangle is equal to 180°.

theorems, or propositions

To prove a geometric theorem, proceed as follows:
1. Write out your theorem, or proposition.
2. Draw the diagram.
3. State the hypothesis—the thing that is given, or admitted, in the theorem.
4. State the thing that you must prove.
5. Proceed with the proof. Write the statements on the left, and the reasons for the statements on the right.

PROPOSITION I

Vertical angles are equal.

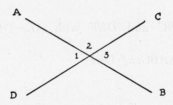

Given: Vertical angles, 1 and 3, formed by the intersection of the lines *AB* and *CD*.
To Prove: $\angle 1 = \angle 3$

Proof:

$\angle 1 + \angle 2 = 180°$	All straight angles $= 180°$
$\angle 3 + \angle 2 = 180°$	" " " "
$\angle 1 = 180° - \angle 2$	Transposing and changing signs
$\angle 3 = 180° - \angle 2$	" " " "
$\angle 1 = \angle 3$	Axiom 1

PROPOSITION II

Two triangles are equal if two angles and the enclosed side of one equal, respectively, two angles and the enclosed side of the other. (Angle, side, and angle of one △ are equal to angle, side, and angle of the other △. This is generally expressed as follows: a.s.a.=a.s.a.)

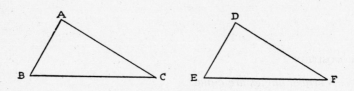

Given: △*ABC* and *DEF* with *AB=DE*, ∠*A=*∠*D*, and ∠*B=*∠*E*.
To Prove: △*ABC=*△*DEF*.

Proof:

Place △*ABC* upon △*DEF* so that side *AB* shall coincide with its equal side *DE*	Hypothesis Axiom 13
Then side *AC* will fall along side *DF*	Since ∠*A=*∠*D* by hypothesis
And side *BC* will fall along side *EF*	Since ∠*B=*∠*E* by hypothesis
Point *C* will fall upon point *F*	Axiom 14
∴△*ABC=*△*DEF*	Triangles are equal if they coincide exactly

PROPOSITION III

Two triangles are equal if two sides and the included angle of one are equal, respectively, to two sides and the included angle of the other. (s.a.s.=s.a.s.)

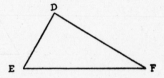

Given: △*ABC* and *DEF* with *AB*=*DE*, *BC*=*EF*, and ∠*B*= ∠*E*.

To Prove: △*ABC*=△*DEF*.

Proof:

Place △*ABC* upon △*DEF* so that *BC* shall coincide with ts equal *EF*	Hypothesis Axiom 13
Then *BA* (or *AB*) will fall along *ED* (or *DE*)	∠*B*=∠*E*, by hypothesis
Point *A* will fall on point *D*	*AB*=*DE*, by hypothesis
AC will coincide with *DE*	Axiom 9
∴△*ABC*=△*DEF*	Triangles are equal if they coincide exactly

PROPOSITION IV

The base angles of an isosceles triangle are equal.

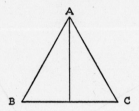

Given: *ABC* is an *isosceles* △, *AB* and *AC* being the equal sides.

To Prove: ∠*B*=∠*C*.

Proof:

Draw the line *AD* to bisect ∠*BAC*

Then ∠*BAD*=∠*CAD*	By construction
AB=*AC*	Hypothesis. Two sides of an isosceles △ are =
AD=*AD*	Identity
△*ABD*=△*ACD*	s.a.s.=s.a.s.
∴∠*B*=∠*C*	Corresponding parts of = △

PROPOSITION V

Two triangles are equal if three sides of one are equal, respectively, to three sides of the other. (s.s.s.=s.s.s.).

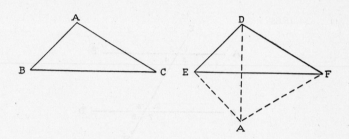

Given: $\triangle ABC$ and DEF, with $AB=DE$, $BC=EF$, and $AC=DF$.

To Prove: $\triangle ABC=\triangle DEF$.

Proof:

Place $\triangle ABC$ so that BC shall coincide with EF and A and D shall lie on opposite sides of EF	Hypothesis Axiom 13
Draw AD	Axiom 9
$\triangle AFD$ is isosceles	$AF=DF$, by hypothesis
$\angle FAD=\angle FDA$	Proposition IV
$\triangle AED$ is isosceles	$AE=DE$, by hypothesis
$\angle EAD=\angle EDA$	Proposition IV
$\angle FAD+\angle EAD=\angle FDA+\angle EDA$	Axiom 2
Or, $\angle A=\angle D$	Substitution
$\therefore \triangle ABC=\triangle DEF$	$s.a.s.=s.a.s.$

PARALLEL LINES

In the figure below, *EF* intersects *AB* and *CD*. It is therefore called a transversal.

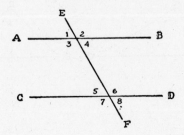

A *transversal* is a line that intersects two or more lines. This intersection produces a number of angles, and the angles are named as follows:

1, 2, 7, and 8 are *exterior* angles
3, 4, 5, and 6 are *interior* angles
1 and 8 are *alternate exterior* angles
2 and 7 are   "   "   "
3 and 6 are *alternate interior* angles
4 and 5 are   "   "   "
1 and 5 are *corresponding* angles
3 and 7 are   "   "
2 and 6 are   "   "
4 and 8 are   "   "

Lines *AB* and *CD* in the above figure are parallel. *Parallel lines* —according to the traditional, Euclidian geometry—are lines which never meet.

Two straight lines parallel to a third line are parallel to each other. Note, for example, the parallel lines on your floor, bureau, and so forth.

PROPOSITION VI

The exterior angle of a triangle is greater than either of the opposite interior angles.

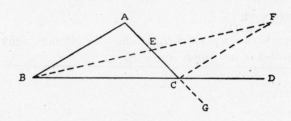

Given: △ABC and the exterior ∠ACD.
To Prove: ∠ACD is greater than ∠A or ∠B.

Proof:

Let E be the middle point of AC. Draw BE and produce it until EF=BE. Draw FC	Construction
In the ▲ ABE and CFE	
BE=EF	Construction
AE=EC	Construction
∠AEB=∠CEF	Vertical ∡
△ABE=△CFE	s.a.s.=s.a.s.
∠ECF=∠A	Corresponding ∡ of equal ▲
∠ACD is greater than ∠ECF	Axiom 7
∴ ∠ACD is greater than ∠A	Substitution

And now, by joining A to the mid-point of BC, and continuing it by the same process as outlined above, we can prove that ∠BCG is greater than ∠B.

| But $\angle ACD = \angle BCG$ | Vertical $\angle$ |
| $\therefore \angle ACD$ is greater than $\angle B$ | Substitution |

PROPOSITION VII

Two lines are parallel if the alternate interior angles made by a transversal are equal.

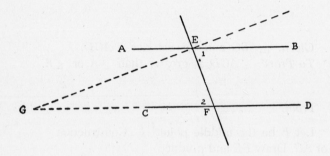

Given: AB and CD are crossed by a transversal at points E and F so that $\angle 1 = \angle 2$.
To Prove: $AB \| CD$.

Proof:

Suppose they are not parallel. In that case they meet at some point. Let that point be G	
Then $\angle B'EF$, or $\angle 1$, is greater than $\angle 2$	Proposition VI
But $\angle 1 = \angle 2$	Hypothesis
$\therefore AB$ and CD cannot meet, and hence are parallel	

PROPOSITION VIII

Two lines are parallel if the corresponding angles made by a transversal are equal.

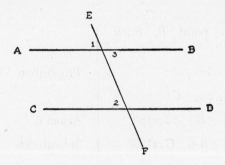

Given: AB and CD are crossed by a transversal, EF, so that $\angle 1 = \angle 2$.

To Prove: AB‖CD.

Proof:

$\angle 1 = \angle 2$	Hypothesis
$\angle 1 = \angle 3$	Vertical $\angle\!\!\!\angle$
$\angle 2 = \angle 3$	Axiom 1
$\therefore AB‖CD$	Proposition VII

COROLLARY:

The alternate interior angles of parallel lines are equal.

PROPOSITION IX

The sum of the angles of a triangle is equal to two right angles (180°).

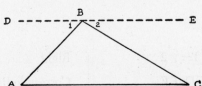

Given: △ABC.

To Prove: ∠A+∠B+∠C=180°.

Proof:

Through point *B*, draw *DE*∥*AC*.

∠1=∠A	Proposition VII
∠2=∠C	" "
∠1+∠B+∠2=180°	Axiom 6
∴∠A+∠B+∠C=180°	Substitution

PROPOSITION X

Two lines perpendicular to the same line are parallel.

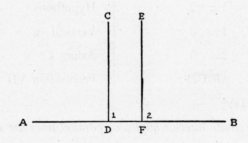

Given: *CD* and *EF* ⊥ *AB*.

To Prove: *CD* is parallel to *EF*.

Proof:

∠1=∠2	Right ∠
∴*CD*∥*EF*	Corresponding ∠ are equal

THE PRACTICAL USES OF MATHEMATICS

This section deals with mathematics not as an abstract science but as a concrete guide to practical living. It contains the answers to the question which, in various forms, arises again and again in our everyday life—*how do you figure it out?*

The mathematical problems of our everyday life may be divided into two parts: *Business Problems* and *Household Expenses*. We shall consider each of these separately.

business problems

THE EXCHANGE OF GOODS

In the buying and the selling of goods, we use the following trade terms:

The *list price* of an article is the price at which it is listed and sold to the public.

The *trade discount* is the reduction from the list price of the article.

The *net price* is the price of the article after the discount has been made.

EXAMPLE: The discount on a radio is 40%. The net price is $252. What is the list price?

$252 is 60% (100%—40%) of what number?

According to our percentage formula, the *base* equals the *percentage* divided by the *rate*. This formula, translated into commercial language, means that the *list price* equals the *net price* divided by the *rate* of the list price.

$$\text{List price} = \$252 \div 60\% = 252 \div \frac{60}{100} = 252 \div \frac{3}{5} = \$420$$

ANSWER, $420

DISCOUNT SERIES

Sometimes a manufacturer finds it advisable to offer a *series* of discounts instead of a *single* discount. Suppose he manufactures silk stockings to sell at a discount of 20% and then suddenly gets a shipment of silk at a very low price. He can now afford an additional discount of 10%. On top of that, he may allow still another discount of 2% to his customers for prompt payments. In other words, he allows a *discount series*.

If he lists his stockings at $24 a dozen, he will compute his discount series as follows:

$24   less 20%, less 10%, less 2%
$24   less 20%=$19.20
$19.20 less 10%=$17.28
$17.28 less   2%=$16.93

When there is a fraction of a cent in a remainder, the fraction may either be dropped or computed as a whole cent.

PROFIT AND LOSS

In computing the profit and loss of any transaction, we apply the principles as explained in our sections on percentage and on trade discount.

EXAMPLES:

1. A haberdasher buys a dozen shirts for $20 and makes a profit of 25%. At what price does he sell these shirts?

    Profit made on transaction=25% of $20=$5
    Price at which shirts are sold $20+$5=$25

2. A grocer buys canned goods at a list price of $125 with trade discounts of 20% and 5%. He sells the goods for $152. What per cent profit based on the cost does he make?

The list price ($125)=100% of the list price
Deducting 20% of the list
  price, we have left   80% of the list price
Deducting 5% of 80%
  we have left   76%

Thus the cost=76% of $125=$95
The profit=$152—$95   =$57

$$\text{The per cent profit}=\frac{57}{95}=.60=60\%$$

ANSWER, 60%

GROSS PROFIT AND NET PROFIT

In the computation of the foregoing examples, we have omitted an important item—the cost of doing business. Let us now consider this item.

Suppose an automobile dealer buys a car from the manufacturer at a net cost of $1555.20. His cost of doing business is 32%, based on the selling price; and his net profit, also based on the selling price, is 14%. (a) What is the per cent of his gross profit? (b) At what price does he sell the car? (c) What is his net profit?

(a) Gross profit   =32%+14%=46%

(b) Selling price (S)=1555.20+.46S
             1.00S=1555.20+.46S
             .54S=1555.20
             S=$2880

(c) Net profit   =14% of $2880=$403.20

ANSWER, (a) 46%; (b) $2880; (c) $403.20

COMPUTING LOSSES

1. A retailer bought 500 shirts at $2.00 each, expecting to sell them at $3.00 each. He ran into a depression, however, and

he was obliged to sell them at $1.70 each. His operating ex
penses in handling those shirts were $75. (a) What was his los
on the sales? (b) What was his net loss?

   (a) Cost of goods sold   =$1000
       Amount realized from sales= 850

       Loss on sales   = $150

   (b) Loss on sales   = $150
       Operating expenses   =   75

       Net loss   = $225

ANSWER, (a) $150; (b) $22

2. A radio dealer bought a number of radios for $3960 and sol
them for $4039. His operating expenses were $375. (a) Wha
was his profit on sales? (b) What was his net loss?

   (a) Amount realized from sales=$4039
       Cost of goods sold   = 3960

       Profit on sales   =$ 79

   (b) Operating expenses   = $375
       Profit on sales   =   79

       Net loss   =$ 296

ANSWER, (a) $79; (b) $29

household expenses

TELEPHONE BILLS

The cost of Mr. Smith's telephone service is $4.50 a month for
100 calls. Additional calls are charged at the rate of 5 cents a call
plus a 3% sales tax.

Find (a) the amount due for additional calls, and (b) the
total amount due, under the following circumstances:

Balance from Previous Month, $6.37
Total Calls for Month, 119
Long-Distance Calls and Telegrams, $1.36

Cost of additional calls	$19\times\$.05$	$.95
	3% of $.95	.03
		$.98
Long-distance calls and telegrams		1.36
		$2.34
Monthly charge for 100 calls		4.50
Balance from previous month		6.37
		$13.21

ANSWER, (a) $2.34; (b) $13.21

GAS BILLS

In order to compute your gas bill, read your meter at the beginning and at the end of each month, and then multiply the difference in cubic feet—that is, the number of cubic feet consumed during the month—by the rate per cubic foot.

EXAMPLE:

On April 1 your gas meter reads 25,000 cubic feet and on May 1 it reads 27,500 cubic feet. The rate is $11\frac{3}{5}$ cents per 100 cubic feet, plus a 3% sales tax. What is your bill for the month of April?

27,500 cu. ft.—25,000 cu. ft.=2500 cu. ft.
=25 units of 100 cu. ft. each.

$$25\times11\frac{3}{5}\cancel{c}=\$2.90$$
$$\text{Tax}=\quad.09$$
$$\text{Total}=\$2.99$$

ANSWER, $2.99

ELECTRICITY BILLS

Suppose the electricity service rates in your community are as follows:

For the first 10 kilowatt hours—$.09 per kilowatt hour (kw. hr.)
For the next 35 kilowatt hours—$.06 per kw. hr.
For the next 35 kilowatt hours—$.05 "   "   "
For the next 50 kilowatt hours—$.03 "   "   "
For all additional service— $.02 "   "   "

In addition to the regular rates, suppose there is a charge of
$.0002 per kw. hr. for "fuel cost adjustment," and a 3% sales tax.
What is your electric bill for June if on June 1 the meter reading
is 5362 and on July 1, 5507?

$$5507-5362=145 \text{ kw. hr.}$$
$$10\times\$.09= \$.90$$
$$35\times\$.06=\$2.10$$
$$35\times\$.05=\$1.75$$
$$50\times\$.03=\$1.50$$
$$15\times\$.02= \underline{\ .30}$$
$$\$6.55$$
$$145\times\$.0002= \underline{\ .03}$$
$$\$6.58$$
$$\$6.58\times\ .03\qquad \underline{\ .20}$$
$$\text{Total bill}\qquad \$6.78$$

ANSWER, $6.78

BUDGETS

It is well for every family with a moderate income to budget
its annual expenditures somewhat as follows:

Rent	20%
Food	25%
Clothing	15%
Household expenses	5%
Miscellaneous expenses	10%
Entertainment	10%
Insurance and medical care	7%
Savings	8%

Suppose the rent is $832 a year.
  (a) What is the weekly income?
  (b) What is the annual amount saved?
  (c) What is the monthly outlay for clothing?
  (d) What is the annual allowance for insurance and medical care?
  (e) What is the weekly allowance for entertainment?

  (a) $832=20% of annual income.
    Annual income $832÷⅕=$4160
    Weekly income $4160÷52=$80
  (b) Annual amount saved=8% of $4160=$332.80
  (c) Annual outlay for clothing=15% of $4160=$624
    Monthly outlay for clothing $624÷12=$52
  (d) Annual allowance for insurance, etc.=7% of $4160=$291.20
  (e) Annual allowance for entertainment=10% of $4160=$416
    Weekly allowance for entertainment=$416÷52=$8

  ANSWER, (a) $80; (b) $332.80; (c) $52; (d) $291.20; (e) $8

REVIEW QUESTIONS IN MATHEMATICS

1. What is the short-cut formula for multiplying a number by 125?

2. For multiplying a number by 999?

3. Divide 22,929 by 67.

4. What is the short-cut formula for dividing a number by 125?

5. Reduce $234/416$ to its lowest terms.

6. Add $\frac{1}{6}$, $\frac{4}{21}$, $\frac{17}{28}$, and $\frac{11}{12}$.

7. Subtract $1\frac{3}{4}$ from $2\frac{2}{3}$.

8. Multiply $8\frac{1}{8}$ by $2\frac{2}{13}$.

9. Divide $16\frac{4}{5} \div 2\frac{2}{11} \div 15\frac{2}{5}$.

10. Divide 789.48 by .0108.

11. Suppose at the beginning of the year your bank balance is $4500, and at the end of the year $1687.50. By what per cent has your balance decreased?

12. How do you represent unknown quantities in algebra?

13. How many fundamental processes are there in arithmetic? In algebra?

14. Add $3a^3+2a^2+2a+1$
$4a^3-2a^2+2a-2$
$9a^3+7a^2-a+14$.

15. From $a^2-5ab+y^2$
subtract $a^2-5ab-y^2$

16. Multiply $4a^2b^3$ by $3ab^2$.

17. Multiply $a^2-2ab+b^2$ by $a-b$.

18. Give the rule for the square of the sum of two terms.

19. Give the rule for the square of the difference of two terms.

20. Give the rule for the product of the sum and the difference of two terms.

21. Divide x^3-y^3 by $x-y$.

22. Solve the following equation:
$8x+12-2x=4x+42-x$

23. What are simultaneous equations?

24. Solve the following equation, eliminating by addition or subtraction:
$2x+y=13$
$3x-y=7$

25. Solve the following equation, eliminating by substitution:
$3x+y=22$
$2x+3y=31$

(Solve the following 13 problems by simple equations.)

26. Of three consecutive numbers, $x+1$ is the largest. Their sum is 54. What are the numbers? (Hint: Let $x-1=$ the smallest number, x the second number, and $x+1$ the largest.)

27. Of three consecutive odd numbers, $2x+1$ is the smallest. Their sum is 69. What are the numbers?

28. Three times a number equals the number increased by 24. What is the number?

29. A man has $2.75 in dimes and quarters. If he has 20 coins in all, how many are dimes and how many are quarters?
(Hint: Let $x=$ the number of dimes
$20-x=$ the number of quarters
$10x=$ *the number of cents* represented by the 10 dimes. And so on.)

30. Ten increased by five times a certain number equals 50. What is the number?

31. Four times a number equals the number increased by 48. What is the number?

32. The sum of two numbers is 56, and one of them is 4 less than 3 times the other. What are the numbers?

33. Brown is twice as old as Smith, and the sum of their ages is 75 years. What are their ages?

34. A man is 35 years old, and his son is 10 years old. In how many years will the son be half as old as the father?

35. In the above example, how many years ago was the son one sixth as old as the father?

36. The four salesmen of an automobile agency together sold 25 automobiles in one week. The second sold twice as many as the first; the third, twice as many as the second; and the fourth, three more than the third. How many did each sell?

37. Five men agreed to contribute equal amounts to a certain fund. Two of them failed to do so, and each of the others therefore had to pay $80 more than originally planned. How much did they agree to pay at the outset?

38. A is 4 years more than twice as old as B. In 16 years A will be three times as old as B is now. How old is each?
(Hint: Let x=B's age at the present time.)

(Solve the following 4 problems by simultaneous equations.)

39. The sum of two numbers is 35. Their difference is 7. What are the numbers?

40. A grocer has two grades of coffee, worth 32 cents and 20 cents a pound. How many pounds of each must he use to make a mixture of a hundred pounds worth 29 cents a pound?

41. A man withdrew from his bank $80 in ten-dollar and five-dollar bills. The number of bills was 10. How many of each did he draw?

42. A man hired 5 men and 2 boys for a day for $31; and the next day, 4 men and 5 boys for $35. How much did he pay each per day?

43. How many degrees are there in a circle? A quarter circle?

44. What is an obtuse angle?

45. What is a pentagon?

46. What are vertical angles?

47. What is an axiom?

48. Complete the axiom, "The whole is equal . . ."

49. What is an isosceles triangle?

50. What is the hypotenuse?

ANSWERS TO THE QUESTIONS IN MATHEMATICS

1. Add three zeros and divide by 8.

2. Multiply by 1000 and subtract the multiplicand from the product.

3. $342^{15}/_{67}$.

4. Multiply by 8 and divide by 1000.

5. $^{9}/_{16}$.

6. $1^{37}/_{42}$.

7. $^{11}/_{12}$.

8. $17\frac{1}{2}$.

9. $\frac{1}{2}$.

10. 73,100.

11. By $62\frac{1}{2}\%$.

12. By x, y, and z.

13. Four in arithmetic—addition, subtraction, multiplication, and division. Six in algebra—the four processes of arithmetic, and raising to powers and extracting roots.

14. $16a^3+7a^2+3a+13$.

15. $2y^2$.

16. $12a^3 b^5$.

17. $a^3-3a^2b+3ab^2-b^3$.

18. The square of the sum of two terms is equal to the square of the first term, plus twice the product of the first term by the second term, plus the square of the second term.

19. The square of the difference of two terms is equal to the square of the first term, minus twice the product of the first term by the second term, plus the square of the second term.

20. The product of the sum and the difference of two terms is equal to the difference of their squares.

21. x^2+xy+y^2.

22. $x=10$.

23. An equation that contains more than one unknown quantity.

24. $x=4$; $y=5$.

25. $x=5$; $y=7$.

26. 17, 18, and 19.

27. 21, 23, and 25.

28. 12.

29. 15 dimes; 5 quarters.

30. 8.

31. 16.

32. 41 and 15.

33. 50 and 25 years.

34. In 15 years.

35. 5 years ago.

36. 2, 4, 8, and 11 automobiles respectively.

37. $120 each.

38. 44 and 20 years.

39. 21 and 14.

40. 75 lbs. at 32 cents; 25 lbs. at 20 cents.

41. 6 ten-dollar bills; 4 five-dollar bills.

42. $5 per man; $3 per boy.

43. 360 degrees. 90 degrees.

44. An angle that contains more than 90 degrees and less than 180 degrees.

45. A figure of five sides.

46. Two angles formed by intersecting straight lines.

47. A fact that requires no proof.

48. The whole is equal to the sum of its parts.

49. A triangle which has two equal sides.

50. The side opposite the right angle in a right triangle.

BIOGRAPHICAL SKETCHES OF GREAT MATHEMATICIANS

Pythagoras (c. 575–c. 500 B.C.). Greek philosopher and mathematician. A native of the island of Samos, he traveled extensively, especially in Egypt, and imbibed the culture of every country that he visited. His studies were concerned mainly with philosophy, mathematics, and astronomy. He finally settled at Crotona, in southern Italy, and tried in vain to "impart wisdom to unwilling minds." A mob set fire to his house and killed a number of his followers. The manner of his death is unknown—it is probable that he, too, was killed by the mob. One of his chief ideas was that the structure of the universe is founded upon the principle of mathematical numbers. He is especially famous for the Pythagorean theorem.

Euclid (fl. c. 300 B.C.). Greek scientist who founded the school of mathematics at Alexandria. His chief contribution to mathematics —among the greatest of all the contributions to that science—is the Euclidian system of plane and solid geometry. He also wrote on astronomy, optics, and the science of musical harmony. There is an interesting story that King Ptolemy of Alexandria, impatient at the elaborate lectures of Euclid, asked him whether there wasn't a quicker way for a king to learn geometry. "Sire," said Euclid, "there is no royal road to learning."

Napier, John (1550–1617). Scotch mathematician. Born in Merchiston, near Edinburgh. Educated at St. Andrews, he traveled extensively on the Continent and finally settled down at Gartness, in Stirlingshire, as a recluse student. The result of his studies was the invention of logarithms. He published his book on this branch of mathematics in 1614. In addition, he was the first to employ the decimal point in writing numbers.

Leibnitz, Baron Gottfried Wilhelm von (1646–1716). German mathematician and philosopher. Born at Leipzig, he entered the university at fifteen and studied law. Upon graduating, he busied himself with politics, philosophy, and mathematics. He entered the service of the Elector of Mainz and wrote brilliant analyses of the political conditions in Europe. Leaving the service of the Elector of Mainz, he took employment with the Duke of Brunswick, and he remained with the princely family for forty years. In addition to this he founded an academy at Berlin and presided over it for life. Among his achievements in mathematics was his independent discovery, about the time of Newton, of the differential and integral calculus. He also devised a calculating machine for dividing, subtracting, multiplying, adding, and extracting roots.

Lagrange, Joseph Louis (1736–1813). The greatest of eighteenth-century mathematicians. Born in Turin, he received his education at Turin College, and in his teens he was appointed professor of geometry at the military academy. He devised, among other things, a method to solve the isoperimetrical problem. From this method stemmed the calculus of variations. He received abundant honors during his lifetime. He was awarded a prize for an essay on the libration of the moon; he served as mathematician under Frederick the Great; he was appointed to the household of Louis XVI and lived in the Louvre. He was chosen professor for the Ecole Polytechnique. His chief publication was his *Mécanique Analytique.*

Gauss, Karl Friedrich (1777–1855). German mathematician. Educated at the University of Göttingen. While still studying for his degree, he succeeded in dividing the circle in seventeen equal parts, a solution that had eluded all geometers before him. Among other accomplishments, he published a classic treatise on transcendental arithmetic. He discovered a method to calculate the planets Ceres and Pallas. He invented the heliotrope, an instrument for reflecting solar light. He accumulated data on terrestrial magnetism. At thirty he was appointed professor of mathematics and director of the observatory at the University of Göttingen. He held this position to the end of his life.

Lobatchevsky, Nicholas Ivanovitch (1793–1856). Russian mathematician. Educated at the University of Kazan, he was appointed professor of mathematics. He administered the business affairs of the university. Dealing critically with Euclidian geometry, he published treatises on his theory of hypergeometry which conceived of space in non-Euclidian terms. The summary of his geometrical studies appeared in his work entitled *Pangeometric*.

Kovalevsky, Sophie (1850–91). Russian mathematician. She studied mathematics at the University of Heidelberg and then, unable to enter the University of Berlin on account of her sex, she took private lessons from Karl Weierstrass. She received her degree at Göttingen. One of the theses she entered for the degree, dealing with partial differential equations, won her fame. She was appointed to the faculty of the University of Stockholm and taught until her death. At thirty-eight she received the Borodin Prize from the Paris Academy. The prize money was doubled for her as a result of her remarkable contributions. She died at the height of her career, at the age of forty-one.

Poincaré, Jules Henri (1854–1912). French mathematician and physicist. He received his education at the Ecole Polytechnique and the Ecole Supérieur des Mines. At thirty-two he was appointed professor of mathematical physics at the University of Paris. His chief studies dealt with the theory of functions. He applied the Fuchsian functions to mathematics. He was noted especially for his painstaking researches. He received numerous awards during his lifetime, and he was elected to the Académie Française.

Riemann, Georg Friedrich (1826–66). German mathematician. Received his education at the universities of Göttingen and Berlin. He was appointed lecturer at Göttingen and finally full professor at thirty-three. Despite his brief life, plagued with tuberculosis, he contributed valuable ideas for a non-Euclidian geometry. He advanced particularly stimulating theories with regard to surfaces and functions.

CAREERS IN MATHEMATICS

There are numerous specialties arising from a career in mathematics. The student of mathematics, for example, may become an actuary for life insurance companies, employed by the government or by private companies. He may be engaged as a statistician by a large corporation or by various federal or state bureaus. He may establish a career as a certified public accountant associated with a firm or in business for himself.

In addition, training in mathematics is essential for the broad and highly creative field of engineering. Thorough knowledge of mathematics is a prerequisite for architectural, electrical, civil, communications, mechanical, aeronautical, and railway engineering. A background in mathematics is essential for meteorology and climatology. Indeed it is vital for a career in any branch of science. And mathematics teachers are proportionately in demand.

actuary

EXPERIENCE REQUIRED: College, major in mathematics. Experience in insurance, training in actuarial work.

DESCRIPTION OF JOB: Analysis, calculating risks in new policies or established ones. Determines dividends, reserves, premiums. Determines probabilities of accident, retirement on old-age pensions or disability.

OPPORTUNITIES FOR ADVANCEMENT: Can rise to managerial duties.

WHERE TO APPLY FOR JOBS: Federal and state departments of insurance. Life insurance companies.

airline meteorologist

EXPERIENCE REQUIRED: Minimum six months' experience in meteorological office. B.A. degree, major in physics, mathematics, or engineering. Mathematics required through calculus and two years of physical science. Or aeronautical school training.

DESCRIPTION OF JOB: Analyzes weather, diagrams, charts, forecasting flight conditions.

OPPORTUNITIES FOR ADVANCEMENT: Flight superintendent.

WHERE TO APPLY FOR JOBS: Government, airlines.

auditor

EXPERIENCE REQUIRED: Training in accounting. College education an asset for advanced work.

DESCRIPTION OF JOB: Analytical checking of records; prepares balance sheets, profit and loss statements, etc.

OPPORTUNITIES FOR ADVANCEMENT: Executive accounting positions, treasurer, controller.

WHERE TO APPLY FOR JOBS: Financial and sales organizations, chain stores' central offices, accounting firms, government and private.

bank teller

EXPERIENCE REQUIRED: College degree often required. Training in mathematics essential.

DESCRIPTION OF JOB: Receives deposits and pays out cash. Prepares cash and records of transactions for other departments.

OPPORTUNITIES FOR ADVANCEMENT: Head teller, junior officer.

WHERE TO APPLY FOR JOBS: Banks.

certified public accountant

EXPERIENCE REQUIRED: Successful completion of state C.P.A. examination. Accounting degree an asset.

DESCRIPTION OF JOB: Prepares statements and reports, tax returns, budgets; installs complete accounting systems; conducts audits. Individual or association practice.

OPPORTUNITIES FOR ADVANCEMENT: Can develop own business, as well as rise to executive position in industry.

WHERE TO APPLY FOR JOBS: Public accounting firms.

communications engineer

EXPERIENCE REQUIRED: Graduation from accredited school of engineering. Thorough training in higher mathematics.

DESCRIPTION OF JOB: Designs manufacture of electrical apparatus. Operation of systems of communication.

OPPORTUNITIES FOR ADVANCEMENT: Executive, consultant, functional divisional head.

WHERE TO APPLY FOR JOBS: Telephone, telegraph, radio broadcasting, electrical manufacturing companies, motion picture industry, television, air lines, government.

electrical engineer

EXPERIENCE REQUIRED: Graduation from accredited school of engineering. Thorough training in higher mathematics. Knowledge of chemistry, physics, and applied mechanics in addition. Graduate work in specialty desirable.

DESCRIPTION OF JOB: Designs electrical machinery and devices, and is concerned with generation, transmission, employment of electrical energy.

OPPORTUNITIES FOR ADVANCEMENT: Executive, consultant, functional division head.

WHERE TO APPLY FOR JOBS: Public utility and telephone companies, electrical equipment manufacturers, government.

insurance office worker

EXPERIENCE REQUIRED: High school minimum. Further study for advancement. Mathematical aptitude. Clerical skill.

DESCRIPTION OF JOB: Employed in insurance office to examine and prepare policies, statistical work, keeping of records, correspondence.

OPPORTUNITIES FOR ADVANCEMENT: May advance in administrative capacity or through outside adjusting and sales work.

WHERE TO APPLY FOR JOBS: Insurance companies.

meteorologist

EXPERIENCE REQUIRED: Graduation from accredited college or university desirable. Training in mathematics essential. Physics, chemistry, mechanical and freehand drawing necessary.

DESCRIPTION OF JOB: Enters records, makes calculations, and charts weather maps. As a climatologist with Soil Conservation Service, concerned with geographical and climatic conditions as they affect erosion of soil.

OPPORTUNITIES FOR ADVANCEMENT: Chief meteorologist.

WHERE TO APPLY FOR JOBS: Government, shipping industries, large commercial firms.

statistician

EXPERIENCE REQUIRED: College degree, thorough training in mathematics, statistics, and economics.

DESCRIPTION OF JOB: Collection, manipulation, tabulation, and presentation of data. Analytic study of data. Intricate advance planning of important statistical investigations.

OPPORTUNITIES FOR ADVANCEMENT: Chief statistician.

WHERE TO APPLY FOR JOBS: Large corporations, independent research institutes, numerous government departments.

BIBLIOGRAPHY: BOOKS ON MATHEMATICS FOR FURTHER READING AND STUDY

Allen, Edwin Brown: *Basic Mathematics.* New York, 1944.

Axelrod, Aaron: *Machine Shop Mathematics.* New York, 1942.

Baer, Zove: *Everyday Mathematics.* New York, 1939.

Bakst, Aaron: *Mathematics, Its Magic and Mastery.* New York, 1941.

Breneman, John William: *Mathematics.* New York, 1944.

Burnham, Reuben Wesley: *Mathematics for Machinists.* New York, 1943.

Cooke, Nelson Magor: *Mathematics for Electricians and Radiomen.* New York, 1942.

Cooley, Hollis Raymond: *Introduction to Mathematics.* Boston, 1937.

Dick, Arthur A.: *Shop Mathematics.* New York, 1943.

Georges, Joel Samuel: *Introductory Business Mathematics.* New York, 1940.

Harkin, Duncan Claire: *Fundamental Mathematics.* New York, 1941.

Hart, Walter Wilson: *Mathematics in Daily Use.* Boston, 1942.

Hobbs, Glenn Moody: *Practical Mathematics.* Chicago, 1940.

Hogben, Lancelot Thomas: *Mathematics for the Million.* New York, 1943.

Hooper, Alfred: *A Mathematics Refresher.* Cleveland, 1946.

Jones, Oscar Bernard: *Applied Industrial Mathematics.* New York, 1947.

Kasner, Edward: *Mathematics and the Imagination.* New York, 1940.

Kokomoor, Franklin Wesley: *Mathematics in Human Affairs.* New York, 1942.

Lasley, Sidney J.: *The New Applied Mathematics.* New York, 1945.

Moore, Justin Hartley, and Julio A. Mira: *The Gist of Mathematics.* New York, 1942.

Palmer, Claude Irwin: *Practical Mathematics for Home Study.* New York, 1942.

Rappolt, Frank A.: *Simplified Mathematics.* New York, 1943.

Schaaf, William Leonard: *Mathematics for Everyday Use.* New York, 1942.

Thomas, Henry: *Mathematics Made Easy.* New York, 1940.

Underwood, Ralph Sylvester: *Living Mathematics.* New York, 1940.

Van Tuyl, George Henry: *Mathematics at Work.* New York, 1935.

Whitehead, Alfred North: *An Introduction to Mathematics.* New York and London, 1911.

CHAPTER SEVEN

biology—life's perpetual miracle

WHAT IS LIFE?

It is difficult to give an exact definition of life, just as it is difficult to give an exact definition of electricity. We know how electricity and life *act,* but we do not know what they *are.*

Yet this much is obvious. Both electricity and life are manifestations of power. Every living thing, like every electrical machine, is a medium for the transformation of energy. How, then, do they differ?

In the first place, living things *move.* They may not be in motion continuously; living seeds may "be asleep" for many years; but they all have the power of movement. As James Russell Lowell poetically expresses it, "every clod feels a stir of might—an *instinct within it* that reaches and towers." This inner instinct is one of the fundamental differences between living and non-living things. A lifeless machine is started only by an impulse from *without;* a living thing is moved by an impetus from *within.* Its motion may be *stimulated,* but it does not have to be *initiated,* by an outside force. *Life moves spontaneously.*

In the second place, living things *feed.* They absorb matter from without, and they transform this matter chemically into the energy for movement and growth. Non-living things may also be said—in a rough sense—to be capable of feeding and growing.

Thus an automobile "drinks" water and gas, and a locomotive "eats" coal, in order that they may be able to move. And a crystal increases in "stature" by the addition of congenial particles. But the food of the engine and the growth of the crystal are poured in, or piled on, by outside forces, whereas the food and the growth of a living thing are absorbed and energized from within. This process of absorbing food and transforming it chemically into energy and growth is called *metabolism*—from the Greek word *metabolos,* which means changeable. And thus *life grows spontaneously.*

In the third place, living things bestow life upon their own kind. Every generation, whether of plant or of animal life, gives rise to the next generation. Individuals do this by the separation and the regeneration of their own substance—in the form of a seed or an egg. A new machine can be "reproduced"—or rebuilt out of the parts of an old machine. But it takes a mechanic to do it. The machine cannot rebuild itself of its own accord. A living thing, however, is moved by *an inner compulsion* to rebuild itself—that is, to pass its life along to something else. *Life reproduces its kind.*

And so there are three manifestations of power that distinguish living from non-living objects: life can move, grow, and reproduce itself from within. A tree, an eagle, a flower, a mouse, and a man possess these characteristics in common: they reach out for their sustenance, they change their sustenance into energy, and they utilize their energy for the production of further life.

LIFE'S ORIGIN

Of all the wonders of creation, the most mysterious perhaps is the miracle of life. At some point in the history of the earth —some billions of years ago—matter became organized in such a manner as to produce a power that could reproduce itself. This point marked the beginning of life.

For life, as we have observed, is an essence which stirs from within, absorbs external matter in the form of food, transforms the food into energy and growth, aims at its own preservation by adapting itself to its surroundings, and propagates itself into other, similar essences capable of self-motion, food absorption, growth, adaptation, and propagation.

So far as we know life can spring only out of life. The first manifestation of life on earth came not from *dead* matter, but from matter that was *potentially alive*. That is, from matter which always possessed the *possibility* of life, but which did not become organized into an *actuality* until the environment of the earth was ready for this organization. Indeed, there are some philosophers and scientists who maintain that *all* matter is *always* alive. But whether or not we are ready to accept this radical theory of an all-pervasive life, we now know quite definitely that life originates from life—*omne vivum ex vivo*. Up to the time of Pasteur it was generally supposed that living things could be "spontaneously produced" out of dead matter. "A horse dies in the street, and almost immediately maggots are generated in its body to devour it." This was the belief of Aristotle, of Virgil, and of most of the leading philosophers and scientists for a very long time. "To question this," declared Alexander Ross, a brilliant writer of the seventeenth century, "is to question reason, sense, and experience. If anyone doubts this, let him go to Egypt, and there he will find the fields swarming with mice, begot of the mud of the Nilus, to the great calamity of the inhabitants."

But Pasteur, in a series of conclusive experiments, dispelled this erroneous idea about the spontaneous production of maggots and mice. He proved that if you screen a dead horse so that no maggots can reach it from *without*, no maggots can be generated from *within*. And he proved further that if you put a liquid into a vessel sealed against the entry of bacteria from the air, no bacteria will be formed in the liquid.

In other words, maggots are born out of maggots, and bacteria out of bacteria. *Life is a continuous unit.* It is therefore not strictly scientific to talk about the "origin" of life upon this planet. Life never *originated* here. It was merely unassembled during the formative period of the earth. It became assembled when the earth was ready for it. At first the cradle was prepared, and then life was born. *But it was born not out of dead matter, but out of the seed of life.*

On this point many of the leading scientists are now agreed. The organization of matter which we call "life" took place at some period in the development of the earth. Before that period there was only *potential* but no *actual* life.

And the first form of life that came upon the earth was plant life. For only plants can live upon the chemical elements contained in rocks. But animals can live upon the chemical elements contained in plants. Therefore animal life came after plant life.

But what kind of plant life first emerged upon the rocks that rose out of the sea? Most likely, bacteria. Without bacteria, there would be no life on earth. For these bits of protoplasm, too small to be seen by the naked eye, perform a function which—to condense a long and complicated process into a few words—trans-mutes the chemicals of the rocks into food for animals and men.

The lowest form of life, then, consists of bacteria; the highest form, of human beings. The microbe is the aboriginal ancestor of man.

THE EARLIEST FORMS OF LIFE

The beginning of life is still shrouded in mystery. But it seems probable that the first living things appeared on the surface of the sea under the warming rays of the sun. At some time in the formative period of the earth the chemical combinations of the elements became such as to produce "sheets and blobs" of proto-plasm—the transparent, vital substance from which all living things are formed. Some of this protoplasm was unable to reproduce itself and lost its life. But it served as food for the few blobs of protoplasm that were able to take nourishment and to stay alive.

These earliest forms of living protoplasm were most likely plantlike. They were prehistoric ancestors of our modern bacteria —the smallest and the simplest of all living organisms. These bacteria are so small that it would take twenty-five thousand of them, placed end to end, to make up the length of one inch.

A bacterium is little more than a blob of protoplasm which consists of a definite shape and is able to grow and to "reproduce" itself by breaking into two halves. Under favorable conditions a bacterium lives for about twenty minutes. When conditions are unfavorable, however, it can turn into a tough-walled spore, or seed. In this "trancelike" form it can "sleep" for as long as three years—a period which, compared to the twenty-minute life span of a bacterium, means a sleep of more than a hundred thousand generations. If a human being were thus capable of a trance between two periods of living activity, he could sleep for three million years and then awaken to a renewed life.

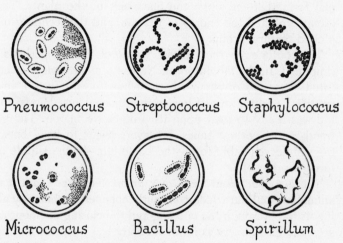

Various disease-causing bacteria.

In its spore-protected state of suspended animation a bacterium may exist on the earth, in the sea, or in the air. It has been found even in icebergs and in hailstones—resisting frost and wind and weather and waiting for the opportunity to come to life again. And when the opportunity arrives, it begins to grow and to reproduce itself as actively as ever. So actively, indeed, that if you put a bacteria-infected needle into a bottle of sterilized broth, every cubic inch of the liquid will contain, within twenty-four hours, about eighty thousand million bacteria. This is about forty times the human population of the entire world.

An interesting fact about bacteria is that they have no sex—that is, no blending of cell with cell. They reproduce themselves, not by uniting but by dividing. And thus they form the link, so to speak, between non-living and living matter.

And they also form the link between vegetable life and animal life. For there are some types of bacteria that wriggle like animals and absorb organic food unlike the mineral food absorbed by plants.

And thus, it seems probable, life began as a plant form that fed upon the chemicals of the earth, and later developed into an animal form that fed upon the chemicals of the plants. The first group exploited the energy of the sun, and the second group exploited the first group.

This outline of the earliest forms of life is perhaps oversimplified. In the laboratory of Nature a great variety of complicated groupings of chemicals must have been effected, rejected, modified, and regrouped before the phenomenon known to us as life was ready to start upon its progressive march. The general trend in the earliest times, however, seems to have been from the simple vegetable form—the bacterium—to the simple animal form—the amoeba.

The *amoeba* (from the Greek *amoibe,* change) is a speck of animal protoplasm which constantly changes its shape by absorbing its food through the opening and the closing of "mouths" that are situated at every point of its body.

These microscopic "animals"—many of them are too small to be visible even through the microscope—encompass the earth in numbers almost beyond human computation. The tiniest drop of water may contain a gigantic city of these microörganisms. The amoeba has no definite organs—no bones or brain or kidney or stomach or heart. Yet it is definitely related to us in the united family of life. For—like other living things—it breathes (by absorbing oxygen and throwing off carbon dioxide) and moves and feeds itself. An amoeba may therefore be said to consist of a single living cell.

The amoeba belongs to a large class of microscopic animals known as *protozoa*—from the Greek *proton,* first, and *zoön,* living thing. When we advance from the simple amoeba to the more complicated members of the class, we come to a group of creatures—still invisible to the naked eye—that possess definite shapes and organs. To this group belongs the euglena, which propels itself by means of a "hairy tail" and takes in food through a regular "mouth" situated somewhere upon its surface. All types of protozoa need moisture to exist. In the absence of moisture they can live only—like bacteria—in a trancelike sleep, under a covering of protective tissue.

In their reproductive processes the protozoa are again like the bacteria—with the addition, however, of one important element. They multiply not only by *splitting* but also by *uniting*. That is, they show a primitive kind of sexual copulation. In general, however, they reproduce themselves by splitting into halves, without benefit of sex.

And their reproduction is extremely rapid. Take, for example, a single protozoön with an average life length of one hour. Suppose that this little creature can get all the food it wants and is not molested by enemies. At the end of one hour it will be split in two. At the end of two hours there will be four; at the end of three hours, eight; at the end of three days there will be enough protozoa, descended from the single tiny and invisible creature, to outweigh the entire earth!

This supposition, however, is never realized in actual life. For the multiplication of the protozoa is limited by two factors: an insufficient supply of food and a continuous aggression of hungry

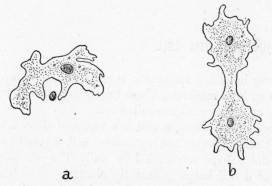

a   b

An amoeba, the simplest form of living organism. At a, the amoeba is about to surround a food particle. At b, the amoeba is shown about to split into two individual organisms.

enemies. Thus countless numbers of protozoa die before they have had a chance to reproduce themselves. Just as in our own biological sphere the bird eats the worm and the man eats the bird, so too, in the lower biological sphere, the tiny fish eats the microbe and the larger fish eats the smaller fish.

So much for the *dividing* method of reproduction among the protozoa. In the *uniting* method of reproduction, the two organisms come into a kind of sexual embrace, and the nucleus of one cell migrates to the nucleus of the other and fuses with it. In effect, the two organisms are now one. The fused body then separates into two bodies, each of which has inherited characteristics from the two parents. Only a few of the protozoa reproduce by this method. The tiny organism known as the paramecium, it is interesting to note, uses both methods.

Each of these methods of reproduction has its own technical name. Reproduction by splitting is called *binary fission,* while reproduction by uniting is called *conjugation.*

But all these divisions and subdivisions of primitive life into classes—from the creation of the plantlike bacteria to the elaboration of the animal-like protozoa—represent a single biological development from an unorganized blob of protoplasm to an organic living form. All life on earth began with a microscopic cell-like speck, and every higher form of life today is an organization of living cells.

LIFE WITHIN LIFE—THE CELL

A living body is a systematic organization made up of a vast number of little machines. These tiny living machines which enable the system to work are called *cells.*

Biologically speaking, a cell is a tiny and slimy bit of protoplasm. Unlike a hermit's or a prisoner's cell, it is not an enclosure of a definite shape surrounded by walls. The protoplasmic substance of a cell keeps incessantly changing in outline; it is a machine in continual motion. Somewhere near the center this cell machine contains a rounded nucleus which floats in a liquid and transparent substance. This nucleus is surrounded by a "planetary" group of smaller bodies—sparkling little globules of oil. Some of these globules move about the cell slowly and in groups. Others appear to be like vagabonds, each of them darting rapidly and "capriciously" over its own individual course.

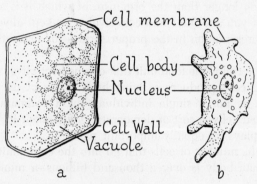

A *plant cell* (a) *and an animal cell* (b).

In addition to the globules the cell contains a number of "threads" that wriggle like snakes over the fluid substance. These threads vary in length and are extremely thin. Sometimes one of the threads breaks into two; at other times two of the threads join end to end and combine into one. They are composed of albumen and seem to constitute an important part of the cell. The exact nature of their function, however, has not as yet been ascertained.

But let us return to the center of all this animated motion—the nucleus. This nucleus, or egg-shaped mass, keeps floating back and forth over the fluid of its cell. And in its motion it carries a freight of two misty little bodies that keep constantly changing their size and their shape and their position. These little bodies, the nuclei within the nucleus, seem to lie at the foundation of life.

Such, then, is the brief picture of a simple cell—the basic material out of which our bodies are built. They are not to be compared, however, to the dead bricks of a stationary building. They are more like the living soldiers of a marching army. Each of them is a different individual and "enjoys" a distinct life of its own. For a cell—like its primitive cousin, the amoeba—can feed itself and eliminate its waste matter and, in some instances, reproduce itself by dividing into two parts. An organism composed of a multitude of *cells* may thus be said to be an organized society of many *selves*. And each cell, or self, may be nursed to live much longer than the organism of which it is a part. Thus a part of you and me could conceivably be kept alive—by means of cell preservation in the proper serum—for many thousands of years.

But the cell is the final unit that can be kept alive. And a union of living cells produces a living body. Each of us, in the final analysis, is not a single individual but a community of individualized cells—a sort of democratic government in which every citizen plays an equally important part.

And the number of cells that go into the community known as the human body is over a thousand billions—a number roughly

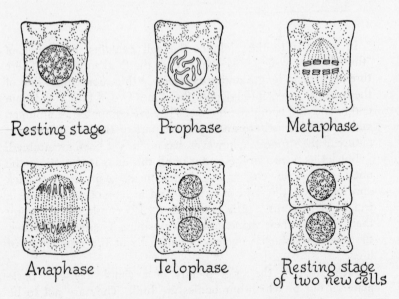

Resting stage   Prophase   Metaphase

Anaphase   Telophase   Resting stage
of two new cells

The various stages of cell division. Notice that the process of division is controlled by particles in the nucleus of the cell.

equal to about ten million times the entire population of the United States.

THE TREE OF LIFE AND ITS BRANCHES

Roughly speaking, all life is divided into two main branches —plants and animals. A plant is a manifestation of life rooted in one place; an animal is a manifestation of life in free motion. Another important distinction—as we have already noted—is that a plant can derive its food directly from the earth and the sun while an animal can derive its food only from plants or from other animals. Still another distinction is that a plant generally possesses a green pigment, called *chlorophyll*, which enables it to "drink" the radiant energy of light. An animal possesses no such pigment. It absorbs the radiance of light only at second hand— through the intake of the chlorophyll in the plant.

Yet there are some forms of life that can be classified neither as distinct plants nor as distinct animals. These forms may be regarded as combinations of the two—links that bind the chain of life into an unbroken unit. Take, for example, the microscopic creature known as the *euglena*. Like an animal, it possesses a lashing tail that enables it to swim about freely, and a mouth and a digestive system that enable it to absorb its food and to eliminate the waste. But, like a plant, it possesses chlorophyll which empowers it to feed directly upon the energy of the sun. It can thus "choose" its own manner of eating—through the mouth or through the chlorophyll.

On the other hand, take an ordinary fungus. It is "rooted" like a plant, yet it has no chlorophyll and therefore it "digests" its food like an animal.

These are but isolated examples of the numerous inhabitants of the earth that live on the border line between the two kingdoms of life. An examination of this border line through the microscope reveals a fascinating variety of green, moving creatures that eat like plants and pale, stationary creatures that eat like animals.

And thus the plant fuses into the animal, and the animal into the plant. There is no sharp dividing line between the one form of life and the other. There is rather a neutral—or mutual—zone inhabited by a transitional form. And this transitional form supplies us with a biological textbook on the progressive continuity of life.

THE PLANT WORLD

Now let us look more closely at the first of the two main divisions of life—the vast group of growing things known as the plant world.

The ancestor of all living things, as we have seen, was a bit of protoplasm similar to what we know today as a bacterium. This bit of protoplasm, in its groping quest for nutrition, reached out toward invisible particles of surrounding matter, drew them together into a unity, and thus the first cell came to life. This cell was an *alga*, a primitive type of seaweed.

As the algae swam about for further nutrition—for the earliest plants had no roots—they developed other, similar cells and reproduced themselves by splitting. At that early period of life's development every living unit was a celibate individualist. Sex, the fusion of two living elements for the creation of a third, was as yet unknown.

As time went on—millions of years as recorded on the dial of Nature's biological clock—some of the "conservative" algae "refused" to branch out into anything new and therefore retained their primitive seaweed form. They withdrew, so to speak, into a "dead-end street" where they continued their isolated and undeveloped existence while the main current of life kept progressing toward new experiments and new types.

And this progressive current is our main concern. We shall therefore disregard the various "stagnant pools" of life that have remained practically unchanged from the earliest times to the present day. Instead we shall try to follow the stream of adventurous experimentation from the simpler to the more complex forms of life.

This adventurous stream of life took up the more "enterprising" of the algae, developed in some of them a "male" or pollen cell and in others a "female" or egg cell, and thus initiated a new kind of propagation through a union of the sexes. The new types of algae spread over the sea and some of them, in their search for food, reached out toward the land. And wherever they arrived, they adapted themselves to their new conditions in their effort to survive. They branched out into thousands of varieties of plants, each variety depending upon its own environment. The sea plants developed in one direction and the land plants in another.

We shall here concern ourselves with the land plants—especially those that bear flowers.

the parts of a plant

Every flower-bearing plant consists of three parts—the stem, the network of roots, and the intertexture of leaves. The stem conducts the sap—or the "lifeblood"—of the plant throughout its frame; the roots keep it anchored in its place and suck up the food from the soil; and the leaves absorb the radiation of the sun from the air.

Unlike an animal, a plant can "afford" to live a simple and sedentary life. It needs no brain, for it has no food to seek—the chief function of the brain from the lowest animals to the highest. It has no digestive apparatus, for it can easily absorb its food without the necessity of transforming it into fuel for energy and motion. It simply sits still and enjoys its banquet from the soil and the sun. It has no need of a heart to pump blood into its veins, since it doesn't waste any strength on useless motion. The slow movement of its sap, up and down its stem, is sufficient for its unhurried and unexcited life.

Yet, aside from its sedentary life, the plant world is closely related to the animal world. The body of a plant, like the body of an animal, consists of an assemblage of cells. And many of these cells are continually in motion even though the entire body is at rest. It is like an established government engaged in the pursuits of peace. The government remains undisturbed while the citizens individually hustle and bustle about in their daily search for food.

The individual cells of the plant organism, like those of the animal organism, are engaged in a constant competition for food.

The roots suck it up from the soil, and the leaves gather it in from the air. The existence of every plant is a lifelong "economic" struggle for survival. And thus, to return to our previous meta-phor, the government of the plant organism is only *apparently* at peace. In reality it reaches downward into the soil and upward into the air in order that it may get its full quota of food. And in this economic struggle the various plants use every possible means to insure their success. The oak tree, for example, stretches its leaves to expel every other tree from its exclusive area of sun-light, and the primrose spreads its petals to stifle every other seedling that may be sprouting in its vicinity. In this competitive race for survival the plants try to outreach one another—mostly in a vertical direction into the air, so as to get a favored position at the banquet of light. And thus a plant, while it cannot *move horizontally* like an animal, can *grow vertically* in a far shorter time and to a far greater size than any animal in the world. In the biological quest for food the dominating activity of the ani-mal is motion; of the plant, growth. But growth is merely another aspect of motion. Hence the living relationship between animals and plants.

how plants reproduce themselves

Animals and plants are related in another respect—their ability to reproduce themselves. Most plants, like animals, reproduce themselves sexually—that is, through the union of two different kinds of cells. But, while the sexes of the higher animals are joined together "in person," the sexes of the plants are married—so to speak—"by proxy." Unable to move about and to embrace, they transmit their life-producing cells to one another by means of insects, winds, and streams. These messengers of procreation are the "marriage brokers" of the vegetable world.

Consider, for example, the "marriage" that takes place in a buttercup. The brilliance and the fragrance of the petals serve as a notice to the insect messengers that they will find something worth while within the cup. And the insects, in answer to the notice, crawl inside and discover a delicious sip of nectar. But inside the cup there is also a cluster of green ovaries—the female part of the flower—surrounded by a ring of yellow stamens—the male part of the flower. When the insects drink the nectar, they become dusted with the powdery grains of pollen emitted by the stamens. And then, in their desire for further nectar, they fly to another buttercup. Here they deposit upon the ovaries of the *second* flower the pollen which they have carried over from the stamens of the *first* flower. As a compensation for their trouble they have received a double "fee" of nectar. But, thanks to their ministration, the "marriage of the flowers" has been consummated and the birth of a new flower is on the way.

But now an important question arises. Since the same flower contains both the ovaries and the pollen, isn't it possible for the flower to impregnate itself without the aid of a carrier from one flower to another? The answer to this question leads to an interesting fact. Plants, like animals, "detest" self-impregnation. They prefer cross-fertilization—the union of two separate individuals for the production of a third. There are some exceptions to this

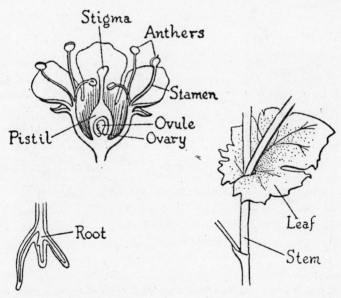

The parts of a flowering plant.

rule. The primrose and other spring flowers, for example, have a capacity for self-pollination. Nature has provided them with this method of reproduction because of the scarcity of insects at that season of the year. As a general rule, however, the reproduction of plants—as of animals—is the result of *crossbreeding* rather than of *inbreeding*. This mode of reproduction insures a more variable type of individual—an individual more able to adapt itself to the ever-changing conditions of the world and therefore more likely to survive.

But to return to the succession of plant life from generation to generation through the union of the sexes. When the female ovum has become fertilized through the male sperm, it develops into an embryo—or seed—protected by a hard shell. This seed contains not only the substance of the embryonic plant, but—like the yolk of an egg—the food for its nourishment. And when the seed is ready to germinate—this is another "precaution" of Nature —it does not drop to the ground side by side with the parent plant. For this would mean a competition between parent and

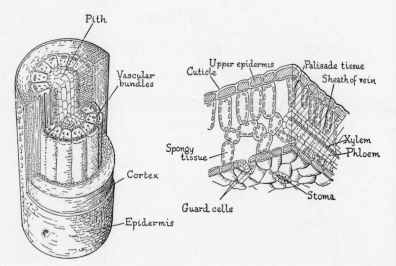

At left, a cross section of the stem of a vine; at right, a cross section of a leaf.

child—their roots would fight for the same patch of moisture and their leaves for the same area of light. Instead the seeds are dispersed from the parent plants so that the species extends over as wide a range as possible.

There is a fascinating variety in the dispersion of the plants. The seeds of the thistle and the dandelion are scattered by the winds. The poppy sways its head and scatters its seed like pepper from a pepper pot. The violet and the sweet pea explode into the air and shoot their seeds out like the sparks of a skyrocket. The seeds of the water lily are provided with spongy little air-inflated "vessels" which float them down the stream. The seeds of the burdock are supplied with "hooks" that attach themselves to the feathers and the furs of creatures that happen to be passing by.

And—to mention but one more of the many methods for the propagation of plants—the blackberry delivers the freightage of its seed, together with the payment of its fruit, to the transport service of the birds. Attracted by the food, the birds eat the seed along with the pulp of the berry. And then, having digested the pulp, the birds eject it, together with the indigestible seed, to germinate into another berry at a spot far removed from its parent plant.

Thus we find a continual tendency among the new generations of plants to move away from the overcrowded environment of the old generations. Life is always in search of a favorable place in which to grow.

THE ANIMAL WORLD

The second main division of life—the animal world—represents a more complicated experiment on the part of Nature. With plants, she began in the sea and then widened her laboratory to include the land. With animals, she added still another region— the air—for the expanding field of her experiments.

But her first attempts at what we now regard as animal life were made in the sea. The fish came into the world many years before the bird and the beast. And the first fish was a creature without a backbone—a sort of marine amoeba. It was born on the day when the first living water thing reached out to eat other living matter. This tiny speck of protoplasm—the amoeba jellyfish —was the ancestor of all the animals alive today.

But for millions of years it reproduced its own spineless sort of jellyfish. And then, as the result of Nature's incessant experimentation and crossbreeding, the jellyfishes developed into creatures with shells and claws. But still they had no backbones.

And finally in the process of this apparently "blind" experimentation we come upon a creature with the first semblance of a backbone. It is a water worm with a thread of stiffened tissue along its back. This marks the first successful step in Nature's struggle to produce vertebrate animals.

Yet it is a slow and—from our narrow human point of view— discouraging process. It takes millions of years for the tiny thread upon the back of the worm to evolve into the primitive "backbone" of the lamprey. It is not much of a backbone as yet—just a soft cartilage that bears only the slightest resemblance to the spinal column of the vertebrate animals that develop out of this creature at a considerably later date. The experimentations of Nature, and the rejections of things that will not work, continue for some further millions of years before we come to the first fish —of the *ganoid* family—with a definite spine of hard bone.

And, together with its backbone, this fish also developed an air bladder—a floating gasbag that enabled it to swim and to rise to different levels of the water by the ejection of air.

And so we find, in the ganoid family of fishes, some of the earliest examples of vertebrae and lungs among living things. And it was one of the branches of the ganoid family that migrated from the sea to the land. The purpose of this migration was the everlasting quest for food. The sea was becoming too crowded. A new realm had to be discovered for the further development of our prehistoric pioneers.

From now on there was a distinction between those animals which remained in the sea and those which migrated to the land. Some of the animals, to be sure, retained—and retain to this day —a transitional form. The toad and the newt, for example, are *amphibians*—that is, they can live both in the sea and on the land. And some animals migrated to the land and then returned to the sea. Among these "renegades" are the seal and the whale. Although they can live under water, they have warm blood—a land-acquired characteristic. But aside from these transitional links, the two types of animals developed each after its own pattern. For breathing, the sea creatures acquired gills and the land creatures lungs. And for locomotion, the sea animals grew fins and the land animals feet. The salamander offers an interesting example of a fin becoming transformed into a foot.

And the frog offers an equally interesting example of a gill becoming transformed into a lung. When it is hatched as a tadpole from its egg, it comes into the world with a pair of gills and is therefore able to live in the water. But when it grows from a

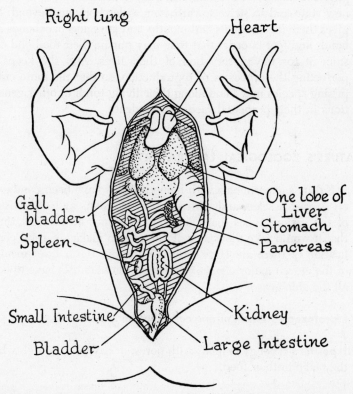

The internal structure of a frog. Compare this with the internal organs of man, shown on page 425.

tadpole into a frog, it exchanges its gills for a pair of lungs. And then it must come up for air after only a brief stay in the water or else it will drown.

The lowly frog is, in one other respect, an important factor in the development of life. It is the first animal in which the bones of the fin have evolved into the thumb and the fingers of the hand.

Thus we can trace the gradual progress of Nature's experiment with life—her rejection of the unfit, her banishment of the less enterprising species into the stagnant pools and blind alleys of existence, and her incessant summons to the more adventurous species to migrate from one realm to another and to develop the physical characteristics that will enable them to survive in their new state and to strive toward ever wider horizons beyond. She gives them fins and tails and mouths and jaws and backbones and hands and feet in order that they may pursue their food and consume it for the preservation of their lives. And she keeps on perfecting the processes of reproduction, so that the more enterprising species may hand along their living torch to other generations in their perpetual race against death.

NATURE'S ZOOLOGICAL LABORATORY

Nature's experiments with living animals have been conducted on so vast a scale, and with so many divisions and subdivisions of the various types that came into existence at different times, that it would take thousands of volumes to make a careful classification of them all. Here we shall attempt but a brief mention of the eleven major classes into which the scientists have divided all the animals:

I **protozoa**—animals of one cell, like the amoeba.

II **porifera**—spongy animals with pores, or cavities, through which they take in their food.

III **coelenterata**—animals without a spine, but with a digestive, stomach-like cavity.

IV flatworms—such as tapeworms and liver-worms.

V roundworms—such as the parasitic worms of the human intestines.

VI wheelworms—microscopic little creatures with "bristling spikes and ruby eyes" that swarm in ponds, damp moss, and gutters.

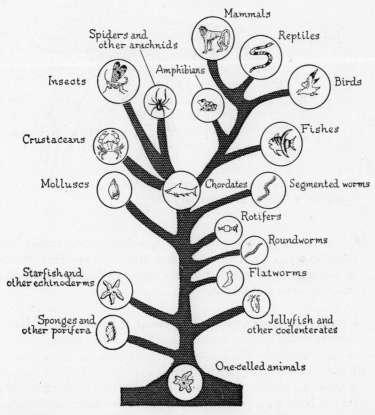

Evolutionary chart of animal life. Shown here are only the present-day representatives of these types of animal life. Each of these types had many ancestors before they evolved into their present form.

VII echinodermata—hedgehoglike animals with a spiny skin forming an external skeleton. This class includes the sea urchin, the sea lily, and the starfish.

VIII annelida—ringed creatures, such as the leech and the earthworm, with segmented bodies but without jointed legs

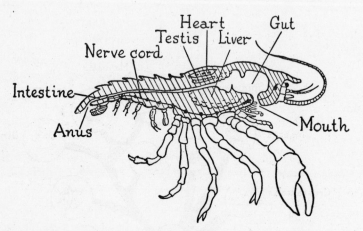

The crayfish, an example of a highly developed animal without a backbone, and a favorite for laboratory study.

IX arthropoda—joint-legged animals; animals with bodies composed of segments, with jointed legs attached (as a rule) to each of the segments. Included in this class are centipedes, lobsters, crabs, spiders, and insects.

X mollusca—animals with soft, spineless, and shell-covered bodies, such as snails, oysters, mussels, and the octopus family.

XI chordata—animals provided with a spinal cord as the basis for a skeleton; vertebrate animals. This class—the final stage (thus far) in Nature's experiments—consists of five main subdivisions:

1. *Fishes.*
2. *Amphibians*—such as frogs, newts, and salamanders.

3. *Reptiles*—including snakes, lizards, turtles, and alligators.
4. *Birds.*
5. *Mammals*—animals that suckle their young. This fifth group of vertebrate animals is further subdivided into eleven orders, as follows:

    a. *Monotremata*—mammals provided with only one opening for their urinary, intestinal, and genital canals. This order includes the duckbill or water mole, and the prickly ant-eater.

    b. *Marsupials*—mammals having an abdominal pouch for carrying their young. Among the animals in this order are the opossum and the kangaroo.

    c. *Edentata*—toothless mammals, such as the armadillo and the sloth.

    d. *Cetaceans*—suckling sea animals, such as dolphins, porpoises, and whales.

    e. *Sirenia*—such as the manatee or sea-cow, the herb-eating "vegetarian" of the deep.

    f. *Ungulata*—hoofed animals, such as horses, sheep, camels, elephants, and pigs.

    g. *Rodentia*—"mammals that gnaw"—rabbits, squirrels, beavers, porcupines, rats, and mice.

    h. *Insectivora*—mammals that feed on insects. Many of them live underground. Among the familiar examples of this order are the shrew and the mole.

    i. *Chiroptera*—hand-winged mammals, such as the bat.

    j. *Carnivora*—flesh eaters, or beasts of prey: cats, dogs, bears, badgers, seals, weasels, otters, and the like.

    k. *Primates*—the leading order of mammals, including lemurs, monkeys, and men.

The above classification is but a brief picture of the innumerable species of animals which Nature has introduced—and is still introducing—into her crucible of life. As an example of the tremendous scale upon which Nature is conducting her experiments, consider the fact that a single subdivision of Class IX—the joint-legged creatures—*contains no less than 450,000 different kinds of insects.* And as a further example of the stupendous variations that govern the pattern of these experiments, consider the difference in the relative weight between the larva and the final growth of a moth as compared to the birth weight and the final growth of a man. The full-grown *cossus*—or *goat moth*—weighs 72,000 times its weight as a larva, whereas the full-grown man weighs, on an average, only about 20 times his weight as an infant. If Nature were to allow the growth of a man to increase as the growth of a moth, you and I would smash the scales at 720,000 pounds each.

But now let us glance at the final stages which enabled Nature to approximate this latest and—we humans are vain enough to suppose—greatest of her biological experiments. We shall briefly examine the order of vertebrate animals leading up from fishes, through amphibians and reptiles, to birds and monkeys and men.

FISHES, AMPHIBIANS, AND SNAKES

The story of the fishes is as varied, and as amazing, as the story of the insects. And to us it is even more interesting because a fish, like a man, is a vertebrate. We are, biologically speaking, related cousins who live in different parts of the world. Our family likenesses—such as the spinal cord, the head, the eyes, the nostrils, and the mouth—are due to our relationship. But our differences —according to the theory of Darwin (1809–82)—are due to our different environments.

Thus, for example, the body of the fish is—unlike the human body—streamlined. This enables the fish to glide swiftly through the water. Moreover, its fins are proportionately shorter than our human legs, and they project to a lesser distance from the trunk, because they must offer a minimum of resistance to the water in their motion. Furthermore, a fish has gills for breathing in the water, while we have lungs for breathing in the air. But, on the other hand, the fish has only a primitive sort of mind because its life in the sea necessitates only a minimum of ingenuity for survival.

These are but a few of the many similarities and differences between the fishes and the land vertebrates. If we examine the human embryo in the various stages of its development, we find that it is the body of a fish being gradually shaped to adapt itself for its life on land.

When the body of the fish has become sufficiently reshaped and provided for its migration to the land, we come—as we have already observed—to the biological border line inhabited by the amphibians.

The amphibians represent the dividing line between those animals that have gills and fins, and those that have lungs and limbs. They have discarded the scales of the sea animals, but they have not as yet acquired the feathers or the hairs of the land animals.

These land-and-sea dwellers are water-breathing animals in their infancy and land-breathing animals in their adult life. As they grow older, they discard more and more of their marine attributes and acquire more and more of the characteristics they will need in their new life on the dry land. They exchange their non-toed fins for limbs with fingers and toes; their tongues are supplied with muscles and their mouths are endowed with a voice—a means for calling their mates when the sex urge is upon them.

Yet the amphibian, even though he has embarked upon his land life, is still compelled to stay close to the water. Possessing neither the scales of a fish nor the hair of a bird, his naked skin has no protection against the excessive loss of moisture. He needs to be continually refreshed by a plunge into the depths. It is not unusual, especially on hot days, to discover the dead bodies of frogs on the roadside. Having ventured too far from the water, they have dried up before they could find their way back again.

And now comes the next step in the migration of life—the evolution of the vertebrate animals into reptiles.

At one period in the development of life the reptiles were supreme both in the sea and on the land. Possessing the scales of fishes and the lungs of beasts, they represented—it would seem —an all-out attempt on the part of Nature to produce a single predominating type of life. For at that period of serpentine supremacy there were neither birds nor mammals in the world.

Originally the reptiles were gigantic creatures which swam in the ocean, or crept over the earth, or soared like bats into the air. Some of these prehistoric reptiles—like the *brontosaur,* or "thunder-sized" lizard—measured eighty feet in length and sixteen feet in height, and weighed about thirty-five tons. Others—like the *pterodactyl,* or the creature with the "flying fingers"—measured twenty feet from wing-tip to wing-tip.

These now extinct reptiles developed out of the amphibians. They were the first creatures to complete the conquest of the land. Their amphibian predecessors had been provided with limbs that protruded *sideways*—like oars from a rowboat. And they had made an oarlike use of these limbs; they had "rowed" themselves, so to speak, over the ground. Their limbs were not able to raise their bellies *off* the ground. But the limbs of the reptiles now began to grow *under* their bodies, serving as pillars to support them and as vehicles to move them.

But their motion was too slow, their bulk too unwieldy, and their food too scarce. Their domination of the world was, biologically speaking, rather brief—only a few million years or so. And then Nature gave up on them and allowed them, for the greater part, to die out. Their only direct descendants today are such reptiles as the alligator, the turtle, the lizard, and the snake —the "degenerate offspring" of a once mighty royal line.

LIFE TAKES TO THE AIR—BIRDS

Though the prehistoric reptiles became extinct, they represented an important development in the adventure of life. For they inaugurated the age not only of the creatures that creep or walk upon the earth but of those that fly in the air. The ancient saurian is the direct ancestor of the snake, and the indirect ancestor of the beast and the bird.

The first living bird that took to the air was a variation of the winged lizard known as the pterodactyl. This primeval bird, as shown by its skeletal remains, was a lizardlike creature. Its body was—for the first time in life's history—covered with feathers. But its tail was long and jointed like the tail of a reptile, and its jaws were lined with reptilian teeth.

This primitive bird, instead of actually flying in the air, probably soared over the ground in a succession of hops, skips, and jumps. To use our modern phraseology for a very ancient phenomenon, the ancestral bird was probably a leaping parachutist rather than a flying aviator. It ran along the ground and then lifted itself for a short distance into the air. Or else it parachuted itself from tree to tree as it allowed its body to be balanced by the fringe of its featherlike scales.

Gradually, as the feathers replaced the scales, the birds acquired the art of aviation as well as that of parachuting.

Yet the varied laboratory of Nature produced a number of birds which, in spite of their wings, were unable to fly. Among these flightless birds were the now extinct *moa* of New Zealand, an ostrichlike species measuring twelve feet in height, and the *epyornis*, or "giant-bird" of Madagascar, whose eggs measured over thirteen inches in length and about ten inches in width.

One of the reasons why such enormous birds were unable to fly is that there is a size limit to a living body which can be carried by a pair of sustaining wings. For the bigger the body, the faster it must fly in order to stay up in the air. This increase of flight speed necessitates an increase in the strength of the wing muscles. Up to a certain point the growing of the wings can be kept proportionately balanced. But beyond that point the wings would overbalance the body and the bird would come crashing to the ground. The crucial balancing point in flying vertebrates is reached, according to scientific estimates, at a body weight of about fifty pounds. And this fact is a fortunate thing for the human race. For otherwise, as J. B. S. Haldane observes, "an eagle might be as large as a tiger and as formidable to man as a hostile aeroplane."

And now, to return to the "ancient bird"—the *archaeopteryx*—that first took to the air. This bird marked an advance over the reptiles. But the advance was different from that of the mammals, of which we humans are a branch. For the birds, like their reptilian ancestors, continued to reproduce their kind in the "old way"—through the laying of eggs rather than through the bearing of living offspring.

The egg of the reptiles and the birds is like the seed of the plants. It enables the young to hatch, or to sprout, *outside* the parent's body. But the shelled egg that grows *inside* the bird's body—before it is laid to be hatched—makes *internal fertilization* a necessity. This means that the female must be courted and won before it can become impregnated with a new life. And thus the shelled egg takes an important place in the evolution of sexual love and family life.

The courting among most birds is the business of the male. The female as a rule is dowdy, but the male is a "coxcomb" of resplendent plumage and aggressive playfulness. In many of the species the male adds the persuasion of his song to the allurement of his dress. The function of all this color and motion and music on the part of the male is the emotional stimulation of the female. If the female is—biologically—not as yet ready for the mating, she will meet the advances of the male either with indifference or with a positive snub. Many of us are familiar with the spectacle of the "lovesick" cock sparrow primping and dancing before his hen, while she repels him again and again with the "heartless" pecking of her beak.

On the other hand, when the female is ready for her mating, it takes but little persuasion on the part of the male to win her over. A solitary female dove in captivity will often lay her eggs— unfertilized, of course—at the mere presence of a solitary male dove in the next cage. The continual sight of his courting maneuvers has resulted in the egg production on her part. Love—among the lower as well as among the higher animals—may be blind; but it has a definite biological function—the reproduction of the species and the continuation of life.

LIFE AMONG THE MAMMALS

We now come to the final—and, to us, the most important— step in the evolution of life. The mammals include the animals which are the most familiar to us and which are, in a biological sense, our *blood brothers*. For all the animals in this class—including ourselves—are warm-blooded. This is a characteristic which the mammals share with the birds; another is a protective covering to prevent the loss of heat from their blood. All mammals are —more or less—covered with hair, just as all birds are covered with feathers.

In the mammalian order, however, there is one great point of departure from the avian—or bird—order. Most of the mammals give birth to their offspring alive, while most of the other living creatures reproduce themselves through the laying of eggs.

And this difference in their manner of reproduction leads to another great difference between the non-mammalian and the mammalian representatives of the living world. In order to suckle their young, the females of the mammal group are provided with milk-producing udders, or breasts, scientifically known as *mammae*.

This necessity of personally providing for their young, not only in their suckling period but throughout their immature life, results in still another tremendous difference between the mammals and all the other living things. In the mammals we begin to find better-developed brains, and therefore more resourceful minds, than in the earlier forms of life.

In the evolutionary development of the mammals, just as in the evolutionary development of the birds, we can observe a definite transitional link. This mammalian link is represented by the group known as the *monotremata*—the order which includes the duckbill and the anteater. Like their reptilian ancestors, the monotremata lay eggs instead of directly producing their young. But like their mammalian descendants, they suckle their offspring. These creatures, therefore, represent one of the great "reformation" periods in biological history—the age in which the reptiles became re-formed into mammals through the acquisition of hair and warm blood and breasts.

These "transitional" stages of evolution—either from one order to another or from group to group within the same order—is one of the most bitterly debated questions in biology. Yet it is generally agreed that the chain of life is continuous even though we have not as yet been able to find every link. For many of the links already *have* been found—so many, indeed, that we can confidently accept the theory (of a continuous evolution) as an almost established fact. The book of life, written in the remains of animals now extinct and in the innumerable creatures of the present day, offers so many unerased paragraphs and chapters that we can pretty nearly understand the entire text.

Take, for example, the story of the evolution of the horse. We have today a collection of the remains of every stage in the development of this creature from the earliest times to the present.

First came the ancestor of the horse—the *hyracotherium*—an animal which, about forty million years ago, roamed over the plains on five toes and fed on grass and leaves and branches. We know these facts from the skeletal remains of the animal (discovered in 1856). The toes of this skeleton are fairly adapted for

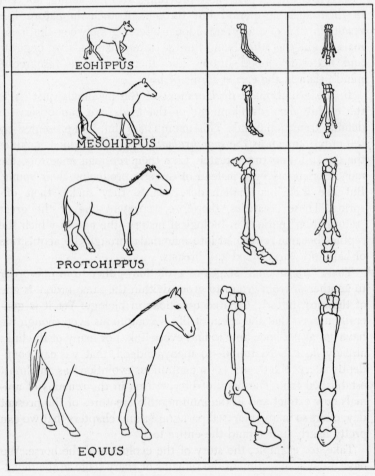

Various stages in the evolution of the modern horse.

running over hard, level land; and its teeth are fairly adapted for grinding tough stems and grasses mixed with flinty bits of earth.

But the handicap of five toes made it difficult for this animal to run speedily over open and grassy plains—and speed was an absolute necessity as a means of escape from pursuing enemies. Moreover, the chewing surface of its teeth was not sufficiently extended for the adequate grinding of the tough vegetation of the plains. And so we see a twofold development in the anatomy of this animal. The hyracotherium evolves into the *eohippus*— or dawn horse—a tiny creature only twelve inches high, built with four toes for greater speed and with (relatively) bigger and stronger teeth for better chewing.

Yet the toes and the teeth of the dawn horse are still inadequate for survival in the hard and level and grassy plains of its ancient abode. A more compact foothold and a more tenacious tooth-hold are necessary for the continuation of its existence. And so we see the next development in its physical adaptation to life. The eohippus becomes transformed into the *mesohippus,* or the horse of the prehistoric noonday. This creature has three toes, or hoofs—a big one in the center, used for running, and two small ones on the sides hanging useless in the air. The teeth of the mesohippus are much more adequate for grass grinding than those of the eohippus. Each of these teeth has now assumed the form of a miniature millstone. Moreover, there are more of these teeth now than ever before in the history of this species. And the more teeth, the longer the jaws and the stronger the mouth muscles for the chewing of the food.

But the mesohippus is still a very small creature—only six inches higher than his paternal eohippus. The added height is due to its longer legs—for swifter running—and to the consequent elongation of its neck in order that it may be able to reach down to its food.

And thus we see the prehistoric ancestors of the horse gradually assuming the pattern of their modern descendant. The next step in the elaboration of this pattern brings us from the mesohippus to the *merychippus.* This immediate predecessor of the modern horse is still burdened with three toes. But the two side toes are mere appendages to the broad, strong hoof in the center. And its teeth are now considerably longer and wider and tougher than the teeth of the mesohippus. Its size, too, has increased notably over the size of the earlier horses. In the final stage of its development—some ten million years ago—it has reached the approximate height of a Shetland pony.

From the merychippus to the modern horse we can similarly trace a slow but continuous development—the gradual displacement of the side toes and the enlargement of the middle hoof, the lengthening and strengthening of the legs, neck, and skull, the progressive enlargement of the teeth, and the final growth of the body to its present-day size.

The above, very briefly, is a partial summary of one of the "deciphered" chapters in Nature's textbook on evolution. We can read this chapter in the language of the fossils and even—to some extent—in the embryonic structure of the modern horse. At the age of six weeks the leg of an embryo horse has three well-developed toes. At eight weeks the side toes are very much smaller than the one in the middle, which is beginning to form into a hoof. At five months the side toes have become reduced to mere splints. At birth the foal has completely lost its side toes and has retained only the hoof at the end of its leg.

And thus the embryo of the individual is, in effect, a recapitulation of the story of the race. This story reveals a progressive pattern in the continual adaptation of life to the incessant variation of its environment. It is the exciting story of evolution forever on the march.

The Darwinian theory of evolution is now regarded, in most scientific circles, as an established fact. The fossil story of the horse has many interesting parallels—in the fossil stories of the sea urchin, the camel, the elephant, the rhinoceros, and other mammalian as well as non-mammalian creatures. These fossils show a complete and regular development from the earliest to the latest forms. Scientists may disagree as to *how* evolution works; but practically all of them are agreed that it does work. There is a steady and unbroken line of development—step by step, change by change, incessantly adaptive characteristic by characteristic—all the way up from the primitive spark of unconscious life to the complicated thoughts and joys and aspirations of modern man.

REVIEW QUESTIONS IN BIOLOGY

1. What three manifestations of power distinguish living from non-living objects?

2. Can life be spontaneously produced out of dead matter?

3. What scientist experimentally demonstrated the answer to the above question?

4. What was the first, and lowest, form of life that came upon the earth?

5. What is protoplasm?

6. How do bacteria reproduce themselves?

7. What is an amoeba?

8. How do protozoa reproduce themselves?

9. What is a cell?

10. About how many cells go into the building of the human body?

11. What are the two main branches of the tree of life?

12. Mention three important distinctions between these two forms of life.

13. Is every form of life either a distinct plant form or a distinct animal form?

14. What was the first form of cell life?

15. What is the name of the "male" cell? Of the "female" cell?

16. Name the three parts of every flower-bearing plant.

17. What is the general difference between the motion of plants and that of animals?

18. How do plants reproduce themselves?

19. Mention three ways in which plants disperse their "offspring" from place to place.

20. Where did animal life begin?

21. About how long did it take for the life process to develop into the first creature with a backbone?

22. Name the animal group that first migrated to the land.

23. What led this group to its migration?

24. Name a familiar animal which exemplifies the transformation from gills to lungs.

25. What other important factor in the development of life do we find in that animal?

26. What are the arthropoda?

27. Name the five groups of animals under the general classification of chordata.

28. What is a mammal?

29. What characteristic puts the kangaroo into the group of marsupial animals?

30. What is a cetacean?

31. Name five "ungulated" animals.

32. Name five rodents.

33. What are the primates?

34. About how many different kinds of insects are there?

35. What physical characteristics are common both to fishes and to men?

36. In what physical respects do they differ?

37. What does the human embryo teach us about the evolution and the migration of life?

38. What is an amphibian?

39. Why does an amphibian have to stay close to the water?

40. What three elements were inhabited by the prehistoric reptiles?

41. Out of what animals did the prehistoric reptiles develop?

42. Into what animals did they develop?

43. What caused their extinction?

44. Who does most of the courting in the kingdom of the birds?

45. What is the "biological function" of love?

46. Why may the mammals be called our *blood brothers*?

47. Name three great distinctions between the mammalian and the non-mammalian animals.

48. Why did the horse, in the process of its evolution, discard its toes and develop its teeth?

49. How long a time did this gradual process consume?

50. How are we able to trace this process in the evolution of the horse?

ANSWERS TO THE QUESTIONS IN BIOLOGY

1. Living objects can grow from within, absorb food, and reproduce themselves.

2. No.

3. Louis Pasteur.

4. Bacteria.

5. The transparent, basic substance from which all living things are made.

6. By separation into two halves.

7. A speck of animal (as opposed to plant) protoplasm.

8. Either by separation, like bacteria, or by copulation.

9. A tiny bit of protoplasm, with a nucleus that lies at the basis of all life.

10. Over a thousand billion.

11. Plant life and animal life.

12. A plant is rooted in one place, derives its food directly from the earth and the sun, and possesses chlorophyll. An animal moves from place to place, feeds upon plants and other animals, and possesses no chlorophyll.

13. No. Some forms of life are combinations of the two kingdoms or transitions from the one to the other.

14. The alga, a primitive type of seaweed.

15. The pollen cell. The egg cell.

16. The stem, the roots, and the leaves.

17. Plants can move (or grow) only vertically; animals can also move horizontally.

18. Like animals, sexually—through the union of two different kinds of cells.

19. By the winds, by the "explosion" of the seeds like the sparks of a skyrocket, or by the deposit of the seeds upon the feathers and fur of passing creatures.

20. In the sea.

21. Millions of years.

22. The ganoid family of fishes.

23. The quest for food in order to survive.

24. The frog.

25. It is the animal in which we find the first crude traces of the fingers and the hand.

26. Joint-legged animals— such as lobsters, spiders, and insects.

27. Fishes, amphibians, reptiles, birds, and mammals.

28. An animal that suckles its young.

29. The possession of the abdominal pouch for the carrying of its young.

30. A suckling sea animal, such as the whale.

31. Horses, sheep, camels, elephants, and pigs.

32. Rabbits, squirrels, beavers, rats, and mice.

33. The leading order of animals, including lemurs, monkeys, and men.

34. Almost half a million.

35. The spinal cord, the head, the eyes, the nostrils, and the mouth.

36. The body of the fish, unlike the human body, is streamlined. Its fins, provided for locomotion in the water, are shorter than our human legs. It has gills for breathing in the water, while we have lungs for breathing in the air. Its brain is far less developed than the human brain.

37. In the human embryo we find the body of the fish being gradually developed into an adaptation for land life.

38. A land- and sea-dwelling animal.

39. Because its skin, unprotected either by scales or by hair, needs a great deal of moisture to keep it alive.

40. The sea, the land, and the air.

41. Out of the amphibians.

42. Into modern reptiles, and into beasts and birds.

43. They were too slow and too unwieldy to find a sufficiency of food.

44. The male.

45. The reproduction of life.

46. Because, like us, they are warm-blooded.

47. Most mammalians give birth to their offspring alive, while most other

animals reproduce themselves through the laying of eggs. Unlike the other animals, mammals are provided with milk-producing breasts. The mammals are provided with better-developed brains than the non-mammals.

48. For the better running over the open and grassy plains, and for the better chewing of its tough vegetation.

49. About forty million years.

50. Through the study of fossils and of the embryonic structures of the modern horse.

BIOGRAPHICAL SKETCHES OF GREAT BIOLOGISTS

Aristotle (384–322 B.C.). Greek philosopher and scientist. Born at Stagira on the peninsula of Thrace of a family of physicians. He came to Athens at eighteen and enrolled in Plato's academy. Achieving a reputation for philosophy, he was summoned by Philip of Macedon in 343 B.C. to serve as the tutor of his son Alexander. Alexander graduated from this instruction to conquer the world. Aristotle returned quietly to Athens, where he founded the Lyceum, a philosophical academy. Growing out of favor with political circles in Athens, he was compelled to go into exile. He died at the age of sixty-two. His writings embrace literally the whole field of knowledge. His writings on biology contain fine samples of the experimental scientist. His observations of animals and fish and his discourse on the habits of bees and octopuses are particularly noteworthy. He made great strides toward the classification of all living phenomena.

Leeuwenhoek, Anton van (1632–1723). Dutch microscopist. Born in Delft, he lived to become the most celebrated lensmaker of his day. Lacking a scientific education, he nevertheless conducted scientific investigations with his microscope and he made a series of remarkable discoveries which form the core of modern physiological knowledge. He first revealed the capillary action of the blood, discovered the red corpuscle, described the spermatazoa in animals, supplied data on the nature of the brain, epidermis, nerves, and hair, the structure of plants. He was the first to draw a representation of bacteria. He set a high standard of scientific research for all who followed.

Linnaeus, Carolus (Karl von Linné) (1707–78). Swedish botanist. Born in Råshult, the son of a Lutheran minister. He was educated at Uppsala, where he later taught botany. In 1732 he went to Lapland on a botanical exploration, and a few years later undertook the study of the plants near Haarlem in Holland. While in Holland he received an M.D. degree and, after travels in England and France, set up a medical practice in Stockholm. However, he continued his scientific work as well and published a number of important botanical books. In one of these, *Species Plantarum,* he laid the basis for the modern system of botanical nomenclature —that is, calling a particular plant by its genus and species name, as *Quercus alba* for white oak. He was named to the nobility in 1761.

Lamarck, Jean Baptiste Pierre Antoine (1744–1829). French naturalist. He was born in Picardy of the nobility. He entered military service and, upon discharge, turned his attention to botany. His chief reputation, however, was gained as a zoologist. He devoted his life to an investigation of living and fossil invertebrates. And he established the science of invertebrate paleontology in which he revealed himself as a definite progenitor of Darwin and the theory of evolution. He postulated a theory of the inheritance of acquired characteristics.

Cuvier, Georges Léopold Chrétien Dagobert (1769–1832). French naturalist. Born at Montbéliard, he was educated at the Academy of Stuttgart. He rose rapidly in educational posts because of his increasing prestige as a naturalist. He taught at the Collège de France and at the Jardin des Plantes. His fame rests on his studies in comparative anatomy and paleontology. He classified and systematically reconstructed the fossils of fish, reptiles, and all species of the animal kingdom. His research on the structure of living and fossil animals is still a classic. He received high honors from Napoleon, was made a peer of France by Louis Philippe, and appointed president of the council of state.

Humboldt, Alexander von (1769–1859). German naturalist, the son of Major von Humboldt, chamberlain to Frederick the Great. Born at the family estate of Tegel, he decided as a young boy to devote his life to travel and the study of nature. He started on his scientific travels at twenty-eight, upon the death of his mother. And he spent his whole long lifetime at the job of studying the Great Book of Nature in every part of the world. In this book, as he explained, "the rolling rock leaves its scratches on the mountain; the river, its channels in the soil; the animal, its bones in the stratum; the fern and leaf, their modest epitaph in the coal." And he translated this Book of Nature, which he had learned to read so expertly, into several fascinating books on biology, zoology, and anatomy. A number of his most important books are known under the general title of *Kosmos—The World.*

Baer, Karl Ernst von (1792–1876). German biologist. Born at Piep in Estonia, he entered Dorpat University to prepare for a career in medicine. But he veered into the field of biology. Investigating intensively the evolution of organisms, he published a paper in which he revealed his discovery of the human ovum. A founder of the science of embryology, he influenced the thinking of a large number of natural philosophers, including Spencer and Huxley. Appointed to the Academy of Sciences of St. Petersburg, he led an expedition into the Arctic to examine the polar life of the empire. Toward the end of his career he carried on investigations in the field of geology. He wrote a classic treatise on the fishes of the Caspian and Baltic seas.

Agassiz, Louis (1807–73). Swiss-American zoologist. Born at Môtier, Switzerland. At fifteen he entered the College of Lausanne. He next studied medicine—especially anatomy—at Zurich. Finally, at nineteen, he matriculated at Heidelberg University. While preparing for his medical degree, he spent his spare time writing a book on fossil fishes. With the help of Alexander von Humboldt, he was appointed professor of natural history at the University of Neuchâtel at the age of twenty-five. His scientific interests had now expanded to include geology along with anatomy and zoology. He wrote a book on the glacial period and was invited to deliver a series of lectures in the United States. He arrived in Boston in 1846, and a year later was appointed to the Harvard faculty. His most important work at Harvard was the establishment of the Museum of Comparative Zoology. He wrote numerous books and articles on the various phases of the sciences. When asked to cite what he regarded as his greatest achievement, he replied: "Observation. I have taught men to observe."

Darwin, Charles (1809–82). English naturalist and father of the theory of evolution. Born at Shrewsbury, and studied at Edinburgh University and at Christ College, Cambridge. After receiving his B.A. degree, in 1831, he joined as a naturalist in the around-the-world exploration cruise of the *Beagle*. The results of his discoveries on this cruise were published in his first two books: *Zoology of the Voyage of H.M.S. Beagle,* and *The Structure and Distribution of Coral Reefs.* For a number of years he made extensive researches in zoology; and in 1858 he published a monograph on his now famous evolution theory. In 1859 he elaborated his theory into a book, *On the Origin of Species.* In this book Darwin did not maintain that man is descended from the ape, but that both can be traced back to a common anthropoid ancestor. He wrote a number of books on various biological and zoological subjects. Among the most famous of these, in addition to his *Origin of Species,* is its companion volume, *The Descent of Man* (1871).

Schwann, Theodor (1810–82). German biologist and physiologist. Born in Prussia, he received his degree in medicine from the University of Berlin at the age of twenty-four. At twenty-eight he taught anatomy at the University of Louvain and nine years later joined the faculty at Liége. An expert physiologist, he investigated the physicochemical basis of life. He wrote papers on the phenomena of putrefaction and fermentation, muscular contraction, the capillaries. He revealed the necessity to the digestion of pepsin. He demonstrated the organic nature of yeast. But his chief claim to fame is as the originator of the cell theory of life. Pasteur and Lister were directly influenced by his researches.

Pasteur, Louis (1822–95). French biological chemist. Born at Dôle; educated at Jena in Germany, and at the Ecole Normale in Paris. In 1867 he was appointed professor of chemistry at the Sorbonne. His first important work was the rehabilitation of the French silk industry by stamping out the diseases of the silkworms. His next researches were concerned with the diseases of the yeast plants. And finally his experiments brought him to the investigation of some of the more dreaded human diseases. He discovered an effective inoculation for hydrophobia, and inaugurated the method of pasteurization—named after him—for the killing of bacteria in wine, beer, milk, and other solutions susceptible to bacterial decay.

Mendel, Gregor Johann (1822–84). German monk and biologist. Born in the Moravian village of Heinzendorf. Twice he failed in his examinations as a high school teacher at Altbrünn. The reason for his failure—"He expresses his own ideas instead of relying upon traditional knowledge." One of history's outstanding scientists, he was too "original" to be accepted as a schoolteacher. He entered the Augustinian order at Altbrünn. The monastery had a small but well-stocked garden. It was in this tiny plot of growing things that Mendel studied the successive generations of plants and formulated his famous Mendelian laws of heredity. It took him seven years to evolve his theory. Mendel published his conclusions in 1866, but it was not until thirty years later that their importance was recognized.

Huxley, Thomas Henry (1825–95). English biologist and a popularizer of science. Born in Ealing and educated at London University. From 1846 to 1850 he sailed around the world as a naval surgeon. In 1851 he was elected a fellow of the Royal Society. In 1854 he became professor of natural history at the School of Mines; in 1863, Hunterian professor at the Royal College of Surgeons; in 1869, president of the British Geographical Society; in 1872, secretary of the Royal Society and lord rector of Aberdeen University; and in 1883, president of the Royal Society. His chief works, as a popularizer of the Darwinian theory of evolution, were *Man's Place in Nature, Science and Culture,* and *Evolution and Ethics.*

Haeckel, Ernst (1834–1919). Born at Potsdam. He studied medicine and the natural sciences at Berlin and Jena. In 1865 he was appointed professor of zoology at Jena. He made a number of scientific expeditions—to Norway, the Adriatic, the Red Sea, the Canary Islands, Ceylon, Corsica, and Java. In his scientific theories he was profoundly influenced by Darwin. His *History of Creation* is a popular summary of the Darwinian doctrine of evolution.

De Vries, Hugo (1848–1935). Dutch botanist. Born in Haarlem, he was a professor at the University of Amsterdam. He was among those who revived Mendel's work on heredity and revealed its importance. He developed the theory of mutations, according to which new species arise through sudden changes.

Davenport, Charles Benedict (1866–1944). American zoologist. Born at Stamford, Connecticut, he received his degree of Doctor of Philosophy from Harvard University. He taught zoology and embryology on the faculty of Harvard and Chicago universities. In 1904 he was appointed director of the station for experimental evolution of the Carnegie Institution of Washington, D.C. He did extensive research in the fields of genetics and eugenics. He devoted his life to the study of the heredity of build and temperament in man.

Morgan, Thomas Hunt (1866–1945). American geneticist. Born in Lexington, Kentucky, he was graduated from the State College of Kentucky in 1886. In 1890 he received his Ph.D. from Johns Hopkins University. From 1904 to 1928 he taught at Columbia University, New York, leaving in the latter year to become director of the Kerckhoff Laboratories of Biological Sciences at the California Institute of Technology. Morgan made significant contributions to an understanding of the mechanisms of heredity. He introduced the use of the fruit fly, *Drosophila*, as an organism for study in genetics. He was awarded the Nobel Prize in medicine in 1933 for his discoveries in the hereditary functions of the chromosomes.

CAREERS IN BIOLOGY

The study of biology is fundamental to a career in medicine, dentistry, pharmacology, research agriculture, and a score of other fields. More than a quarter of a million Americans earn a living in jobs that require training in biology. The government has employment for bacteriologists who do research work in foods and drugs, who serve the dairy and refrigeration industries, who test water and milk, explore better methods of sanitation, perfect antitoxins and serums. Still others perform research in hormones and vitamins, or enlist in the fight against heart disease and cancer. The War Department engages biologists to investigate the effects of chemical and atomic warfare.

The biologist may specialize as an expert in soil conservation and the breeding and nutrition of animals. He may become a plant pathologist, applying chemicals to increase and modify the growth of plants, or employing methods to control plant and fruit diseases. As an entomologist, he may study the effect of insects on the development of plants, crops, livestock, and on the general health of the population. He may work for the government's Biological Survey, conserving bird and animal wild life, or for the Department of Forestry, where he would battle the diseases of trees. By keeping the forests healthy, he would be contributing to the nation's soil and water supply.

The student trained in biology may become a nurseryman, an expert in landscape gardening, a director of greenhouses. Today this is a nationwide business with an investment of more than a hundred million dollars. He may become an expert in the processing of wood employed in private industry. He may teach, administer an aquarium, or supervise a museum.

animal geneticist
EXPERIENCE REQUIRED: College degree. Graduate work or experience in research in animal genetics.
DESCRIPTION OF JOB: Assists, researches, supervises animal breeding.
OPPORTUNITIES FOR ADVANCEMENT: Civil service upgrading.
WHERE TO APPLY FOR JOBS: Government.

biologist

EXPERIENCE REQUIRED: College graduation with biology degree. Graduate work desirable.

DESCRIPTION OF JOB: Usually specializes in research work in a specific field of biology.

OPPORTUNITIES FOR ADVANCEMENT: Laboratory director, government job opportunities related to particular specialty.

WHERE TO APPLY FOR JOBS: Government, manufacturers of products derived from animals, plants, foods, and drugs.

biometrician

EXPERIENCE REQUIRED: College degree with a major in mathematics or in biology, anatomy, bacteriology, genetics, etc.

DESCRIPTION OF JOB: Supervises, assists, directs research concerning mortality and sickness in connection with environment.

OPPORTUNITIES FOR ADVANCEMENT: Civil service upgrading.

WHERE TO APPLY FOR JOBS: Government.

dairy technician

EXPERIENCE REQUIRED: Degree from agriculture college desirable. Training in bacteriology, chemistry, animal husbandry, elementary physics. Good health.

DESCRIPTION OF JOB: Tests for acid content, butter fat; makes bacteria count in milk or cream for grading purposes. Determines amount of moisture in dairy products, amount of sediment in milk and cream.

OPPORTUNITIES FOR ADVANCEMENT: Managerial and executive positions.

WHERE TO APPLY FOR JOBS: Dairy organizations, milk laboratories, creameries.

dietitian

EXPERIENCE REQUIRED: College degree with training in chemistry, bacteriology, biology and dietetics studies, etc. For advanced work, experience as hospital dietitian or teaching dietetics.

DESCRIPTION OF JOB: Procures food, prepares diets, supervises servicing of food.

OPPORTUNITIES FOR ADVANCEMENT: Civil service upgrading.

WHERE TO APPLY FOR JOBS: Government.

entomologist

EXPERIENCE REQUIRED: Degree in entomology. Some training in livestock and crop production.

DESCRIPTION OF JOB: Studies life of insects, their habits in relation to growth of plants, health of animals and of the population.

OPPORTUNITIES FOR ADVANCEMENT: Research expert, college department head.

WHERE TO APPLY FOR JOBS: Agricultural colleges, state departments of entomology, experiment stations, Department of Agriculture.

forester

EXPERIENCE REQUIRED: Graduation from accredited school of forestry.

DESCRIPTION OF JOB: Fire prevention, flood erosion control, insect control, checking of tree diseases, maintenance of forest roads, trails, etc.

OPPORTUNITIES FOR ADVANCEMENT: Administration or specialization in private employment.

WHERE TO APPLY FOR JOBS: United States Forest Service, National Park Service, Soil Conservation Service, lumber companies, pulp and paper mills, mining companies, state and municipal bureaus.

medical technician

EXPERIENCE REQUIRED: College degree with training in chemistry, biology, physics. Laboratory experience in specialty desirable.

DESCRIPTION OF JOB: Assists, supervises, or directs in clinical laboratory activities.

OPPORTUNITIES FOR ADVANCEMENT: Civil service upgrading.

WHERE TO APPLY FOR JOBS: Government.

plant pathologist

EXPERIENCE REQUIRED: Broad training in botany, chemistry, physics.

DESCRIPTION OF JOB: Concerned with causes and control of plant diseases. Investigates in field and laboratory. Researches on insects, bacteria, fungi, and other causes of plant diseases.

OPPORTUNITIES FOR ADVANCEMENT: Executive.

WHERE TO APPLY FOR JOBS: Government bureaus, manufacturers of fungicides and insecticides, greenhouses, seed companies.

research specialist (agriculture)

EXPERIENCE REQUIRED: Degree in agriculture and graduate work in specialty. Several years' experience with government agency desirable.

DESCRIPTION OF JOB: Researches in plant and animal breeding, animal nutrition and feeding practices, crop fertilization, agricultural economics and farm management, marketing of farm products, and crop-production methods.

OPPORTUNITIES FOR ADVANCEMENT: Administrative.

WHERE TO APPLY FOR JOBS: Government bureaus, processors and marketers of agricultural products.

wild-life worker

EXPERIENCE REQUIRED: College degree. Training in biology, zoology, agriculture, and forestry desirable. Good health.

DESCRIPTION OF JOB: Manages habitat, production, protection of various species of wild life. Conservation and management of wild-life resources.

OPPORTUNITIES FOR ADVANCEMENT: Wild-life farming, refuge manager of private estate.

WHERE TO APPLY FOR JOBS: Federal and state governments, private refuges.

BIBLIOGRAPHY: BOOKS ON BIOLOGY FOR FURTHER READING AND STUDY

Baitsell, George Alfred: *Manual of Animal Biology*. New York, 1932.
——: *Human Biology*. New York, 1940.
Barrows, Henry Robbins: *Elements of General Biology*. New York, 1936.
Crampton, Henry Edward: *The Coming and Evolution of Life*. New York, 1931.
Fenton, Carroll Lane: *Our Living World*. New York, 1943.
——, and Paul E. Kambly: *Basic Biology*. New York, 1947.
Fitzpatrick, Frederick Linder, and R. E. Horton: *Biology*. Boston, 1935.
Hauber, Ulrich Albert, and Sister Ellen O'Hanlon: *Biology*. New York, 1937.
Haupt, Arthur Wing: *Fundamentals of Biology*. New York, 1940.
Hogben, Lancelot Thomas: *Principles of Animal Biology*. New York, 1940.
Holmes, Ernest J., and R. D. Gibbs: *A Modern Biology*. New York, 1937.
Huxley, Julian S.: *What Dare I Think?* New York, 1931.
Kenoyer, Leslie Alva, and Henry N. Goddard: *General Biology*. New York, 1945.

Lillie, Ralph Stayner: *General Biology*. Chicago, 1945.
Lindsey, Arthur Ward: *The Science of Animal Life*. New York, 1937.
Mavor, James Watt: *General Biology*. New York, 1947.
Meier, William Herman Dietrich: *Essentials of Biology*. Boston, 1944.
Moon, Truman Jesse, and Paul B. Mann: *Biology*. New York, 1941.
Parshley, Howard Madison: *Biology*. New York, 1940.
Peattie, Donald Culross: *This Is Living*. New York, 1938.
Stanford, Ernest Elwood: *Man and the Living World*. New York, 1940.
Strasbaugh, Perry Daniel: *Elements of Biology*. New York, 1944.
Thomson, John Arthur: *Biology for Everyman*. New York, 1935.
Wells, Herbert George: *The Science of Life*. New York, 1934.
Whaley, W. Gordon: *Biology for Everyone*. New York, 1948.
Woodruff, Lorande Loss: *Foundations of Biology*. New York, 1930.
Young, Clarence Whitford: *The Human Organism and the World of Life*.
    New York, 1938.

anthropology—man's place in nature

MONKEYS, MICE, AND MEN

In 1918 the geologist Freudenberg discovered the first "human" footprint known on earth. This footprint, made about ten million years ago in the sand now hardened into sandstone, is the prehistoric monument of our earliest ancestor. It is not the footprint of a "manlike" ape, since the foot of the ape has no thumb-toe but five finger-toes of equal length. The outline of the foot imprinted in the sandstone, however, shows definitely not only a big thumb-toe at the one end but a little finger-toe at the other end. It is a *human* foot.

We are unable, from this mere footprint, to reconstruct prehistoric man. But we have enough evidence, from many other sorts of fossils, to assume that the earliest humans bore a strong resemblance to the apes. Let us briefly examine this resemblance —first, by comparing the human body to some of the other vertebrates; and next, by comparing it to the ape.

Thus, for example, a man is physically closer to a frog than— let us say—to a cuttlefish or to a crab. For both the man and the frog are vertebrates, while the cuttlefish and the crab are not. A man and a frog possess in common an internal skeleton, a pair of eyes and ears, a nose, a mouth, a set of teeth, and two pairs of limbs.

Yet even among the vertebrate animals a man is physically closer to a mouse than to a frog. For both the man and the mouse have hair, both have warm blood, and milk and breasts for suckling their young—characteristics which the frog does not have. In other words, the man and the mouse belong to the same family group—the mammals—while the frog does not belong to this mammalian family. Of mice and men it may be said that they are cousins—a rather unfriendly relationship, to be sure, but a blood relationship nonetheless.

And now we come to a still closer relationship—between the man and the chimpanzee. These two mammalian creatures possess, in common, limbs for walking and climbing, hands with thumbs, fingers with nails instead of claws, and well-developed brains with many folds and furrows. As a further departure from the other mammals, these two *primates*—or *leading order* of animals—have lost their tails, have developed a single pair of breasts, and their females have acquired a menstrual period.

Moreover, their skeletons are alike almost bone for bone; their apparatus for hearing and the range of sound intercepted by their ears are practically the same; and their emotions—such as fear, anger, hatred—are almost equally varied and intense.

Furthermore, both apes and men are able to anticipate experience by learning from their mistakes. That is, they are able to *reason,* to put ideas and things together—an inventive faculty which, so far as science has been able to discover, is absent from all other animals, even in the tailed monkeys. A chimpanzee and a man alone, among all the living creatures, possess the intelligence to fix the solid end of one stick into the hollow end of another in order to fetch an object that is beyond the reach of either of the two sticks alone. From the fitting together of two sticks to the construction of a bridge, there is a mental development that varies in degree but not in kind.

In short there is a very close relationship between the simian and the human forms of life. This relationship is even more apparent in the fetus than it is in the adult of the two species. Both embryos are covered with a short coat of hair before birth; and both are practically hairless at birth. The man retains this condition—with the exception of the hair on the head—while the ape acquires a permanent long covering of hair shortly after its birth.

The two embryos are also alike in the shape of the skull and the formation of the limbs. The differences arise later, when they grow into maturity.

Indeed, man may be regarded as a more mature ape. When the human race emerged from its simian environment, it was provided with a faculty which enabled it to advance into a new world of experience and thought. This faculty was the acquisition of speech. It is the faculty of speech which, on the one hand,

This is how we think man's earliest manlike ancestor, Pithecanthropus erectus, *appeared.*

raises the savage above the ape, and on the other hand, elevates
Shakespeare above the savage. From the scientific point of view,
however, the inarticulate ape, the stuttering savage, and the sublime poet are brothers under the skin.

THE COMING OF THE HUMAN RACE

Science has pretty clearly established the fact that the human
race is descended from an apelike ancestry. Though the fossils
of prehistoric simians and humans are not nearly so numerous as
the fossils of prehistoric horses, we are nevertheless able to reconstruct the story of man with but very few blurred or missing
paragraphs.

This story teaches us that the dawn of the human race arose
when the "manlike" apes had learned to walk erect, on two feet.
The footprint of this early race, as we have noted, has been preserved in the rock. Perhaps this footprint belonged to the so-
called "missing link"—the creature that marked the transitional
stage between the "manlike" apes and the "apelike" men.

A skeleton of this transitional link has been discovered in Java
(1892). It has been named the *Pithecanthropus*, or *Ape Man*.
This prehistoric Adam of the human family, roaming over his
island paradise, had a brain "capacity" about halfway between
the largest simian brains of the orangoutang and the smallest
human brains of the Australian savages. He had beetling ridges
over his eyes, like a monkey; but he stood erect, like a man. And
his teeth, too, were manlike rather than apelike. Strangely enough,
this skeleton of the first and perhaps the ugliest of humans possesses one thing in common with the statue of Venus de Milo,
regarded as one of the most beautiful reproductions of the human
form. Both the skeleton and the statue were dug out of the earth
with the arms missing.

But to return to our human ancestry. In addition to the Ape
Man, various other types of transitional Man Creatures have been
discovered. For example, the *Eoanthropus*—or Dawn Man—unearthed in Sussex must have looked more like a gorilla than a
man. For his eyeteeth were long and sharp, his jaws heavy, and
his brains very small and undeveloped. Yet, like the Ape Man,

he walked erect. And his skeleton, upon its discovery, was surrounded with crude implements—the earliest known instance of the human shaping of tools.

And then we have the *Sinanthropus*—the prehistoric *China Man* and the *Rhodesian Man* and the *Kanam Man*. The fossils of these subhumans are incomplete; yet they are sufficient evi-

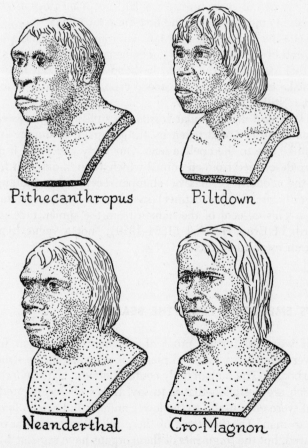

Heads of some of man's prehistoric ancestors. (After busts in the American Museum of Natural History.)

dence of a new race emerging from the brutes and raising its eyes to the heavens.

Next in our prehistoric survey of our human pedigree we come to the *Neanderthal Man*—the first living creature who not only walked erect but buried his dead. For the remains of this creature were discovered in a grave fitted out with utensils for a life beyond death. Apparently the Neanderthals had acquired the first glimmerings of a religious faith and an immortal hope.

Neanderthal Man, while he resembled modern man more than did any of the early forms, was still not a member of the same species as modern man. The first ancestor of that species—*Homo sapiens*—was Cro-Magnon Man, who appeared on the scene at the end of the last Ice Age to challenge the supremacy of Neanderthal Man. Like the latter, he lived in caves, but he was able to make tools of a more advanced type, and his art was of a sort that is still admired today.

These and many similar fossils are sufficiently consistent signposts along the road taken by the progressive journey from the manlike ape to the apelike man. Our early ancestors, it appears, were descended from an animal which, though different from any of the modern gorillas or chimpanzees or orangoutangs, was nevertheless a (now extinct) member of the general family of apes. This descent of the human from the simian race is, in the words of Ernst Haeckel (1834–1919), "not a vague hypothesis, but an established fact."

MAN'S EMERGENCE FROM THE BEAST

If we need further proof of our human evolution from the lower animals, we can find plenty of evidence in the structure of our bodies. The human body contains *almost two hundred* organs which are vestigial—that is to say, traces of degenerated organs that were once useful to the lower animals but are no longer useful to man. The *functions* of these inherited organs have disappeared, but the *fragments* of these organs have remained to prove their inheritance.

Let us glance at a few of them:

1. Our body hair, which is no longer essential for protection against the cold. Every one of these useless hairs is attached to an equally useless muscle, or goose-pimple. These hairs and muscles once served their purpose among our furry ancestors. Among ourselves they are merely a telltale reminder of our lowly pedigree.

2. Our abbreviated tails at the base of the spine. These atrophied tails of ours, no longer useful for our human activities, are nevertheless supplied (in our embryonic state) with all the muscles necessary for brushing away insects and clinging to branches. Merely another genealogical reminder of our animal origin.

3. The motive muscles of our ears. These muscles still exist in all humans but have become—except in the case of those who can "wiggle" their ears for the amusement of their friends—vestigial and useless. Among the lower animals, however, these muscles were used as a means of turning the ears in the direction of sound from approaching enemies.

4. The fleshy projection in the inner corner of the eye. This bit of flesh, though useless in man, remains as a vestige of the "third eyelid" which many of the lower animals can sweep across the eye from side to side just as easily as we can sweep our two eyelids up and down.

5. The capacity of the newborn babe to support his own weight by clinging with his hands. This is a "surviving symbol" of the time when the baby ape was obliged to cling to its mother's fur as the mother used all her limbs in traveling over the branches.

6. The ability of the newborn babe to grasp things with his feet —an ability which fades away as he grows older but which remains intact in his maturing cousin, the ape.

Many of the vestigial organs are more pronounced in the human embryo than they are in the human adult. The embryo, in fact, tells the entire story of evolution in condensed form.

Every one of us begins his earthly existence as a single cell, develops into a cell colony, and then passes successively through the stages of a *polyp* or flower-animal, an *amphioxus* or pulpy thing with the merest outline of a spine, a vertebrate fish that swims in the "liquid pond" of his mother's womb, a mammal with tail and fur, an apelike creature with short legs and long arms and clinging fingers and grasping toes, and finally develops into the beginnings of a man.

MAN DESCENDS FROM THE TREES

The earliest men, like their simian ancestors, lived in trees. The human hand today is merely the development of a "gadget" used originally for holding onto branches. And the erect position of the human body is the result of the up-and-down motion of the prehistoric tree climbers and tree dwellers.

Also man's ability to throw things must have had its origin in his tree-dwelling experience. The early animals, as they moved over the branches, inadvertently loosened bits of bark and fruits that fell upon the ground. Little by little these animals—like the monkeys and the squirrels of today—learned to throw things down deliberately. And, as man descended to the ground in his evolutionary progress, he gradually perfected the art of throwing things *horizontally* as well as *vertically*.

The descent from the trees was the first great migration of the human race. This migration was due—as seems likely—to the increasing numbers of humans in the forests. As they kept growing in population—for Nature had found them to be a species adaptable for survival—they spread out toward the edges of the forest and finally to the plains beyond. At first they must have foraged on the plains in the daytime and returned to the safety of the trees at night. But as time went on some of the pioneers wandered too far away from the trees and were compelled, for safety's sake, to seek shelter in the caves.

And so—this is but one of several theories—the forerunners of the human race took up their new habitation and began to acquire the characteristics necessary for their new life. They now stood more erect than before; they depended upon their legs alone, without their front limbs, for walking; and they developed these front limbs into arms and hands for the various uses of their more advanced existence.

Now this advanced existence was rather precarious. In spite of his ability to throw sticks and stones and—later on—to fashion crude weapons for his defense, man was surrounded on all sides by prowling animals—such as tigers and lions and leopards and wolves.

But fortunately, like the wolf, man had acquired the habit of running in a pack. And *hunting* in a pack. He had become a gregarious—or social—animal.

HOW TOOLS ORIGINATED

In this brief outline of our human evolution it is important to remember that every single step must have taken thousands of centuries. Our education from primitive beasthood to mature manhood has been fairly steady but exceedingly slow. Little by little—as we measure the process by millions of years—we see the development of the hands and the feet, the shortening of the snout, and the enlargement of the brain.

And the first human making of tools.

The toolmaking ability of man is one of the chief characteristics that distinguish him from the ape. The first tool ever used

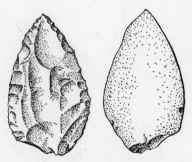

The flint knife, one of the earliest known tools.

by man was probably a stick—a reminder of his tree-dwelling days—which he picked up from the ground and carried about for knocking down fruits and nuts.

Somewhat later—let us not forget our thousand-century unit for measuring the various stages of evolution—our ancestors learned to fashion their sticks into clubs and spears.

But as time went on they observed that wooden tools were too soft and therefore too easily broken. And so they began to make tools and weapons out of another material which they could find in large quantities. This new material was bone.

Yet even bone, as the slowly dawning mind of man must have realized, was not the proper stuff for sharpening into a hard and durable tool. In order to cut his meat and his skins he needed a tough and solid substance that could be fashioned into a keen edge. Some sort of rock. And experience showed him that the best kind of rock for this purpose was flint. The "manufacture" of the first flint knife was a great step in human development. For it enabled man not only to use a new tool but to find new uses for his old tools. With the help of his sharp flint he could now sharpen his implements of wood and bone for an ever-widening variety of objects—such as spearheads for hunting, hatchets for

Skillful drawings like these have been found on the walls of caves which were probably occupied by Cro-Magnon Man.

chopping, knives for cutting up the skins of animals, scrapers for removing the fat from the skins, and needles for stitching them into clothes and blankets.

And also various crude instruments for engraving the pictures of animals upon fragments of wood and stone and bone, and upon the walls of their cave dwellings. For with the dawning human hunger for knowledge came the dawning human thirst for beauty. Man was henceforth to be distinguished from the other animals not only as a maker of tools but as a creator of art.

THE BEGINNING OF HUMAN SPEECH

There are sufficient details in the skull formation of the Java Man to show that he was able to articulate. He probably had acquired a limited number of words to express his primitive feelings and thoughts. Thus he could tell his companions—in monosyllables that accompanied his gestures—that he had seen a beast on the prowl, that night was coming on, that he was tired from the hunt, or that he had discovered a spring of cold water in the woods.

But just how this power of speech originated is still a debated question among the scientists. One of the most plausible theories is that the early cave men had probably learned to sing before they learned to speak. At first their song was a communal grunt or concerted howl. When they were uncomfortable, they moaned in unison; and when they were elated over some happy kill or a brightening sun, they uttered together a cry of joy that after a time developed into a guttural chant. Little by little the more progressive among them began to communicate their dawning individual thoughts and desires by simple inflections of the voice—a primitive sort of modulation which gave their grunts a more distinctive character. And in this way the first syllables of human language were born.

With the discovery of language, man had hit upon the most important of his tools. For speech is an instrument not only for *translating*, but for *creating* thought. Words are the bricks out of which all ideas are built. And they are also the symbols—like the numerals in mathematics—that enable us to arrange and to classify and to summarize the objects of the external world for our human understanding.

And thus the invention of speech had carried *Homo sapiens* another long step away from the ape.

THE PRODUCTION OF FIRE

Fire, as the result of lightning, was known to the living things on earth many centuries before the advent of man. But man alone among the animals was able to *produce* fire and to *harness* it to his use.

Just how the human production of fire came about is as yet uncertain. It seems plausible, however, that the earliest men at first *used* the fires already kindled by the lightning. They had discovered that they could bring warmth as well as death. And so they learned to huddle about the smaller fires, and to keep them alive with dry branches, in order to drive away the cold and the attacks of wild beasts. And to cook their meats—probably an accidental discovery when one of our pioneering ancestors ventured to taste the carcass of an animal that had been burned to death.

But from this *employment of an existing fire* to the *kindling of a new fire* was a long step. We therefore owe a great debt to the prehistoric inventor of the "friction spark"—the production of fire through the twirling of one stick in the hollow of another stick.

The invention of fire was one of the turning points in the road that carried man farther away from the beasts. An ancient Greek legend tells us that Prometheus—the "giver of fire" to mankind—incurred the displeasure of Zeus because this gift threatened to bring the human too close to the divine. Unlimited divine powers with limited human minds. For, as the messenger of Zeus explains in this legend, fire is too dangerous a weapon for the foolish race of men.

This legend, like so many others, expresses a profound truth. Too many great inventions of the past—from the kindling of fire to the splitting of the atom—have been used for destructive even more efficiently than for constructive ends. The development of men's morals lags far behind the development of their minds.

THE RACES OF MEN

All the different races today are descended from a single human stock. Biologically speaking, all mankind is a related species, for the various existing races are able to interbreed. This is Nature's stamp of identity—the scientific evidence of our common relationship throughout the world.

When mankind began to spread out over the face of the earth, the human life stream became divided into many tributaries. And the course of each of these tributaries assumed a different direction and a different shape, depending upon the landscape over which it flowed. Thus gradually there arose, under the different environments, the different pigmentations and physical conformations of four main groups—the white, the yellow, the African and the Australian black.

In the march of civilization some groups lagged behind simply because they drifted into the out-of-the-way fringes of the earth and remained isolated there. Removed thus from any contact with the rest of the world, they never emerged from their state of primitive savagery.

For human progress is a matter not of race but of locality. Civilization is possible only on the so-called "highways" of the world—the regions where many different kinds of people intermingle and exchange their ideas and experiences.

PRIMITIVE WARS

When man first descended from the trees, he was a forager; that is, he roamed about for his food and picked it up wherever he found it. But later, as he developed his tools, he became a hunter; he began to pursue animals and to kill them for his food.

The instinct for hunting led to the further development of another human instinct—the desire to gang together. For, united, a group of hunters found it much safer to attack a herd of animals. And in each group, as it set out for the chase, there arose someone who, by his superior cunning or courage, became a leader. He literally *led* the rest in the stalking of the prey and in the final attack. But these bands of hunters did not always confine themselves to the chasing of animals. Sometimes they took to hunting their fellow humans in organized groups.

This method of competitive fighting arose—very likely—when two bands, intent upon hunting the same herd of animals, happened to sight each other. This led to "economic rivalry"—each of the bands insisting upon its exclusive right to the hunting grounds. The rivalry for territorial possession was aggravated as the result of a universal human trait—the dislike of the unlike. When the people of one hunting group met the strangers of another group, both sides surrendered to a feeling of fear mingled with contempt. And thus, instead of becoming co-operatively acquainted to their mutual advantage, they became belligerently embroiled to the common disaster of all.

PRIMITIVE RELIGION

Primitive religion, in the opinion of many anthropologists, arose partly out of fear and partly out of hope. When men saw their shadows in the water, and the images of their friends in their dreams, they concluded that people had two bodies. One was the "living body" that you could touch, and the other was the "shadow body" that appeared only on special occasions but remained hidden away all the rest of the time. When anyone died, his first body was buried in the earth; but his second body, his shadow body, kept coming to you sometimes in your dreams. The shadow body, therefore, must be still alive, somewhere.

Now suppose the leader of a tribe died. During his lifetime he was a man greatly to be feared. But now that he was dead he was even more to be feared. For his shadow body was invisible, and nobody knew just when or how he was likely to attack those unfortunate creatures who might happen to displease him.

In order to gain his good will, therefore, it was necessary to bribe him with many gifts. For he was a terrible spirit and a mighty one. He thundered in the tempest, he raged in the fiery mountain, and he brought disease and death to those he disliked. This powerful shadow spirit, furthermore, controlled a peculiar, mysterious something that floated in the air. The name of this thing was *Luck.* Sometimes it came to help you, and sometimes it didn't. You and your friend went out to battle one day. Your friend was killed, and you escaped. Luck was with you but against your friend. Why? Perhaps it was because of something important that you did and your friend failed to do. But how could you tell? Well, there were wise men in your tribe who made it their business to find out. They became experts in Luck, magicians, seers. They told you what you must do, and what you must not do, in order to win favor in the eyes of your Shadow Chief and to get your fair share of Luck. These magic men, or primitive seers, were to be strictly obeyed. The consequence of disobedience was death—and punishment in the shadow world beyond the grave.

So much for the fear element in the awakening of the religious consciousness of man. The other element—hope—must have arisen early in the development of the human mind. For hope is but the reverse side of the coin of fear. Fear is the expectation of evil, and hope is the expectation of good. And all expectation is based upon the projection of the human mind into the future. When men vaguely began to think of the future, they must have visualized it as a shadowy image of the past. The past was the living body of the world; and the future, the shadow body, or the world of their dreams.

Now in this dream world, as they observed, some of the spirits were evil and some good. Perhaps their own guiding spirits were good—or could be rendered good by presents and prayers. And so they placed in the graves of their departed friends various utensils and articles of food. These were meant to insure the comfort of the dead and to secure their good will toward the comfort of the living.

But the images of their dead—and living—friends were not the only shadow bodies that they saw in their dreams. Some of them were "spirits" whose likeness they had never seen. Powers outside of this world. Chiefs who lived, most likely, in the heavens among the stars. Devils who were feared as the bearers of pain, and gods who were to be revered as the bringers of hope.

FROM HUNTING TO AGRICULTURE

We have now followed the human race as it emerged from its simian ancestry, acquired the use of tools, learned how to think and speak, produced and harnessed fire, began to travel over the world, developed into manifold groups with various external characteristics depending upon the variety of their environment, invented war, and learned to worship God.

And then, as time went on, some of our primitive forefathers discovered—probably by accident—that the planting of seeds resulted in the growing of plants. As a result of this discovery there was in many regions—especially in the fertile flatlands—a movement away from hunting to farming.

This transition, like all the other transitions in the slow-paced process of evolution, must have taken many thousands of years. Temperamentally, as we have seen, many of us still possess the impetuous aggressiveness of the hunter rather than the patient tenacity of the planter. We have not as yet come to the end of our transformation from wandering fighters to settled workers. But the beginning of that transformation came about through the discovery of the new method for securing food.

This new method—the raising of crops—led to another revolutionary step in human development—the taming of animals as beasts of burden and as producers of hides, wool, meat, milk, butter, and cheese.

And thus planting was added to foraging and hunting, as the activities of man expanded with the environmental changes of time. But this new step brought its evil as well as its good results. For it served to supply a new source of plunder for the foragers and the hunters. And thus the primitive instinct for war received another spur.

Yet in spite of these interruptions of primitive warfare, the human race went progressively on. Civilization had taken a tremendous stride forward with the growers of wheat and barley and the tamers of wild beasts.

EARLY LIFE IN THE VILLAGES

While the hunters still remained in their camps, the settlers gathered into villages and harvested their grain and tended their flocks and herds.

These villagers were the progressives of their day, the breakers of the old traditions, the founders of the "new way of life." They lived in the so-called *Neolithic,* or New Stone Age—as opposed to the *Paleolithic,* or Old Stone Age. They had learned to sharpen their stones into fine edges for hoes with which to dig their fields, and for axes with which to clear their brushwood and to chop down their trees.

And with the timber of these trees they had learned to build permanent houses, unlike the movable tents and tepees of the hunters. The log cabins of the primitive villagers served not only

A family unit in a primitive village. Notice the division of labor among the villagers. (After a model in the American Museum of Natural History.)

as dwelling places for themselves but as stables for their domestic animals. These stables, or huts, were often built on piles in the middle of a lake and were connected to the shore by means of a wooden bridge removable for protection against marauders at night. The floors of these huts were covered with trodden cow dung. The human inhabitants were quartered at one end of the main room, and the domestic animals at the other. All of them —men, women, children, and animals—made up a rather noisy but congenial group. The people sat and ate and slept on the ground, for they had not as yet discovered how to make chairs or tables or cots.

But, on the other hand, they had learned to make a good many useful things. Mats and baskets woven out of rushes and withes. Pottery fashioned out of clay and baked into lasting food containers. And clothing, plaited out of goat's hair and sheep's wool and—much later—woven out of flax.

And thus there arose in the village a diversified life of industrial activity. Some of the inhabitants attended to the farming; others to the herding; still others to the weaving of baskets or the shaping of pottery or the making of cloth.

This new kind of communal existence tended to stimulate the personal ingenuity as well as the social instinct of man. The competitive urge for a livelihood compelled the villagers to run a race with one another. But the social necessity for protection kept every one of them from running too far away from the others. They had learned the important lesson of mutuality—mutual laws for their individual safety through their social coherence. The human race had discovered the fine art of government.

In other words, the primitive villagers (about twelve thousand years ago) had traveled a long way from their simian origin.

The inhabitants of the ancient villages had developed a primitive sort of art—painting and whittling and modeling in clay. They played musical instruments; they danced; they sang; they told tales of heroism—the dawning of poetry; they created folk tales; and they indulged in mimicries of life—the origin of the drama.

And thus we can see, in the village life of the New Stone Age, the first complete outline of that definite human nature which binds us all alike into the single family of man.

THE CRADLE OF CIVILIZATION

In the foregoing outline of man's development from the lower animals we have adopted an arbitrary sequence of events. A word of caution, therefore, is necessary. Science has not as yet been able to establish the *exact order* of the earliest steps taken in the evolution of man. We do not know, for example, whether the invention of tools came *before* or *after* the production of fire. The same is true of several of the other steps in earlier evolution. The *order* of the various events, however, is of minor importance. Of *major* importance is the fact that the human animal developed by slow but definite gradations out of the apelike animal.

And the final step toward what we call our "modern" civilization began, about six thousand years ago, in the valley of the Nile.

This valley had once consisted of a long, narrow plateau of limestone. When the ice melted in the last glacial period, a huge stream of water tumbled down upon the plateau, scooping out a channel about thirty miles wide. Little by little the water subsided, the valley became covered with a strip of fertile soil, and wandering tribes from many regions came to settle down in that spot, to exchange experiences and ideas, and to weld themselves gradually into a united nation.

For the tendency of the gregarious human animal is to unite individuals into groups, groups into villages and towns, and villages and towns into states.

And the Egyptian state—a combination of the Nile settlements —possessed the natural environment for the first human experiment in living together on a large scale. The climate of the Nile Valley was excellent and the water plentiful. As you advanced from the flat deltas to the mountains, you could find the proper soil for all sorts of growing things and building materials. Wild barley, wild wheat, grasslands for the grazing of cattle, meadows, groves, forests of oak, pine, and cedar—food and housing for the living—and, in the foothills and the mountains, quarries of granite for the more permanent houses of the dead.

And so the pioneers of the "national idea" settled down in the Nile Valley, and their population increased rapidly. The river served as a thread that joined them together into a friendly and powerful and prosperous community.

Yet life in the Nile Valley was not always pleasant. For every once in a while—in those days the human race had not as yet learned how to reckon time—the Egyptians noticed that the river was not so friendly to them as usual, and that the barley and other foodstuffs failed to come up as plentifully as in other years. And so it began to dawn upon them, little by little, that if you can't eat up all your food at once you can store the rest of it away for future use.

And thus arose the human custom of saving for a rainy—or, as in Egypt, for a dry—day.

The inundations and the recessions of the Nile led the human race to another important discovery. As the river kept regularly rising and dwindling, some of the keener minds among the Egyptians began to count the number of days between one floodtime and another. In this way arose the first crude calendar in history, and its inventors were regarded with a feeling of deep reverence. They were able to forecast the activities of the Nile. They could —so it seemed—anticipate the caprices of the gods. Indeed, they appeared to be in *very league* with the gods. They were the earliest priests of Egypt, the "wise old men" who interpreted the will of the Nile to the people whose life depended upon it.

At first they communicated their thoughts by word of mouth. But later on they invented a rather complicated system of hieroglyphics—or sacred picture symbols—in order to make their decrees more binding upon the people.

And thus it was the Egyptian priests who invented writing—as a means for interpreting "the will of the gods for the guidance of men."

But hand in hand with the priests, who *interpreted* the will of the gods, there arose in Egypt another powerful group—the men who *enforced* the will of the gods. The priests foretold the days of plenty and the days of hunger, and the men of action stored away the barley against the lean days when their neighbors would need it. Having thus acquired the means for keeping the rest of the people alive, these men of action became the lords and masters over their fellow men. Little by little the cleverest or the most powerful or perhaps the most unscrupulous among them got rid of his competitors; and in this way, as seems likely, the first king arose among men.

The other so-called "cradle of civilization"—Mesopotamia, or the "land between the [Tigris and Euphrates] rivers"—has a similar story to tell. The Mesopotamian Valley is really a continuation of the Nile Valley. This region extends from Egypt, across Palestine and Syria, and into the Iranian plateau. It formed, at the end of the glacial period, one of the leading "highways of traffic" for the diverse groups of people who were migrating from a colder to a more temperate environment. The meeting of all these different tribes resulted in a cross-fertilization of the human mind —a necessary prelude, as many scientists believe, to any significant step in the progress of man. Civilization began in Egypt and in Mesopotamia because the settlers of that region were the products of many different sorts of knowledge garnered in many different parts of the world. Civilization is a process of *mental interaction* —the contribution of all kinds of humans to the advancement of humankind.

THE SAIL AND THE WHEEL

One of the chief factors in civilization is the development of our human ability to utilize the materials and to harness the forces of nature. It was during the great migrations of the glacial period that man discovered new ways of transportation—across rivers and lakes, and over the land. In his earlier days he had learned to sit astride a log as it floated down the current, and to guide his course by paddling his "boat" with his arms and legs. Later, as the need arose for more extensive travel, he learned to tie two or more logs together into a crude raft, and to propel it along the water by means of sticks. In this way he was able to cover longer distances and to carry bigger loads—himself and his family and his goods.

But this, too, was a rather inconvenient way to travel. A raft was difficult to steer, especially over a rapid current. And so the men of the New Stone Age invented a new kind of boat—a log of wood hollowed out in the center and "streamlined" for easy handling.

This dugout canoe led to various similar types of "hollowed" boats. One of the most interesting among them was a craft of inflated skins, used in ancient Egypt and Mesopotamia—and, on the upper reaches of the Nile, even today. Several of these skins —of oxen, sheep, or goats—were blown up like bladders and placed under a platform of light logs. This sort of boat not only was easy to manipulate but was able to carry heavy loads.

Another early type of Egyptian river craft was the "papyrus canoe"—a boat made out of bundles of papyrus reeds with up-turned ends.

But all these boats were designed for traffic on rivers or on comparatively small lakes. They kept the roving spirit of man confined to the land. As they cast their eyes over the sea, the Egyptians and some of the other coastwise nations invented larger boats—or seagoing vessels—made of heavy timber and pro-pelled by the oars of human slaves.

Yet even this was not enough: too little accomplished with too much work. Now here was a great and unused force—the wind —a thing that you couldn't see but could definitely feel. It lashed the branches and whirled the dust and piled the waves into mountains. It drove everything before it. Why not harness it to drive the ships? A simple matter, once you happened to think of it. Set up a stick in your boat, and tie a "wing"—or sail—to the

An Eskimo and his team of dogs. This means of transportation, while quite primitive, is well adapted to the Eskimo's environment, as is the igloo seen at the right.

stick. The wind will strike the sail, and your boat will be carried along without any oar pulling on your part.

And thus began a mode of transportation—the use of wind power to save man power—which continued practically unchanged from about 4000 B.C. to the beginning of the nineteenth century.

Along with his inventiveness in sea transportation, man developed his ingenuity in land transportation. In his early hunting stage he traveled on foot and carried merely his weapons and the animals he killed. If a tribe migrated from one hunting region to another, the men piled the heavier loads—such as baskets, hides, and materials for tents—on the backs of the women while they themselves were left free for the chase.

Later on they trained their domesticated animals—the ox, the ass, the camel, and the horse—to carry their heavy burdens. Still later, as civilization advanced and the traffic between the various settlements became heavier and more frequent, somebody hit upon the idea of hitching an animal to a pole, or combination of cross poles, that would offer a bigger carrying surface for the freightage.

This primitive vehicle, however, had no wheels. It was a sleigh moving on runners even in regions, like Egypt and Mesopotamia, where there was little or no snow. In Egypt the sleigh was used for transporting the gigantic stones required for the building of the Pyramids.

But this was a clumsy method of transportation that consumed time and muscle. In an effort to make the motion of their vehicles speedier and easier, some of the more ingenious "mechanics" of the New Stone Age recalled a simple fact in nature. A rounded object, like a tree trunk or a stone, could either be *dragged lengthwise* or it could be *made to roll in a circle* over the ground. Why not cut a trunk into *rolling sections* and attach them, in place of runners, to a sleigh?

And this is (probably) the way in which the invention of the wheel came about.

At first the wheels were made out of one solid piece of wood. But as soon as the idea of rotation had become familiarly associated with rapidity, the wheels developed into larger disks consisting of a narrow rim supported by four or more spokes.

And then, as the rim of the wooden wheel was found to wear out too easily, a tire made of harder substance was added to the wheel in order to support it as it traveled over the rough ground. But this brings us to the next stage in our human development.

THE AGE OF METAL

One of the most important events in the early development of man was the discovery that the earth contained certain materials which could be melted in the fire and molded into any required shape. These materials came to be known as *metals*—from the Greek *metallon*, a substance which has to be sought for, or unearthed.

The discovery of metals meant not only better transportation, through the reinforcement of wooden wheels with more durable rims, but greater opportunities for progress, through the shaping of finer tools.

Yet the first metal pressed into the service of man was not use-

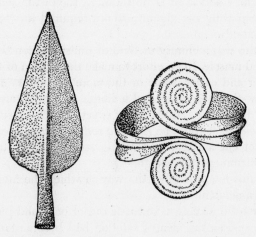

Two early objects made of metal: at left, a spearhead; at right, a bracelet.

ful but ornamental. Gold, it seems, was discovered before any of the other metals. Our primitive ancestors paid more attention to their physical beauty—a biological urge to procreation—than they did to their material comfort. Owing to its brilliant color, a nugget of gold was far more likely to attract early attention than a piece of any other metal.

Next to gold came the discovery of copper. This metal, too, occurs in nuggets; but its surface, in its unpolished form, is a tarnished purple or a greenish black. At first it was overlooked in favor of gold. Later on, however, it was discovered that copper could be made to shine with a little rubbing. And then it became even more useful, because it was more plentiful, than gold. The ancient graves of Egypt and of Mesopotamia have yielded up various copper ornaments and utensils—such as beads, bracelets, fishhooks, axes, chisels, and the like.

At first gold and copper were *hammered* into shape. It was not until much later that man learned to *cast* them into shape, through melting. The discovery of metal casting served as a great spur to man's material and aesthetic development. It enabled him to make machines and statues—huge outpourings of nature's bounty combined with his own fantasy. One of the earliest known products of copper casting is the lion that adorns the Temple of the Moon Goddess at Ur in Chaldea, the birthplace of Abraham. This copper figure is about seven thousand years old.

The next metal used in early history was silver. This metal was known to man—in various sections of Asia—as early as five thousand years ago. The excavations of Babylonia, for example, have yielded up silver headdresses worn by the attendants slain at the funeral of Queen Shubad—to serve her in death as they had served her in life. This fleeting glimpse of the Babylonian funeral enables us, incidentally, to get an excellent picture of man's material, mental, and moral development as he stood upon the threshold of civilization. It is a strange picture of beauty and savagery—physical splendor, religious faith, poetical imagination, and artistic skill intermingled with primitive superstition, sacrificial stupidity, slavish obedience to custom, and utter indifference to human suffering.

But humanity kept on advancing, with new discoveries, new ideas, and new arts. After silver came tin—a lusterless ore which cannot be reduced as readily as copper to a metallic state. It is therefore a tribute to the ingenuity of man that he discovered the use of tin at so early a period in his life. He first used this metal as an alloy with copper to produce bronze. Since bronze was found to be more durable than copper and at the same time less subject to gas bubbles in its melted form, it gave rise to a greater variety and better quality of ornaments and weapons and tools.

The discovery of another metal—lead—resulted in one of the first human attempts at organized sanitation. The Romans used it for the making of pipes to conduct water into their villas. Hence our modern word, *plumbing,* which is derived from *plumbum*—the Latin word for lead.

The last of the important metals discovered in ancient times was iron. Among the earliest known objects of this metal are the beads and the daggers recently found in the Egyptian tomb of Tutankhamen. These iron objects are about thirty-five hundred years old.

It appears that man first became acquainted with iron through its presence in meteorites. The ancient Greek word for this metal is *sideros,* which means "from the stars." This would tend to show that the ancients regarded iron as a metal fallen from the sky, in a shower of meteors.

From the very first iron seems to have been used largely for military purposes. Discovered in large quantities in Asia, it was forged into swords and spears and daggers. And in the warlike temper of the period it became a commodity of considerable commerce among the nations. We have an ancient letter of the Egyptian king, Rameses II (about 1300 B.C.), sent to the Hittite king, Hattushil, with an order for a shipment of iron weapons. In his reply to this letter King Hattushil informed King Rameses that, owing to the heavy demand upon his iron war works, he had no weapons available at the moment.

The discovery of iron ushered in a new phase of human development. Man had advanced successively from the Stone Age to the Age of Copper, of Bronze, and of Iron. And the Age of Iron has not as yet come to an end. We are still living in an environment dominated largely by iron buildings, iron machinery, iron tools, and iron weapons for war.

REVIEW QUESTIONS IN ANTHROPOLOGY

1. About how long ago was the first human footprint made on earth?

2. What animal does man most closely resemble?

3. What faculty enabled man to advance into a new world of thought?

4. What is the name (1) of the so-called "missing link"? (2) Of the so-called "Dawn Man"?

5. What evidence of human progress was discovered together with the skeleton of the Neanderthal Man?

6. Mention four "vestigial" organs in the human embryo.

7. Where did the earliest men find their lodging?

8. Where did they lodge next?

9. Why were our early ancestors gregarious?

10. What, probably, was the first tool ever used by man?

11. What was the next material used for the making of tools? The next after that?

12. What two faculties now distinguished man from the other animals?

13. What was (probably) the earliest method for the production of fire?

14. Are the different races of men descended from different kinds of animals?

15. In what sort of localities was civilization most likely to advance?

16. What caused the transition of mankind from hunting to agriculture?

17. What other important step resulted from this transition?

18. Where were the first houses built?

19. Who lived in these houses?

20. What two human instincts stimulated the progress of the early villagers?

21. About how long ago was this?

22. What is the name of that period?

23. Where did "modern" civilization begin?

24. When?

25. How?

26. Why was this region so favorable for the human experiment in living together on a large scale?

27. Why was life not always pleasant in this region?

28. How did the first calendar arise?

29. Who invented writing?

30. For what purpose?

31. How did the idea of "kingship" arise among men?

32. What was the second "cradle" of modern civilization?

33. What was the earliest type of boat?

34. Mention three other types of primitive boats.

35. About how long did the sailboat rule the sea?

36. Who were the first "beasts of burden"?

37. What was the earliest type of land vehicle?

38. What was the earliest type of wheel?

39. What was the first metal discovered by humans?

40. What was the probable reason for the early discovery of that metal?

41. What was the next metal discovered?

42. About how long ago was the first statue cast out of metal?

43. About how long has silver been known to the human race?

44. What is the nature of the silver ornaments unearthed at Babylonia?

45. How did men first use tin?

46. What is the derivation of the word *plumbing*?

47. What was the last important metal discovered in ancient times?

48. What are the earliest known objects of this metal?

49. How, judging from its Greek name, was this metal discovered?

50. What was the reason for the importance of this metal in ancient times?

ANSWERS TO THE QUESTIONS IN ANTHROPOLOGY

1. About ten million years ago.

2. The ape.

3. The acquisition of speech.

4. (1) Pithecanthropus, or Ape Man.
   (2) Eoanthropus.

5. The skeleton of this creature was surrounded with utensils for a life beyond death—evidence of a primitive religious faith.

6. The body hair, the abbreviated tail at the base of the spine, the "movable" muscles of the ear, and the fleshy projection in the inner corner of the eye.

7. In trees.

8. In caves.

9. For mutual protection against wild beasts.

10. A stick.

11. Bone. Flint.

12. The ability to make tools and to create art.

13. The twirling of one stick in the hollow of another stick.

14. No.

15. On those "highways of traffic" where many different kinds of people intermingled and exchanged ideas and experiences.

16. The discovery that things could be made to grow out of the planting of seeds.

17. The domestication of animals.

18. On wooden piles in the middle of a lake.

19. Humans, together with their animals.

20. The competitive urge for a livelihood and the social instinct for mutual protection.

21. About twelve thousand years ago.

22. The Neolithic, or the New Stone Age.

23. In the valley of the Nile.

24. About six thousand years ago.

25. Through the gathering of wandering tribes from many regions.

26. Because of the excellent climate, the abundance of water, the fertility of the

soil in the valley, and the abundance of granite in the mountains.

27. Because sometimes the waters of the Nile failed to irrigate the soil.

28. Through the counting of the days between the inundations of the Nile that fertilized the soil.

29. The Egyptian priests.

30. In order to interpret "the will of the gods for the guidance of men."

31. Through the "cornering" of the grain against the lean days, and thus holding in their hands the means for keeping the people alive.

32. Mesopotamia.

33. A floating log.

34. A raft, a log hollowed out into a canoe, and a craft of inflated ox- or sheep- or goatskins.

35. Almost six thousand years —from about 4000 B.C. to the beginning of the nineteenth century.

36. The women.

37. A pole—or combination of cross poles—hitched to an

animal, but without wheels.

38. The round section of a tree trunk.

39. Gold.

40. The human preference for adornment—a biological urge—rather than for comfort.

41. Copper.

42. About seven thousand years ago.

43. About five thousand years.

44. They are the headdresses worn by the attendants slain at the funeral of Queen Shubad.

45. As an alloy with copper to produce bronze.

46. It is derived from *plumbum,* the Latin word for lead.

47. Iron.

48. The beads and the daggers found a few years ago in the tomb of Tutankhamen.

49. In the form of meteors, "visitors from the stars."

50. It was used largely for the manufacture of military weapons.

BIOGRAPHICAL SKETCHES OF GREAT ANTHROPOLOGISTS

Blumenbach, Johann Friedrich (1750–1840). German anthropologist. Born at Gotha, he studied medicine at Jena and received his degree as Doctor of Medicine from Göttingen at twenty-three. He joined the faculty of Göttingen as professor. He taught here until he died. He was the first to apply the science of comparative anatomy to anthropology. He did extensive research in human crania, on the basis of which he divided the human race into five great families, the Caucasian, the Malayan, the Mongolian, the Negro, and the American (redskin).

Morgan, Lewis Henry (1818–81). American ethnologist. Born near Aurora, New York, he was educated at Union College and practiced law in Rochester. Becoming interested in the Iroquois tribe of Indians, he went to live with them and observed their culture. His adopted name was "Ta-ya-da-o-wub-rub," given him by the Hawk clan of the Seneca tribe. He published his researches on the Iroquois and followed it with other books on ethnology, notably *Ancient Society, or Researches in the Lines of Human Progress from Savagery, through Barbarism, to Civilization*. In addition to his scientific accomplishments, Morgan served in the New York State Assembly and Senate.

Galton, Sir Francis (1822–1911). British anthropologist. A cousin of Charles Darwin, he was born in Birmingham, England, and studied medicine at the Birmingham Hospital and King's College, London. He continued his education at Cambridge University, graduating in 1844. He explored unknown regions of South Africa and published his experiences in a book. Devoting his life to investigations in anthropology and heredity, he established the science of eugenics. He left his fortune to found a chair in eugenics at the University of London. He did research in mental imagery, color blindness, and fingerprints as a means of identification.

Broca, Paul (1824–80). French anthropologist. Born at Ste. Foy la Grande, he studied medicine at Paris and was appointed to the chair of surgical pathology. Founder of the Anthropological Society, he has been considered the father of the science of craniology. He devoted a great portion of his life to the study of the brain. He is celebrated for his revelation of the seat of articulate speech in the left frontal lobe of the brain, known thereafter as the convolution of Broca.

Tylor, Sir Edward Burnett (1832–1917). British anthropologist. Born in London, the son of a brass founder, he was educated at Grove House, Tottenham, by the Society of Friends. He first achieved recognition as an anthropologist with the appearance of *Researches into the Early History of Mankind*. He first clearly defined the concept of animism, the "doctrine of souls." He published *Primitive Culture: Researches into the Development of Mythology, Philosophy, Religion, Language, Art and Custom*, which became a classic on anthropology. In 1896 he was appointed the first professor of anthropology at Oxford University.

Powell, John Wesley (1834–1902). American ethnologist. Born at Mount Morris, New York, he attended Illinois and Oberlin colleges. He entered the Union Army during the Civil War and lost his arm at the battle of Shiloh, but he continued in the service and rose to the rank of major. In 1867 he embarked on a series of scientific expeditions to the Rocky Mountains and the Colorado River, studying the Indians and their languages. He established a bureau of ethnology at the Smithsonian Institution and assumed directorship of the geological survey. Previously he had been curator of the museum of the Illinois Wesleyan College and at the Normal University. On one occasion he traveled the length of the Mississippi in a rowboat.

Brinton, Daniel Garrison (1837–99). American ethnologist. Born in Pennsylvania, he was educated at Yale. He studied medicine at the Jefferson Medical College and at Paris and Heidelberg. He served as a surgeon in the Union Army during the Civil War. At its conclusion he practiced medicine in Pennsylvania. In 1884 he was appointed professor of ethnology and archaeology in the Academy of Natural Sciences in Philadelphia, and he afterward taught linguistics at the University of Pennsylvania. Among his published works are *The American Race, Races and Peoples, American Hero Myths, Religions of Primitive People.*

Frazer, Sir James George (1854–1941). Scottish anthropologist. Born in Glasgow, he was educated at Glasgow and Cambridge universities. In 1907 he became professor of social anthropology at the University of Liverpool. Frazer's name is linked with the study of primitive religion and myths; his many-volumed masterpiece, *The Golden Bough,* first published in 1890, is a landmark in the history of anthropology.

Pearson, Karl (1857–1936). British educator. Born in London, he was educated at Cambridge University and admitted to the bar. Eventually he became an outstanding authority in the field of eugenics, and was appointed to the chair of eugenics at the University of London. In addition he became director of the Francis Galton Laboratory for National Eugenics. He made important contributions to the mathematical theory of heredity and evolution. He was chosen fellow of the Royal Society and he received the Darwin Medal.

Boas, Franz (1858–1942). German-American anthropologist. Born in Minden, Westphalia, he received his education at Heidelberg, Bonn, and Kiel universities. At the age of twenty-seven he was appointed assistant in the Royal Ethnological Museum in Berlin. He came to the United States and joined the faculty of Clark University as instructor in anthropology. Shortly afterward he was appointed professor at Columbia University and curator of ethnology in the American Museum of Natural History. He took part in the Jesup North Pacific expedition, which revealed significant links between the northwest American and north Asiatic cultures. In 1907 he was elected president of the American Anthropological Society.

Hrdlička, Aleš (1869–1943). Bohemian-born American anthropologist. He came to the United States at an early age and studied medicine, but never pursued a medical career. Between 1899 and 1903 he went on a number of expeditions sponsored by the American Museum of Natural History. In 1904 he joined the United

States National Museum in Washington, D.C., organizing its division of physical anthropology. He became curator in 1910. Hrdlička was never an armchair anthropologist; he traveled to almost every country in North and South America on anthropological expeditions. He contributed to many phases of anthropology, and is known particularly for his support of the theory that the American Indian is of Asiatic origin, having migrated from Siberia to Alaska across the Bering Strait.

Wissler, Clark (1870–1947). American anthropologist. Born in Wayne County, Indiana. He was named curator of anthropology of the American Museum of Natural History in 1906, and professor of anthropology at Yale in 1924. He was one of the foremost students of the American Indian and formulated the culture-area concept to explain the spread of culture.

CAREERS IN ANTHROPOLOGY

There are limited opportunities for anthropologists—on the teaching staffs of universities, and on the research staffs of museums. The Smithsonian Institution, the American Museum of Natural History in New York, the Museum of the University of California, the Field Museum of Natural History in Chicago, employ highly trained specialists in the field of anthropology.

The government offers positions for trained ethnologists. The Office of Indian Affairs, for instance, employs ethnologists who are experts in the field. During World War II anthropologists were consulted by various governments on matters dealing with foreign cultures. Anthropologists are especially needed to develop in the white races a greater understanding of the role of colored races in the world of tomorrow. A background of anthropology is desirable for a number of allied fields: sociology, biology, linguistics, history, geography, psychology.

BIBLIOGRAPHY: BOOKS ON ANTHROPOLOGY FOR FURTHER READING
AND STUDY

Bean, Robert Bennett: *The Races of Man.* New York, 1932.
Boas, Franz: *General Anthropology.* New York, 1938.
Calverton, Victor Francis: *The Making of Man.* New York, 1931.
Cattell, Raymond Bernard: *Human Affairs.* New York, 1937.
Feibleman, James: *The Theory of Human Culture.* New York, 1946.
Goldenweiser, Alexander A.: *Anthropology.* New York, 1937.
Hooton, Ernest Albert: *Apes, Men, and Morons.* New York, 1937.
——: *Twilight of Man.* New York, 1939.
——: *Up from the Ape.* New York, 1946.
Linton, Ralph: *The Study of Man.* New York, 1936.
Lips, Julius Ernst: *Origin of Things.* New York, 1947.
Lowie, Robert Harry: *An Introduction to Cultural Anthropology.* New York,
    1940.
Malinowski, Bronislaw: *A Scientific Theory of Culture.* Chapel Hill, 1944.
Penniman, Thomas Kenneth: *A Hundred Years of Anthropology.* New York,
    1936.
Radin, Paul: *Social Anthropology.* New York, 1932.
Siegel, Bernard J.: *Anthropology for Everyone.* New York, 1949.
Stewart, George Rippey: *Man, an Autobiography.* New York, 1946.
Venable, Vernon: *Human Nature.* New York, 1945.

physiology—the mechanism of the body

THE HUMAN ENGINE

The human body is a machine—governed by the same physical and chemical laws that govern all other machines. But there are several important differences between the mechanism of the living body and the lifeless machines made by man. The human machine can observe its own functions, make its own repairs, refuel and lubricate its own engine, and reproduce other machines to take its place when it is worn out.

Every human machine is compelled to go through the same physical routine. Every man has to feed his stomach, eliminate the waste, supply his lungs with air, and refresh his body with sleep.

For the human body is constantly spending its energy. Not only is it always at work—even in sleep the blood flows and the heart beats and the lungs breathe—but it is always losing heat to the outside air and replacing it from the reservoir of energy within.

The human body, in other words, is a combustion engine. A man, like a motorcar, will burn up a definite amount of energy upon the intake of a definite amount of fuel. Both the man and the motor are driven by the oxidation of fuel into power. When the fuel stops, the power stops and the engine goes dead. For the only way to generate power in any machine—whether human or otherwise—is through the combustion (or burning) of food.

HEAD, TRUNK, AND LIMBS

The human machine is a symmetrical body consisting of three main sections—the head or the engineer, the trunk or the engine, and the limbs or the instruments of locomotion.

1. The head—or skull—is the seat of the brain, and the brain is the director of the body. Yet the *directorship* of the brain is not a *dictatorship*. It is rather a representative center of government which gives out instructions dependent upon a continuous stream of information that pours in from every part of the body. And the agents of this information are the various sense organs—of sight, hearing, taste, touch, smell, warmth, coldness, pleasure, pain, and the like.

The continuous messages from the sense organs to the brain and the consequent orders from the brain to the body are carried over an elaborate system of telegraph wires, or nerves. These message carriers are tough cords of interwoven fibers held together by delicate sheaths. They weave a pattern of sense impressions and motor impulses over the entire body, so that every healthy muscle has its functioning nerve system. When a nerve is severed or diseased, the muscle becomes paralyzed. For it has lost its means of communication with the central government of the brain.

2. The trunk is connected to the brain of the human machine by means of the spinal cord—the great central channel through which the messages travel between the brain and the rest of the body. The spinal cord is really the elongated continuation of the brain. It is—so to speak—the body branch of the cerebral government in the human organism.

As a protection against injury, the spinal cord—like the brain—is encased in a compartment of bone. This bony compartment—or spinal column—forms the "tie beam" that binds together the skeletal framework of the trunk. The tie beam is thus a hollow tube that houses the spinal cord. But it is a *flexible* tube, consisting of twenty-six vertebrae—or knobby rings—jointed together and reaching down from the top of the neck to the bottom of the spine.

At (approximately) its center, the spinal column supports the ribs which form a protective cylinder around the chest, or upper part of the trunk. The cavity—or thorax—thus enclosed by the ribs is further protected by the breastbone, which is situated in front of the chest. And housed in this protective cylinder lie some of the most important parts of the human engine—the lungs which circulate the air, the heart which pumps the blood, and the esophagus or canal through which the food passes into the stomach.

At the bottom of the chest cavity there is a muscular platform called the diaphragm, or midriff. This platform divides the trunk of the human engine into an upper and a lower story. The upper story, as we have already seen, contains the heart, the lungs, and the esophagus. The lower story—or abdomen—contains several of the other important parts of the human engine: the furnace of the stomach, which transforms the food into energy; the plumbing of the bowels, the bladder, the liver, and the kidneys, which carry off the waste matter; and—especially significant as a distinguishing feature of the living machine of the body—most of the organs of reproduction.

3. Lastly we come to the outreaching sections of the human engine: the arms, which do the lifting and the carrying and the throwing; and the legs, which perform the walking and the leaping and the running. These limbs—with their tentacles of fingers and toes at the extremes—are united to the engine of the body by a complicated leverage of jointed bones, and they respond to the promptings of the brain by an equally complicated system of contracting and expanding muscles.

And this, in very brief outline, is the basic structure of the self-moving, self-observing, self-feeding, and self-reproducing machine known as man. It is a machine whose various parts are propelled by hundreds of muscles, stimulated by thousands of nerves, and controlled by the central direction of the brain. And the entire surface of this machine is held safely together under an elastic covering of skin, and every nook and cranny of its mechanism is washed continuously in a life-preserving stream of blood.

But let us look a little more closely at some of the organs and functions of this remarkable machine.

THE MUSCLES

The muscles—derived, interestingly enough, from *musculus,* the Latin word for "a little mouse"—constitute the red meat of the human machine. Many of our muscles are connected to the extremities of two separate bones, and they are able to manipulate these bones by changing their own shape—that is, by stretching out to become longer and thinner, or by pulling together to become shorter and thicker. Thus, for example, the thirty-two bones of the arm and the hand can be made to assume many different kinds of positions—and thus to perform many different kinds of work—through the contraction of the fifty-eight muscles to which these bones are attached. The various expressions of the human face are the results of the various motions of our thirty-one face muscles. The muscles of the neck enable us to move the head without turning the body—a defense mechanism in the evolutionary struggle for existence. A neckless animal—like the frog, for example—is compelled to shift its entire trunk with the turning of its mouth as it goes about clumsily snapping for its food.

The muscles of the shoulders are connected both to the shoulder bones and to the arm bones. The same double connection is true of the muscles of the chest. And thus the movements of the arms are harmonized with the movements of the trunk, since there is a common set of muscles that provides a leverage for their different sets of bones.

In like manner the muscles of the hips and of the buttocks are so joined to the various bones of the legs and of the trunk as to bind them together into a harmony of motion. Moreover, some of these muscles control the hip joints along with the hips and the legs and thus they provide for the support of the entire body in action.

These are but a few of the many hundreds of muscles which, in conjunction with the bones, constitute the coherence and the leverage and the motor agency of the human machine.

THE FIVE FUNCTIONS OF THE BODY

The mechanism of the human body is sustained, repaired, and replaced through five fundamental sets of organs. These five sets of organs, working harmoniously together, take care of the *circulation,* or the diffusion of the blood throughout the body; the *respiration,* or the inbreathing of wholesome air and the outbreathing of poisonous air; *alimentation,* or the conversion of food into tissue and energy; *elimination,* or the excretion of the waste matter from the human engine; and *reproduction,* or the process of building new machines to maintain the continuity of life.

We shall consider, in turn, each of the above functions and the organs through which they operate.

circulation—the composition of the blood

The entire expanse of the body's muscular mechanism—indeed, every nook and cranny of its living tissue—is continually irrigated by an intricate river traffic of blood. This blood stream, with its principal channel and its hundreds of tributaries, serves as the "water route" of commerce between the various sections of the living organism. It brings to the muscles the fuel and the oxygen necessary for their health, and it carries away from them the sewage that would poison their life.

Yet the blood stream is more than a mere medium for traffic. It is not, like a river in a landscape, a current of lifeless fluid. It is a living tissue, like a muscle or a bone. But unlike a muscle or a bone, it is a liquid rather than a solid tissue.

This liquid bodily tissue called *blood*—from the Anglo-Saxon *blowan,* to bloom—is an organization of innumerable living cells that float in a watery stream. The cells—or *corpuscles,* little bodies —are of two kinds: red and white. The red color of healthy blood is due to the fact that it contains a predominant number of red cells. These red corpuscles—their color is due to a red pigment called *hemoglobin*—are exceedingly small. The average human body, whose blood component is about one gallon, contains within it a vastly greater number of these red little living crea-

tures than the entire human population of the world. And these
red corpuscles have an active duty to perform. They carry the
oxygen throughout the body, and they eliminate some waste
products. When they diminish greatly in number, the blood
stream becomes *anemic* and the body suffers from too little oxygen
and too much waste.

Red Cells   White Cells

The two types of blood cells.

Yet the white corpuscles, too, have their uses—in conjunction
with a sufficient supply of their red collaborators. While the red
cells serve as the *workers* of the human body—distributing the
oxygen and removing wastes—the white cells serve as the *soldiers*
—fighting off the many bacterial parasites that are continually
laying siege to the body.

This working and fighting community of cells keeps circulating
through the body over a liquid stream known as the *plasma*—a
waterlike compound of various chemicals. The containing
plasma, just like the contained corpuscles, plays an important
role in the life of the human body. For the plasma serves as the
medium not only for the sailing of the cells in the performance of
their various duties, but also for the solution and the transportation of all the food nutrients necessary to the healthy organization of the body.

One of the most interesting properties of the plasma is its
ability to form its own protective shield when the surface of the
body is cut and the blood begins to flow out. In most bodies this
outflow of blood solidifies into a clot which automatically seals
the wound. Were it not for this "self-bandaging" power of the
blood, the slightest scratch might result in the victim's bleeding
to death. There are some people, indeed, whose blood can never
clot. This disease—ironically called *hemophilia,* a love for bleeding—is hereditary. Several members of the last royal dynasty in

Spain were afflicted with hemophilia—a possibly contributory factor in their political as well as their physical decay. This blood defect is at times so serious in its consequences that patients suffering from it have been known to die in the dentist's chair.

But, on the other hand, the tendency of the blood to coagulate —that is, to thicken into clots—is not always an unmixed blessing. For one of the most dreaded diseases today is *thrombosis*—the formation of a clot which obstructs a blood vessel and frequently results in death.

So much for the composition of the blood. And now let us glance at the manner in which it flows over the body.

The blood is kept in continual circulation over the body through a network of major and minor channels. The major channels are the thick arteries, along which the purified blood is pumped out of the heart; and the minor channels are the thin veins, along which the impure blood flows back into the heart.

This system of circulation is regulated by the manipulation of the heart valves which keep the blood flowing in one direction only. The circuit made by the arteries and the veins may be roughly compared to a hollow ring filled with water and fitted with a knob—the heart. This ring contains a set of valves which open and close in such a way as to keep the water flowing always in a clockwise direction.

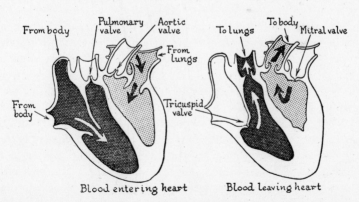

The heart shown receiving blood from the body and the lungs, at left, and pumping blood out to the body and lungs, at right.

And now, attached to this central system of circulation, there are a great many branches—or tributaries—which carry the blood to the various parts of the body, transform the food into flesh, cleanse away the impurities, and keep the organism alive.

But this is only part of the story. As we have noted above, the blood is pure when it leaves the heart to perform its work, and impure when it returns to the heart after its work has been per-

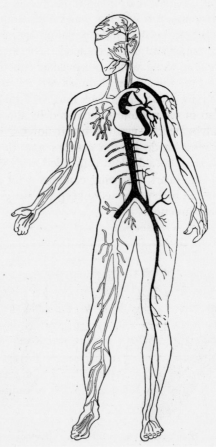

The circulatory system. Arteries are shown in heavy black lines, veins in open lines.

formed. Another process is now necessary to purify the blood for its next circuit. This process takes place in a smaller circular journey of the blood stream—from the heart to the lungs, where it is purified, and then back again into the heart, where it is ready for its next larger journey over its circular course.

And thus the revolution of the blood stream is double rather than single. Its course describes a figure eight instead of a circle. To return to our former comparison, the circuit of the blood is similar to the passage of water over *two* hollow rings—one larger and the other smaller, and both of them joined together at the common projection or knob, the pumping heart.

The human heart consists of two pumps that work side by side. The larger pump distributes the blood for its irrigation throughout the body, and the smaller pump sends it for its purification to the lungs.

And this irrigation and purification system of the blood stream consists of so many tributary canals—or *capillaries*—that if you were to join them end to end they would stretch into a river about sixty thousands miles in length!

respiration—the mechanism of breathing

Our human breathing apparatus consists of the nose, the mouth, the windpipe (*trachea*), and the lungs.

The outer air that is taken into the nostrils needs considerable cleansing before it can be transferred to the lungs, for the air is full of irritating dust and injurious bacteria. And therefore the nose is supplied with a network of filtering chambers. These nasal chambers are divided by bony partitions and fitted with tiny brushes of hair and with glands that produce a sticky substance called mucus. The brushes remove from the atmosphere the heavier particles of dust, and the layers of mucus imprison the lighter bacteria like so many flies caught on sheets of flypaper. This shows how important it is to breathe through the nose rather than the mouth.

Yet even the nose is an insufficient safeguard against the excessive dust and bacteria of our densely populated areas. In such districts a considerable amount of impure air escapes through the nasal barriers and "crashes" into the lungs. People who live in smoke-ridden cities, or who work in stuffy factories or in coal mines, become so saturated with dirt that their lung tissue gradually turns black.

Under ordinary conditions, however, the nose is an adequate filter for the impurities of the air.

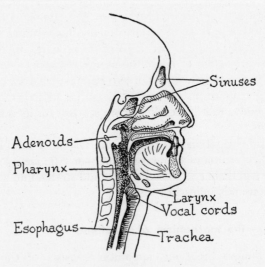

The respiratory system in the head.

As the outer air is filtered through the nostrils and into the mouth, it passes to the trachea—a narrow tube that leads from the mouth to the chest. When the trachea enters the chest, it branches out into two sections called *bronchi,* and these two sections in turn branch out into many little air canals of the lungs.

The lungs gather up the air into these canals and use it as a cleanser for the blood that keeps arriving from the heart. The action of this upgathering of the pure air into the lungs is called *inspiration,* or *inbreathing.* Along with this, the lungs perform another action—*expiration,* or *outbreathing*—the expulsion of the impure air from the body.

This rhythmical breathing of the lungs—the bellows of the human mechanism—is produced through the movements of the walls that enclose the chest. These walls are the ribs and the diaphragm. When the muscles that move the chest walls become tensed, they cause a sucking of the air *into* the lungs; and when they become relaxed, they cause a pushing of the air *out* of the lungs.

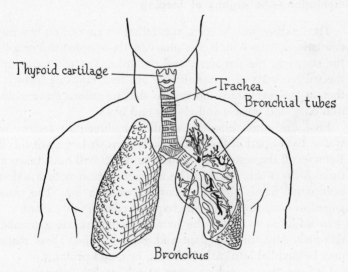

The respiratory system in the neck and chest.

And here is an interesting point. Men breathe largely through the movements of the diaphragm, while women breathe principally through the actions of the ribs. The reason for this difference in the respiration of the two sexes is due to a precaution of nature. For the diaphragm, in its rhythmical breathing, induces a constantly repeated pressure upon the abdomen—a disturbance which, during a woman's pregnancy, might result in serious injury to the embryo.

But, both in the male and in the female, the respiration of the lungs performs a double service. It frees the blood of its carbon dioxide, and it supplies it with oxygen. And the blood uses this oxygen to oxidize body tissue and some digested foods, thus liberating heat which helps to maintain the body temperature at

98.6° F. But the burning of the food and tissue serves not only as a means for heating the body but—as we have already observed—for the production of the energy that keeps the human machine in motion.

alimentation—the organs of feeding

The feeding process—or alimentation—is carried on in a factory consisting of the mouth, the pharynx, the esophagus (or gullet), the stomach, the pancreas, and the liver. Let us glance first at the various sorts of materials that are sent into this factory, and then at the mechanical operations that transform these materials into bone and muscle and energy and blood.

First, and most important of all, our alimentary factory needs water. Every part of the human body consists largely of this fluid. Remove all the water from a man, and you will have taken away three fifths of his weight. The average person with a sedentary occupation needs almost a quart of water a day. The man engaged in hard physical labor requires considerably more.

In addition to water the human factory needs a number of materials consisting of plant and animal tissue. These materials may be divided into carbohydrates, fats, and proteins.

Carbohydrates—such as sugar, starch, and the glucose of many fruits—are substances compounded of one part carbon and one part water. Fats—including vegetable oils—are substances that are insoluble in water. Both carbohydrates and fats are easy to burn, and therefore they make a good fuel for the body. Indeed, one of these substances may suffice if the other is hard to get. Thus the inhabitants of the Arctic Circle live largely on fats, while the people of the Torrid Zone subsist mainly on carbohydrates.

Finally, the human food factory requires materials containing protein. These materials consist not only of carbon, hydrogen, and oxygen, but also of nitrogen—a chemical absent in fats—and (frequently) phosphorus, sulphur, and iron. Such foods as meat, cheese, eggs, peas, and beans are rich in protein. Like the fats and the carbohydrates, the proteins make a good fuel for the generation of energy. But they perform one additional service which the other two kinds of food cannot perform. They supply the *stuff for*

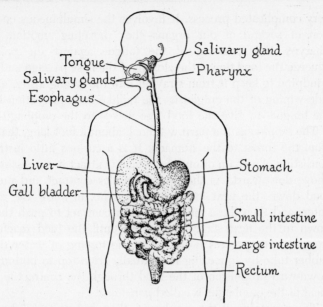

The digestive system.

the building, as well as the *fuel for the burning,* of our human machines.

And now, having glanced at the materials that go into our digestive factory, let us look at the process of their digestion. The word *digestion,* from the Latin *digestio,* means "an orderly distribution." The mechanism that transforms and distributes the food into the tissues of the body begins with the mouth. This little engine, by means of its sharp prongs, or teeth, grinds up the food into minute particles and mixes them thoroughly with saliva. The function of the saliva is twofold: it lubricates the food as an aid to easier swallowing, and it begins the digestive process of the food by transforming its starch into sugar.

When the food has been thus chewed and saturated with saliva, it is passed along to the next step in the "assembly line" of our factory. This step is the transmission of the food, through the contraction of the pharynx, into the esophagus. The familiar name for this action is *swallowing*—a very simple word for a

very complicated process. It involves the simultaneous co-operation of several of our organs—the "shoveling" motion of the
pharynx, the thrusting of the tongue against the palate to
squeeze the food down, the closing of the nose passage and of the
windpipe to keep it from straying into the wrong aisles, and the
sideswiping of the epiglottis—the taillike little projection behind
the tongue—to give the food free access to the esophagus.

The *esophagus* is a narrow tunnel, about a foot long, that leads
from the throat to the stomach. It is a curious little instrument
consisting of a chain of muscles which contract in succession from
above downward. As the upper muscles contract and push the
food down, the next lower muscles relax to allow the food to
enter; and then these muscles in turn contract to push the food
down to the next stage; and so on until the food reaches the
stomach. The process is similar to the forcing of water down a
rubber tube by squeezing it gradually from top to bottom. This
downward propulsion of the food through the contractile movement of the esophagus is called *peristalsis*.

The peristalsis of the esophagus, then, brings each "shovelful"
of food from the mouth to the stomach. The stomach is a little
furnace—with a capacity of about two quarts—having an upper
opening and a lower. The upper opening is the *esophagus,* which
brings the food *into* the stomach; and the lower is the *duodenum,*
or small intestine, which carries the food *out* of the stomach.

The mechanism of the stomach consists of two important operations—the muscular action of the outer wall, and the glandular
action of the inner wall. The muscles churn the food as it boils
in the stomach, and the glands manufacture the gastric juices
which enable the food to become digested.

As the food undergoes its digestion in the stomach—a process
that takes from about one to four hours—it becomes soaked with
the gastric juices and boiled into a soft and acidy pulp, or *chyme*.

During this digestive period in the stomach the opening between the stomach and the duodenum is automatically closed
against the too early entrance of the food into the intestines. But
as rapidly as a portion of the food becomes thoroughly digested
—that is, completely transformed into chyme—it is thrust, by the
churning motion of the stomach muscles, against the opening of
the duodenum as a signal that it is ready to pass on.

And, in answer to the signal, the gate is "unlocked" and the food is conveyed to its next stage along the "assembly line." This stage—the small intestine—is a tube about an inch in diameter and seven yards long. It lies, in an intricate arrangement of coils, within the cylinder of the abdomen. This intestine is divided into two parts. The first part, aided by its two collaborators—the *liver* and the *pancreas*—which are connected to it by a narrow channel, continues the transformation of the food into suitable material for the building of the body tissues. This process of transformation in the smaller intestine, like the process of digestion in the stomach, is maintained through a rhythmical contraction of the muscles. And thus the food is gradually rechurned and fortified with the necessary juices of the liver and the pancreas—an operation of about three hours—until it is ready for its journey to the second part of the small intestine.

Here it undergoes its transmutation from food into blood. And the agency of this transmutation consists of a multitude of little "fingers"—called *villi*—which gather up the molecules of the digested food and send them into the blood stream to replenish the energy and the tissues of the body.

As for the balance of the food—the part found unsuitable for body building—it is taken up into the large intestine, or *colon*. This intestine, about five feet in length, starts at the bottom of the smaller intestine and surrounds it, like a frame around a picture, up one side of the abdomen, across the top, and down the other side, until it reaches the rectum, or the opening for the elimination of the waste matter.

And this brings us to the fourth of the five essential functions of the human mechanism.

elimination—the plumbing system of the body

The sewage system of the human body consists of several organs—the colon, the rectum, the bladder, the kidneys, the sweat glands, the mucous membranes, and the salivary (or spittle) glands. In addition to these some of the organs that perform other important functions are also called upon to help in the ejection of poisonous matter from the body. Thus the lungs expel the impure air; and the liver converts the harmful ammonia, which gathers in the combustion engines of the body, into harmless urea and sends it to the kidneys to be thrown out in the form of urine.

Of all the "exhaust" agents of the body, the most important are the *colon*, the *liver*, and the *kidneys*. We have already glanced at the first two; we shall now look at the third.

The kidneys are the "bouncers" of the undesirable elements that enter the body. They stand in the small of the back, one on either side—a pair of "eliminators" shaped like boxing gloves—full of "blood and fight." They take up the matter that passes into them through the blood stream, sort out the good molecules from the bad, return the good molecules to the blood, and filter the bad ones down in a trickle of watery fluid—urine—to the bladder. Here the fluid gathers, little by little, for its periodic expulsion when the reservoir of the bladder becomes overfilled.

The apparatus of the kidneys is an interesting contraption of millions of little tubes. Each of these tubes gathers up its quota of blood for its particular job of "inspection" and elimination. Thus there is a tremendous activity in this part of the human factory. The kidneys are the exhaust organs of the *liquid* poisons of the body, just as the colon is the exhaust organ of the *solid* or *semiliquid* poisons. And the two organs—like *all* the organs in the healthy body—are in constant co-operation. For example, there are certain solids—like phosphate of lime and other insoluble minerals—in the blood. These minerals, if they came into the kidneys, would form into masses of crystals and clog up their action. But in the co-operative provision of nature, the colon takes these crystals out of the blood into its own channel of sewage disposal, and thus saves the kidneys from unnecessary work and pain.

For the healthy human mechanism is an engine of many parts, working harmoniously together toward a single end—the preservation of life.

reproduction—the replacement of the human machine

The last of the five important functions of the body—the process of reproduction—constitutes the most important difference between the human mechanism and the man-made machines. And therefore, from the biological standpoint, the organs of reproduction are among the most interesting of all the organs in the human body.

These organs are extremely complicated—not only in themselves, but in their relation to the entire body. And our scientific knowledge regarding their nature is still far from complete. Yet, in spite of this, it is possible to get a fairly accurate picture—in simple outline—of their general service in the continuity of life.

The elements of reproduction are the cells known as *gametes* —from the Greek word *gamein,* to marry. They are the cells which unite the two sexes in marriage. These gametes are of two kinds —the female *ova,* or eggs, and the male *spermatozoa,* or living seeds. The only way for the human machine to reproduce itself is through the union of these two cells. For the egg of the female must be fertilized by the seed of the male before a new life can begin.

The female egg is spherical in shape and so small that it would take about one hundred and twenty-five of them, lying side by side, to measure one inch. These eggs are manufactured in the *ovaries,* of which there are two in the female body. The process of their manufacture follows a rhythmical trend. Once every

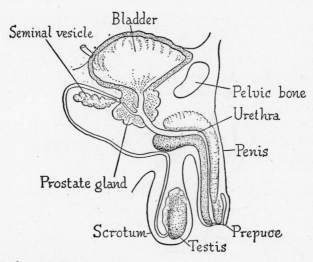

The male reproductive system.

month an egg ripens in one of the two ovaries and is discharged, through muscular action, to the "marriage chamber," where it is ready to be fertilized by the male sperm—or seed.

The sperm that performs the fertilization is the one successful candidate among the *two hundred million* that have entered the female body in their effort to "consummate the marriage." All the unsuccessful candidates die a natural death without the privilege of creating a new life.

The successful seed, like all the others, is considerably smaller than the ovum. But, if inferior in size, it is superior in agility. Consisting of a rounded head and a long, lashing tail, it whips itself furiously along the passages leading to the "bridal chamber." And when the "bridegroom" meets the "bride," the resulting embrace brings about the fertilization of the egg.

Then an interesting thing happens. The fertile sperm burrows its head into the fertilized ovum, sheds its tail for which it has no further use, and merges its own male substance with the female substance of the egg. Then the two creatures, having become one, begin their development into the embryo of the new living organism called a human child. This new organism—through the

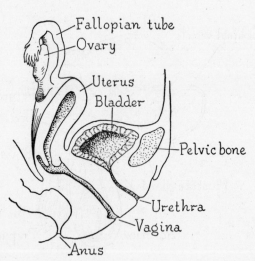

The female reproductive system.

union of its female parent, the ovum, and its male parent, the sperm—is now adjusted to inherit the characteristics of both.

As for the factors that determine the sex of the new life, and the organs responsible for the secretions that produce the rhythmic changes in the ovaries—such as the monthly ripening of the one egg for its fertilization and the expulsion of all the unnecessary eggs from the body—these are still subjects for scientific research and theoretical detours. We shall therefore by-pass these subjects and go on with the more certain knowledge dealing with the development of the newly created embryo.

When the united egg-sperm is ready for the next stage of its development, it is taken up into the *uterus,* where it becomes embedded in a cradle of soft muscular cushions and purifying glands and nourishing blood. Here the original egg cell undergoes *segmentation,* or cutting up. This is a process of *multiplication through division.* The first cell is divided into two, the two are divided into four, the four into eight, the eight into sixteen, and so on. The cells keep on dividing, and multiplying, and growing into the substance of the new life. At first this growth is extremely slow; at the end of two weeks the entire embryo is only about one twenty-fifth of an inch in diameter. But from that time on the growth becomes much more rapid, and the first

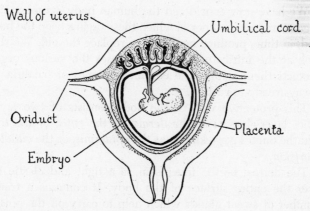

A human embryo in the uterus.

visible organs of the body and the brain begin to appear. At the end of six weeks the multiplying cells of the embryo have developed into the definite traces of a beating heart, a set of limbs, a digestive system, a pair of kidneys—and the rudimentary gametes for the generation of the next successive life when its own life is ready to be replaced.

But at this early stage the embryo has such strange elements as the tail of a monkey, the gills of a fish, and other vestiges of the early ancestors of man. All these telltale vestiges, however, are gone by the end of the second month, and the embryo begins to have a distinctly human appearance.

From this time on the *form* of the embryo undergoes very little change. The only development until the time of its birth consists in its *growth*.

This growth is stimulated by the food that passes from the mother into the child through the *placenta*—the connective tissue between the life that is spending itself and the life that is about to begin.

And thus the old machine pours its blood and its energy into the new, and the reproductive evolution of life goes incessantly on.

THE RAMPART BETWEEN THE BODY AND THE WORLD

We have now considered the human body, its most important organs, and the manner in which these organs keep the body alive and, in time, produce new lives to replace the old. We shall now look at the intricate wall that encloses the various organs and protects them against the enormous armies of bacteria that are always ready to rush in.

This protective wall of the body consists of two layers: the inner layer—known as the *derma,* or the *cutis,* or the *true skin;* and the outer layer—known as the *epidermis,* or the *cuticle,* or the *scarfskin.*

The derma, or the inner skin, is a tight and elastic covering over the entire surface of the body. It contains a tremendous number of sweat glands which help to carry off the poisons that accumulate in the various organs. It serves as a further protection against injury through its function as the medium for the sense of touch. This sense of touch makes the skin highly susceptible to pain—another defense mechanism against the approach of danger. It is irrigated, like the rest of the body, by a copious system of blood vessels, intersected by a telegraphic network of nerves, and kept fresh by an active multiplication of living cells. Through its intimate connection with the body, its cellular activity, and its sensitiveness to touch and pain, it forms the *inner defense* of the rampart that surrounds the human individual.

The epidermis, or the scarfskin, forms the *outer defense*. This outer layer of the skin consists of a covering of dry, horny cells that have died because of their remoteness from the blood supply which nourishes the body. These cells, in a literal sense, may be said to form a rampart of dead soldiers who have "sacrificed themselves" for the good of the living cells within.

For this outer rampart keeps the bacteria from invading the body and causing disease. Sometimes, indeed, a breach is made in the wall when the skin is cut. And then a terrific battle takes place between the invading bacteria and the defending tissues of the body. The blood vessels in the vicinity of the breach become dilated, and a host of *leucocytes*—or white corpuscles—is rushed along the widened channels of the blood vessels to fight the bacteria at the invaded spot. These leucocytes try to conquer the bacteria by eating them up and throwing them out as digested dead waste. And they succeed in doing this when the bacteria are few in number or insufficient in strength.

But when the bacteria are numerous and strong, the battle lasts longer and becomes more intense. And then the battlefield —or the area of the infection—begins to show the signs of the conflict. The skin becomes swollen and sore. The bacteria keep increasing in numbers as they overrun the invaded territory and destroy the healthy tissue. And the leucocytes, in their effort to consume both the bacteria and the destroyed tissue, are taxed beyond their strength and are themselves destroyed. After a while the dead matter—including both the leucocytes and the bacteria—becomes collected into a heap on the battlefield and converted into an abscess, or cavity of pus.

And this leads to a new phase in the battle. The leucocytes try to form a protective ring around the abscess, and the bacteria

try to spread into the body beyond the borders of this ring. If
the bacteria succeed in their efforts, the infection may reach
the blood stream and serious injury—even death—may result. But
if the leucocytes prevail, the abscess breaks open at the surface
of the skin, the pus is expelled from the body, the invading bacteria are driven off, the breach in the rampart is healed, and the
skin is ready once more for its defensive duty against the outer
world.

THE LIFE CYCLE—GROWTH, MATURITY, DECAY, DEATH

The human body grows for about twenty-five years. But the
human brain keeps on developing for about forty or fifty years.
Thus the maturity of the body and the maturity of the brain are
reached at different periods of a person's life. It takes much
longer to develop a full-grown thinker than a full-grown athlete.
This natural disharmony between the development of the body
and the development of the mind is of great disservice to the
athlete, who is generally forgotten long before he dies. But it is
of great advantage to the thinker, who can keep working at his
best—or almost at his best—until the very twilight of his life.

When the life of the human body—or of the human brain—has
reached the maturity of its growth, it remains at a standstill for
a while and then begins its decay. Yet these stages—of growth,
maturity, and decay—have been only roughly defined in the above
discussion. Strictly speaking, the three stages go on simultaneously throughout the body. The various bodily tissues—such as
the first and the second sets of milk teeth, the wisdom teeth, and
the like—undergo development along different periodic rhythms
in the current of life. One part of the body may be wearing out
while another part is just beginning its development. And still
another part at that selfsame period may be going through the
transitional stage between growth and decay. And thus there is
in reality no standstill in the movement of the human mechanism
from the beginning to the end. Through one or another of its
parts the body is always undergoing a triple process of growth,
maturity, and decay. Even in disease, when the entire body may

be disintegrating, there may be tissues that are enjoying an uninterrupted process of growth.

Yet there comes a period when the body and the brain as a whole may be definitely said to be going downhill. This is the period of old age. Its beginning is heralded by the telltale lines on the forehead and at the corners of the eyes and of the mouth—a "written announcement" that the elasticity of the skin, the outer defense of the body, is becoming impaired.

From now on the vital organs of the body keep on deteriorating, their reactions become less efficient for the storing of energy and the struggle against disease, and the old machine is ready to be thrown into the scrap heap while the newer machines of its own creation are preparing to take its place in the perpetual activity of life.

Then comes the final breakdown of the machine through the complete failure of one of the vital organs—and the body dies. The exact chemical basis for our physical decay and death is undetermined as yet. There are some animals that can survive for several centuries, and some plants whose life span can extend into thousands of years. When we can thoroughly understand the chemistry of our mortal decay, we may be able to prolong our human life up to a hundred years and even beyond.

In time our increasing knowledge may very likely result in a substantially longer span of life. But the individual life—whether longer or shorter by a few years—seems always destined to end in death after it has provided for the continuation of life in the mass. For this is Nature's way of scrapping the old machines to make way for the new.

REVIEW QUESTIONS IN PHYSIOLOGY

1. What are the chief distinctions between the mechanism of the human body and that of a man-made machine?

2. What sort of engine is the human body?

3. What are the three main sections of the human body?

4. Mention seven of our physical senses.

5. What happens to a muscle when its nerve system becomes dissevered?

6. What is the spinal cord?

7. How is it protected against injury?

8. What is the thorax?

9. What three important organs are situated in the thorax?

10. What is the diaphragm?

11. Mention the important organs contained in the abdomen.

12. What are the muscles?

13. How are the movements of the arms harmonized with the movements of the trunk?

14. What are the five sets of organs that sustain the mechanism of the human body?

15. What are the two main functions of the blood stream?

16. When does the blood stream become anemic?

17. What is the function of the white corpuscles?

18. What property of the blood prevents the excessive bleeding of wounds?

19. What is thrombosis?

20. What are the two main groups of channels for the circulation of the blood?

21. What organ directs the circulation of the blood?

22. What organ purifies the blood?

23. What figure does the blood stream describe in its circulatory course?

24. What are the duties performed by the two heart pumps?

25. About how long is the total stretch of the capillaries that carry the blood stream to every part of the body?

26. What is the function of the nose in breathing?

27. What service does the air perform in the lungs?

28. Mention the principal alimentary (not to be confused with elementary) organs.

29. What is the most important of the foods required by the human body?

30. What are the three kinds of plant and animal tissue required by the body?

31. Mention some of the foods rich in protein.

32. What is the meaning of digestion?

33. What double duty is performed by the saliva?

34. What is the esophagus?

35. What is the function of the muscles in the outer wall of the stomach?

36. What is the function of the glands in the inner wall of the stomach?

37. Name the agency that transmutes food into blood.

38. What are the three most important "exhaust" agents of the body?

39. What is the function of the kidneys?

40. What are the gametes?

41. Name the two kinds of gametes.

42. About how many seeds enter into the competition for the creation of a single life?

43. About how big is the human embryo at the end of two weeks?

44. At the end of what period does the embryo show the first traces of a heart, a pair of kidneys, and a set of limbs?

45. At the end of what period does the embryo assume a distinctly human appearance?

46. Name the two layers of the skin.

47. What corpuscles of the blood protect the skin against infection?

48. What happens when the bacteria put up a strong fight?

49. How long does the human body keep developing? The human mind?

50. What are the first telltale symptoms of old age?

ANSWERS TO THE QUESTIONS IN PHYSIOLOGY

1. The human body, unlike the man-made machine, can observe its own functions, make its own repairs, refuel and lubricate its own engine, and reproduce itself.

2. A combustion engine. It generates power through the burning of food.

3. The head, the trunk, and the limbs.

4. Sight, hearing, taste, touch, smell, pleasure, and pain.

5. It becomes paralyzed.

6. The elongated continuation of the brain—the central channel through which the messages travel between the brain and the rest of the body.

7. Through its encasement in a covering of bone—the spinal column.

8. The chest cavity enclosed by the ribs.

9. The lungs, the heart, and the esophagus.

10. The muscular platform that divides the chest from the abdomen.

11. The stomach, the bowels, the bladder, the liver, the kidneys, and most of the reproductive organs.

12. The red meat of the human machine.

13. Through the leverage provided by the common sets of muscles to the different sets of bones.

14. The organs of circulation, respiration, alimentation, elimination, and reproduction.

15. It supplies the muscles with fuel and oxygen, and carries away the poisons.

16. When the red corpuscles diminish greatly in number.

17. They fight against the bacteria that besiege the body.

18. The ability to form a clot shield which seals up the wound.

19. The formation of a clot which obstructs a blood vessel.

20. The arteries and the veins.

21. The heart.

22. The pair of lungs.

23. The figure eight.

24. The larger pump distributes the blood for its irrigation, and the smaller pump sends it to the lungs for its purification.

25. About sixty thousand miles long.

26. It filters the air before its passage into the lungs.

27. It cleanses the blood that keeps arriving there from the heart.

28. The mouth, the pharynx, the esophagus, the stomach, the pancreas, and the liver.

29. Water.

30. Carbohydrates, fats, and proteins.

31. Meats, cheese, eggs, peas, and beans.

32. The orderly distribution of the food taken into the body.

33. It lubricates the food and transforms its starch into sugar.

34. A narrow, foot-long tunnel that conveys the food from the throat to the stomach.

35. They churn the food as it boils in the stomach.

36. They manufacture the gastric juices for the digestion of the food.

37. Villi.

38. The colon, the liver, and the kidneys.

39. They are the "bouncers" of the undesirable food elements that enter the body.

40. The reproductive cells of the two sexes.

41. The female ova and the male spermatozoa.

42. About two hundred million.

43. About one twenty-fifth of an inch in diameter.

44. At the end of six weeks.

45. At the end of the second month.

46. The inner layer of the derma or the cutis or the true skin, and the outer layer of the epidermis or the cuticle or the scarf-skin.

47. The leucocytes, or white corpuscles.

48. The area of infection becomes swollen and sore.

49. About twenty-five years. About forty or fifty years.

50. Lines on the forehead, and at the corners of the eyes and of the mouth.

BIOGRAPHICAL SKETCHES OF GREAT PHYSIOLOGISTS

Galen (131–A.D. 201). Greek physician. Born in Pergamum, Mysia, he studied medicine as a career and was appointed official physician of his native city. He went to Rome to practice, and he achieved such renown that emperors clamored for him. He was celebrated as an anatomist and physiologist; he reinterpreted and clarified all medical knowledge up to and including his times. He was a facile writer, publishing almost a hundred treatises on philosophy and grammar as well as medicine. Although he shared many of the superstitions of his day, he taught emphatically that disease had natural origins and could be overcome only by natural means. His writings had a tremendous influence for centuries after his death.

Servetus, Michael (1511–53). Spanish physician. Born in Tudela in Navarre, the son of a notary, he first embarked on the study of law. But the theological discussions of the day excited a religious interest in him. He devoted his life to theology and medicine. He was a successful practicing physician, esteemed especially for his skill as a dissectionist. He is said to have reached the threshold of discovering the circulation of the blood. His theological radicalism plunged him into difficulties with the orthodox prelates of the day, and he was finally burned at the stake as a heretic.

Harvey, William (1578–1657). British physician. Born at Folkestone, he was educated at Cambridge University. He went to Italy to study medicine under Fabricius and Galileo. He received his medical degree in 1602 and returned to England as a practicing physician. His patients included the leading men of England, among them Francis Bacon. In 1618 he was appointed physician to the king. In 1628 he published his celebrated *Essay on the Motion of the Heart and the Blood* in which he demonstrated his theory of the circulation of the blood. During the regime of Cromwell, Harvey, in his late sixties, withdrew from public life. He occupied his last years studying the physiology of sexual generation. He lived to see his medical contributions acclaimed by the leading physicians of Europe.

Haller, Albrecht von (1708–77). Swiss physiologist. Born at Berne, he studied medicine at Tübingen in Germany and Leyden in Holland. At the age of twenty-one, he returned to Berne and practiced medicine. His reputation soon earned him an appointment at the newly established University of Göttingen. He remained at Göttingen as a professor for seventeen years, during which time he wrote several thousand medical articles for a local journal. He spent the final two decades of his life in Berne attending to civic duties. A great physiologist, Haller contributed classic information on the development of the embryo, the sexual organs, the arteries, and the brain. He demonstrated the phenomenon of bodily respiration and the actions of the heart. He contributed, in addition to his scientific writings, poetry and political essays.

Bernard, Claude (1813–78). French physiologist. Born at St. Julien, he decided at first upon a career in literature. But he abandoned this for medicine. At twenty-six he entered the Hôtel Dieu as an intern, and he studied under the celebrated physiologist Magendie. At forty-two he succeeded to the chair of medicine at the Collège de France. He became celebrated all over Europe for his researches. He lectured on experimental physiology at the Sorbonne, and he was chosen president of the Société de Biologie. Among his contributions to physiology was his demonstration of the role of the pancreas gland in the phenomenon of digestion. He revealed the vasomotor system, experimented with the physiological reaction of poisons, made classic observations on the function of the liver, publishing valuable hints on the causes of diabetes. His printed lectures alone comprise seventeen volumes.

Virchow, Rudolf (1821–1902). German pathologist. Born in Prussia, he studied medicine in Berlin and entered the Charity Hospital at twenty-three as surgeon's assistant. At twenty-six he was appointed lecturer at the University of Berlin, but owing to political activities, he was compelled to leave his post. However, in 1856 he returned as professor of pathological anatomy, and he resumed, at the same time, his political career. He became leader of the progressive party in Prussia, entered the Reichstag, and became Bismarck's chief opponent, scoring his policy of militarism.

As a scientist, he won fame as the establisher of cellular pathology. He revealed the nature of the umbilical cord, demonstrated neuroglia of the spinal cord, and made a series of significant contributions to the study of morbid anatomy.

Pavlov, Ivan Petrovich (1849–1936). Russian physiologist. Born in the district of Ryazan, the son of a priest, he studied medicine at the St. Petersburg Medical Academy. He did research work in Germany and returned to Russia to become director of the St. Petersburg Institute of Experimental Medicine. In 1907 he was chosen a member of the Russian Academy of Sciences. He is particularly celebrated for his investigations in digestion and his revelations concerning the conditioned reflexes. He made significant observations dealing with cerebral functions and the circulation of the blood. He received the Nobel prize in 1904 for his researches on the work of the digestive glands. He was elected a foreign member of the Royal Society. And he was awarded the Copley Medal.

Loeb, Jacques (1859–1924). German-American physiologist. Born and educated in Germany, he came to the United States and joined the faculty of Bryn Mawr College as a professor of biology. Shortly afterward he was appointed to the faculty of the University of Chicago, and he received a professorship at the Rush Medical School, transferring in 1902 to the University of California. He devoted his life to elucidating complex biological phenomena in terms of physiochemical laws. He demonstrated that the fertilizing power of spermatozoa could be duplicated by chemical solutions. He linked physiological instincts to the heliotropism of plants. He experimented with the influence of salts upon regeneration and heteromorphosis.

CAREERS IN PHYSIOLOGY

The study of the functions of the human body is a prerequisite for a sizable number of occupations. Training in physiology is essential for careers in medicine, dentistry, pharmacology, toxicology, bacteriology, anatomy, biology. The government employs expert physiologists to study the diet of the American people.

There are many practical applications in the field. World War II has necessitated the large-scale rehabilitation of the wounded. There is an unprecedented demand for physiotherapists. Jobs are available at veterans' hospitals, mental institutions, hospitals for the disabled, public health agencies. The demand is great; the supply of trained physiotherapists is still relatively small.

Not merely veterans but all sections of the population require physiotherapy. The physiotherapist treats injuries by means of exercise, heat, massages, electricity, light, hydrotherapy. Moreover, there are various specialties within the specialty. The chiropodist, for instance, prescribes for various types of foot ailments. The occupational therapist heals injuries and trains the disabled occupationally by means of educational and industrial exercises, arts and crafts. The field of physiotherapy provides excellent professional opportunities.

chiropodist

EXPERIENCE REQUIRED: Graduation from accredited school, passing of state licensing examination.

DESCRIPTION OF JOB: Diagnoses and treats foot ailments. Prescribes corrective shoes and appliances. May serve on staff of industrial clinic, hospital, school.

OPPORTUNITIES FOR ADVANCEMENT: Professional advancement.

OWN PROFESSION: Independent.

occupational therapist

EXPERIENCE REQUIRED: Generally graduation from accredited school of occupational therapy.

DESCRIPTION OF JOB: Through use of arts and crafts, games, educational and industrial activities, restoring injuries, retraining in skills, and effecting mental readjustments. Works under supervision of a doctor.

OPPORTUNITIES FOR ADVANCEMENT: Chief therapist, executive.

WHERE TO APPLY FOR JOBS: Veterans Administration, mental institutions, community workshops, social service agencies.

physical director

EXPERIENCE REQUIRED: College degree, training in physical education and experience in physiotherapy in hospital for mentally ill, or directing physical education in schools or universities.

DESCRIPTION OF JOB: Supervises, assists, directs physiotherapy for mentally ill.

WHERE TO APPLY FOR JOBS: Government.

physiologist

EXPERIENCE REQUIRED: College degree with major in biology. Graduate work or research experience in physiology.

DESCRIPTION OF JOB: Investigates vitamins and other problems in dietetics.

WHERE TO APPLY FOR JOBS: Government.

physiotherapist

EXPERIENCE REQUIRED: Graduation from approved school of physiotherapy. Knowledge of physiology, anatomy, physics, and biology.

DESCRIPTION OF JOB: Treats injuries, diseases, mental ailments, disabilities by massage, application of heat, light, electricity, or exercise. Works under direction of doctor.

OPPORTUNITIES FOR ADVANCEMENT: Assistant therapist, chief therapist.

WHERE TO APPLY FOR JOBS: Public health hospitals, veterans' hospitals, mental institutions, institutions for the crippled.

veterinarian

EXPERIENCE REQUIRED: Graduation from accredited college of veterinary medicine. Must pass examination for licenses in most states.

DESCRIPTION OF JOB: Deals with cure, prevention of animal disease; care, feeding, management of animals; inspection of foods and other products of animal origin.

OPPORTUNITIES FOR ADVANCEMENT: Private practice. Executive.

WHERE TO APPLY FOR JOBS: State-operated veterinary schools, United States Department of Agriculture, meat-packing houses.

BIBLIOGRAPHY: BOOKS ON PHYSIOLOGY FOR FURTHER READING AND STUDY

Bainbridge, Francis Arthur: *Essentials of Physiology.* London, 1940.

Best, Charles Herbert, and Norman Burke Taylor: *The Living Body.*

Bundy, Elizabeth Roxana: *Bundy's Anatomy and Physiology.* Philadelphia, 1940.

Cannon, Walter Bradford: *The Wisdom of the Body.* New York, 1939.

Carlson, Anton Julius: *The Machinery of the Body.* Chicago, 1941.

Clarke, James: *Picture of Health.* New York, 1940.

Clendening, Logan: *The Human Body.* New York, 1945.

Gerard, Ralph Waldo: *The Body Functions.* New York, 1941.

Greisheimer, Esther Maud: *Physiology and Anatomy.* Philadelphia, 1945.

Haggard, Howard Wilcox: *The Science of Health and Disease.* New York, 1938.

Hickman, Cleveland Pendleton: *Physiological Hygiene.* New York, 1942.

Kahn, Fritz: *Man in Structure and Function,* tr. by George Rosen. New York, 1943.

Keith, Sir Arthur: *The Engines of the Human Body.* London, 1930.

Kimber, Diana Clifford, Carolyn E. Gray, and Caroline E. Stackpole: *Textbook of Anatomy and Physiology.* New York, 1942.

Kirkpatrick, Thomas Bruce: *Fundamentals of Health.* Boston, 1941.

Martin, Henry Newell: *The Human Body.* New York, 1937.

Tokay, Elbert: *Fundamentals of Physiology.* New York, 1944.

——: *The Human Body and How It Works.* New York, 1949.

Wiener, Renée: *Fearfully and Wonderfully Made.* New York, 1938.

Williams, Jesse Feiring: *Healthful Living.* New York, 1947.

——: *A Textbook of Anatomy and Physiology.* Philadelphia, 1939.

psychology—the function of the mind

THE MEANING OF PSYCHOLOGY

Psychology is that branch of science which deals with the nature, properties, behavior, emotions, thoughts, aspirations, and hopes of man. Psychology is the study of the mind in action.

This action may be conscious, or subconscious, or—at times— even unconscious. There are some psychologists, like Watson, who would completely do away with the concept of consciousness in psychology. The term *consciousness,* they maintain, is so vague that it belongs to philosophy rather than to psychology. The scientific psychologist, according to this school, must disregard the so-called "inner sensations and ideas" of the mind and concern himself only with its "outer behavior." The majority of the psychologists, however, are interested in both phases of mental activity—the subjective states of emotions and thoughts, and the objective manifestations of their actions.

For all mental processes are accompanied by physical actions. And, vice versa, all physical objects are reflected by mental images. We are so constituted that we cannot understand the one phenomenon without the other. Yet at the same time we cannot explain the one in terms of the other. No amount of mental instruction will make a blind man understand redness; and no amount of description will make an insensitive man understand love.

In order, therefore, to get a complete picture of our human mentality—most of the psychologists maintain—we must look upon it subjectively, as a storehouse of consciousness, and objectively, as a springboard of action. Thus it is the business of psychology to discover a common denominator that will show, if possible, the relationship between the inflowing consciousness of the brain and the outflowing activity of the mind.

THE HUMAN THINKING MACHINE

The relationship between the brain and the mind—that is, between the body and the mind—poses one of the most baffling questions in psychology. Do these two aspects of our human personality represent a *dual* world or merely the two-sided picture of a *single* world?

In an effort to answer this question let us for a moment look into our own minds. These minds of ours tell us that we *know* what we are thinking and feeling and doing—in other words, that we are *conscious of ourselves*. But this consciousness of our individuality is something that each of us knows, at first hand only, *for* and *of* himself. I definitely know that I am I. But I merely infer that you are you. I get this inference from your words, your behavior, your appearance, and so forth. But I cannot get under your skin and into your brain and *feel* your individuality as you do.

Yet I have every reason to believe, and therefore I accept it as a fact, that *you* know *your* individuality as clearly as *I* know *mine*. And this personal consciousness of ours is a mental energy that resides in the physical realm of the brain. Consciousness, therefore, seems to be a *body-mind* activity. It is a two-in-one aspect of the physicomental instrument through which our actions and our thoughts have become interrelated. The brain does not make the mind, and the mind does not make the brain. Yet the two *interact* upon each other in such a way that every mental process is accompanied by nervous action. If we could thoroughly understand the nervous system of a man—the chemical and the physical laws that control its operations—we should be able to understand the conduct of that man. And in like manner, if we thoroughly understood the consciousness of a man, we should be able to understand his nervous reactions.

For the body and the mind, according to many psychologists, are but two ways of looking at the same unity—the personality of the human individual. Modern psychology, therefore, tends to be both *objective* and *subjective*. The experimenter in psychology tries to observe a man's *reactions* (the objective method) as well as to study a man's *introspections* (the subjective method).

This two-in-one method of modern psychology recognizes the human individual as a *thinking machine*—an object confronted by various physical conditions, and at the same time a subject capable of choosing between one physical condition and another. Man, as the modern biological psychologist sees him, is a creature governed by fate and yet endowed with a free will. And this free will enables him to modify his fate to his own advantage.

The body-mind of man is thus the latest—and, it seems, the highest—stage in the evolutionary effort of life to adjust the individual to his environment.

THE BODY-MIND AT WORK

Suppose you have made up your mind to buy a Blankmobile car. Just what do you mean by the words *made up your mind?* It is the unified response of your person to a certain situation. And this response is the result of a great number of factors that have led to a definite step. To mention but a few of these factors:

You have learned from experience that you need rapid transportation in your business or professional or social activities. You have noted, or you have been told by your friends, that some cars are more satisfactory in some respects, other cars in other respects. You have tested various cars and compared their merits and their defects. You have discussed these cars with your family and your friends. You have driven in these various cars and watched them in action. You have tentatively decided upon one car in preference to the others.

And now, very likely, you have begun to look upon the matter from a somewhat different angle. You have examined your finances to see whether you could afford this particular type of car. You have figured out your bank balance, your *actual* income and expenses during the *past* year, and your *possible* income and expenses during the *coming* year. Can you afford the car without sacrificing any of your necessities? Any of your luxuries? If you *must* sacrifice something else, is the car worth the sacrifice?

And so on, and on. Many additional factors will occur to you if you analyze your decision about buying a Blankmobile or any other car. Or about doing any of the innumerable things about which you are continually making up your mind. But all these factors that bring you to a decision may be condensed into a simple phrase—*the summation of past experience*. And your action resulting from the consideration of these factors may be expressed in another simple phrase—*the behavior responsive to past experience*.

Thus the physicomental reaction to any situation—or the body-mind activity of man—is *the capacity of the entire organism to behave in accordance with experience*. A man's mentality is the ability of his body-mind to translate learning into action. The greater the mentality, the wider the capacity to absorb experience and to modify it into appropriate behavior.

HOW WE BEHAVE, AND WHY

As we have already noted, the words *behavior* and *behave* are used here in a psychological rather than in an ethical sense. *Behavior* means *action*, whether good or bad. Let us now see how and why we act as we do.

In the forecasting of a person's behavior at any moment—a matter which is even more difficult than the forecasting of the weather at any moment—it is necessary to determine two important groupings of facts:

1. The composite nature of the stimuli that act upon the person at the moment.

2. The physicomental structure of the person at that moment.

The stimuli that act upon the person are of less importance than the person himself. The selfsame stimulation—a series of unhappy events, let us say—may turn one man into a murderer and another into a reformer. For a man's momentary reaction to his stimuli depends upon his entire organism. And his organism, in turn, depends upon a number of contributory factors:

A. HIS HEREDITY. The characteristics transmitted to him through his parents' germ plasm, which is itself the product of a long line of ancestors.

B. HIS STATE OF MATURITY. A child, an adolescent, and a full-grown person will react in three different ways to the same set of stimuli.

C. HIS PAST EXPERIENCE. A man brought up in the belligerent atmosphere of a dictatorial and aggressive nation will most likely be "conditioned" to fight at the drop of a hat; while another man nurtured in the peaceful atmosphere of a Quaker society will probably be prepared to *reason* it out instead of *fighting* it out.

D. HIS STATE OF HEALTH. A well person sees life through rose-colored spectacles and reacts accordingly. But an ill person sees the same life through black glasses, and his reaction therefore will reflect his own unhappy vision.

E. THE STATE OF HIS HUNGER. For food, companionship, fame or fortune, or sex. These, too, are important factors in determining the condition of a man's organism at the moment of a particular stimulation and his reaction to that stimulation.

And thus our behavior is due secondarily to the totality of our stimuli but primarily to the organic structure of our body-minds. And the individual reaction of any organism to its stimuli at a given moment depends upon its heredity, maturity, experience, health, and state of satisfaction or want. By and large we react to our stimuli not as the lower animals, creatures of undisciplined impulse, but as humans, persons of experienced judgment. Yet within this human pattern there are wide variations of psychological activity—aligning us all the way, in different individuals and at different times, between the angels and the beasts.

THE STRUCTURE OF THE BRAIN

Our thinking machine is an organization with a central office connected by many wires to every part of the body.

The central office—about the size of half a grapefruit—consists of a pinkish-gray soft material and is divided into two parts: the *cerebellum* and the *cerebrum*.

The *cerebellum*—or the *little brain*—lies at the bottom and at the back of the skull. It acts as a sort of intermediary between the mind and the body. It takes the orders from the mind to the body, and it supervises the general distribution of these orders

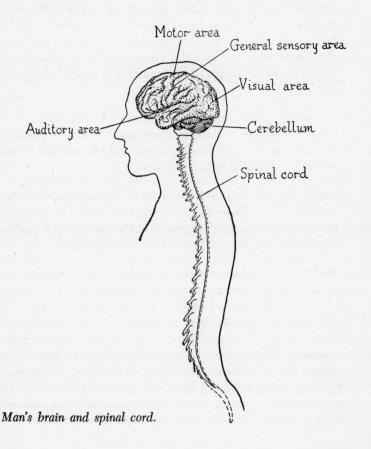

Man's brain and spinal cord.

and their effective execution through the co-operation of the various organs involved.

The *cerebrum*—or the *large brain*—lies above and in front of the cerebellum. It occupies the entire upper part of the skull and acts as the commander in chief which plans the mental activities of the body and gives out the orders. It is the part that manages our memory associations—that is to say, it co-ordinates our past experiences into recollections, ideas, imaginations, emotions, desires, and dreams.

The human brain differs from the brains of other living creatures not so much in the *structure* as in the *proportion* of its parts. The brain of a man has a greater complexity of folds, and therefore a wider area for its associative functions, than the brain of an ape. A man is superior to an ape in the matter of speech, for example, because his "cerebral office" has more room for the development of articulation than the "cerebral office" of the ape. The lower animals possess all the elements of the human brain. But these elements exist in a cruder form among the earlier products of evolution, and in a more advanced form among the later products. Man's brain is equipped with no special parts that are lacking in the brains of other animals. But the parts of his brain have evolved into a more complicated system of reactions—that is, a more educated mind—than the corresponding parts in the brains of his more primitive cousins, the dogs and the apes.

OUR REFLEXES, INSTINCTS, AND THOUGHTS

There has been a great deal of misunderstanding about the three words—*reflex, instinct,* and *thought.* The general public frequently confuses these words, substituting them indiscriminately for one another. And even the intelligent person, in his ordinary speech, is rather vague about their exact definitions. He generally assumes, in an offhand way, that the most primitive forms of life react upon reflex, the higher forms upon instinct, and the highest form—or man—upon thought.

Psychologically speaking, however, the above three responses to external stimuli are but the three different aspects of the same response. There is a very close interrelationship between them, for reflex merges into instinct, and instinct merges into thought. In the evolutionary current of life there is a single line of mental development from the first to the last. A complicated reflex becomes an instinct, and a complicated instinct becomes a thought. Yet our human mentality embraces all these three types of responses to the promptings of the world.

For example, the presence of an irritant in the nose results in the reflex of a sneeze, and the presence of a red-hot iron near the hand results in the reflex of a hasty recoil. These and similar reactions possess the following characteristics: (a) they are automatic; (b) they invariably respond in the same way to the same stimulus; (c) they are (as a rule) not susceptible to education; (d) and they involve a part of the body rather than the whole body.

A reflex, therefore, is a simple response to a simple stimulus. Among the commoner reflexes of our human organism are the processes of breathing, coughing, yawning, vocalizing, grasping, swallowing, smiling, laughing, weeping, and the involuntary winking of the eye at the approach of a threatening object. These

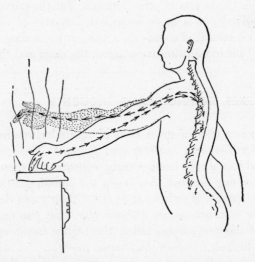

How a simple act like withdrawing the hand from a hot object takes place. Notice that the only part of the central nervous system involved here is the spinal cord.

reflexes have to do with the nervous system but not with the mechanism of the brain. Remove the cerebral hemispheres by surgery—and this has actually been done in frogs and in other animals—and the reflexes remain intact. But the powers of learning, understanding, and recollecting are gone. Thus a "decerebrated" animal can still breathe, and swallow, and recoil when it is hurt. But its mentality is completely lost. It can neither feel consciousness nor remember past stimuli. If you strike it, it will jump away. But if you threaten to strike again, it will have no recollection of, and will thus be unable to profit by, its former blow. The mutilated animal has retained its reflexes, though it has lost its mind. For the reflexes lie—so to speak—upon the threshold of the passageway between the body and the mind.

When we pass beyond the threshold, we come into the realm of the instincts. An instinct is an innate, unlearned tendency to respond in a certain way to a set of stimuli that is universal in the species. An instinct differs from a reflex in that while a reflex involves a specific response to a stimulus—the eye winks when an object approaches it—an instinct does not express itself in so rigidly patterned a reaction. For a long time psychologists ascribed many instincts to human beings—the maternal instinct, the mating instinct, food seeking, acquisitiveness, sneezing, laughing, pugnacity, curiosity, etc. But in recent years much doubt has been cast on the whole idea of instinct because it has been found that man is not born with a tendency to react in certain ways, but actively learns them after birth. To take but one example. In our society it is considered "natural" for a mother to love and care for her children, and consequently this tendency was described as instinctive. But anthropologists have found that among certain peoples of the world it is considered just as "natural" for a mother to be virtually indifferent to her children. Clearly then, if the "natural" response of two human beings brought up in different societies is so varied, the response must have been learned.

For this reason most psychologists today prefer not to use the term instinct at all, but rather to talk of basic drives which may be expressed in a variety of ways.

The mechanism by which the drives develop is known as the *conditioned reflex,* or *conditioned response,* a concept first introduced by the Russian scientist Ivan Pavlov. Pavlov conducted a series of interesting experiments which demonstrate the development of a *simple reflex* into a *conditioned reflex*. Pavlov had noticed that the reflex of swallowing food is accompanied by the secretion of saliva. With this knowledge as a start, he tried to see whether he could teach a dog to generate saliva as a result of its *mere recollection* of food. And so he put a dog into a quiet room and conditioned it to have its meals a few seconds after the ringing of a bell. The experimenter watched the dog through a peephole in the wall.

At first the dog had no conception as to the relationship between the food and the ringing of the bell. But after repeated experiments the sound of the bell began to arouse conditioned

Schematic representation of Pavlov's experiment for the conditioned reflex. At the top the dog salivates when the food is presented while the bell sounds. After a while the mere sounding of the bell is enough to cause the dog to salivate, as at the bottom.

expectations in the dog. A licking of the lips, a watering of the mouth, and a general excitement were definite proof that the dog was reacting instinctively to the *pleasant memory* of food. The dog *had learned* to respond to the *impending arrival* of its meals.

In other words, *its mentality was at work*. The sound of the bell had telegraphed the idea of food to its brain, and the brain had relayed the idea to its lips, its jaws, and its salivary glands. A dog with its brain cut out, as previous experiments had shown, could not have reacted in this way to the sound of approaching food, or even to its sight or smell.

Thought, or thinking, is a judgment of the mind. And judgment is a product of intelligence, or of learning through experience. Let us take a simple example to illustrate this point. Suppose we place some food in a wire box, so that the food can be smelled and seen; and then we put a bolt upon the door of the box, so that the food can be reached only through the unfastening of the bolt. And now suppose we allow a squirrel, a dog, and a child of five to get at the food, if they can, through their own ingenuity. We shall note—as repeated experiments have shown—a very interesting series of results. The squirrel will run around the box aimlessly in an effort to reach the food. It may try to find a weak spot in the wiring so that it may dig its way in. But its actions will not be correlated. That is to say, the squirrel will not have learned, from any of its past actions, how to act in the future. Its responses to the impulses of hunger and to the proximity of food, in other words, will be *reflexive*.

The dog, on the other hand, will undergo a series of trial-and-error attempts. After a number of failures it will find the bolt and discover how to manipulate it in order to open the door and to get at the food. If we shut the door, the dog will be able to open it again. For it will have become conditioned to its reaction. But this conditioning will have been a process of *movement* rather than of *reasoning*. Thus, if we alter the arrangement of the fastening or change the position of the box, the dog will have to start all over again. For it has learned a series of actions, but it has not acquired a process of reasoning.

And now let us watch the child, whose responses will be entirely different from those of the squirrel and of the dog. He will find the bolt, he will learn how to unfasten it, he will reason about its combination, and he will be able to repeat the action as a result of his *learning* and his *reasoning*.

Human beings have acquired the faculty of intelligent judgment. They have learned to think. They are the only animals capable of conceiving ideas. The healthy human mind is a steady current of immediate perceptions and stored memories which it keeps channeling into (more or less important) thoughts. The simplest human act is the result of a complicated process of conscious, subconscious, and unconscious recollections translated into mental images and directed into physical motion.

Take, for example, the ordinary process of eating an apple. You sit at the table and you see a round object. You know, from past experience, that this object is not a rubber ball, or an empty bubble, or any one of a thousand other objects that are round and smooth. It is a *solid* thing; your memory tells you that this is so because it *looks* like so many of your accumulated mental images of similar objects. You pick it up, and your sense of *touch* corroborates the memory of the images aroused by your sense of *sight*. And now your sense of *smell* enters into the current of your perceptions. The thing has the appetizing odor of a series of fruit images that have become stored away in your memory— *apple images*. All these stored memories are *images of recognition*.

Added to these are *images of education*—such as your experienced knowledge that an apple is good for your health, that it may be best for you to eat it skin and all, that it is more polite—if less satisfactory—to cut the apple into slices than to bite into it and to spatter the juice all around, and so on.

And, finally, the eating of the apple may arouse in you a number of other ideas—or *images of association*. The fruit may remind you of the story about the eating of the apple in the Garden of Eden. And this recollection in turn may direct your mind to the doctrine of original sin—"in Adam's fall we sinnèd all." Or the eating of the apple may set your thoughts adrift upon a lighter current of reminiscences—the occasion when you spent a month in the country—apple orchards, wholesome people, the farmer's attractive children, their desire to leave for the city, the relative merits of city and country life, and so on and on.

We have purposely taken a simple example to show the complexity of our most elementary thoughts. A single stimulus—the sight of an apple or the knock upon a door—may arouse a chain of ideas that will culminate in Newton's *Law of Gravitation* or Beethoven's *Pastoral Symphony*.

THE PROCESS OF EDUCATION

The body-mind is a thinking machine which specializes in the production of educated humans, whether in the formal academy or in the "school of hard knocks."

Education is the process of readjustment—through repeated experience—between the individual and his environment. The educated man has learned, as a result of his mental or physical discipline, to modify his responses to his stimuli. And the purpose of this modification is to make him less susceptible to the dangers of the world.

Experience has shown that there are certain conditions under which a person can be most efficiently trained to modify his responses—that is, to become educated. Some of the more important of these educational conditions are the following:

1. Education cannot be forced. An organism finds most satisfaction in acting when it is most ready to act. A man, or a child, will learn only when and what he is willing to learn. You cannot pump knowledge into a person; you can merely prompt him to acquire his knowledge out of his inner needs. The word *education* means a drawing out.

2. The process of education is repetitious. We learn through constant practice. To express this idea scientifically, the connection between a stimulus and a response becomes perfected through exercise and atrophied through disuse. And the more frequent the exercise, the more "educated" the response.

3. The process of a person's education is the cumulative attempt to abandon his painful states and to retain or to repeat his pleasant states. The Old Testament dictum that we learn through our suffering is psychologically true—in the sense that we learn to

reject our suffering in order that we may be free to *accept* our happiness.

For education is the way to human happiness. And the goal of education is the Roman ideal of *mens sana in corpore sano*—a healthy mind in a healthy body.

This ideal of a healthy physical and mental organism, working in "educated" harmony, may be attained through the method of *co-ordinating responses*. This method elicits from a person the *proper responses* by subjecting him to such stimuli as will teach the *proper co-ordination* of his responses. There is a school of psychologists—the so-called *Gestalt* school—who strongly believe in this method of education. They maintain that all education is the result of activity—the act of *putting together* the parts of an object or an idea into a whole, or the act of *visualizing together* the relationship of these parts toward one another and toward the whole. The mere *repetition* of a response to a stimulus is of no importance, declare the Gestaltists. The important thing in learning, they say, is to enable the learner to discover the *meaning of the relationship* between the stimulus and the response. It is the ability to *correlate images* and to *understand their connection*—according to the Gestalt school—that distinguishes the human mind from that of the lower animals.

In the teaching of multiplication, for example, it is helpful to the pupil—believe the Gestaltists—to point out to him that certain combinations of figures, when multiplied together, will result in products that bear a relationship to one another. Thus they have found it comparatively easy to teach a backward pupil the table of tens by showing him—or, still better, by enabling him to discover for himself—that in this table *the products always begin with the first number of the multiplier and end in zero:*

$$10\times1=10 \qquad 10\times 6=60$$
$$10\times2=20 \qquad 10\times 7=70$$
$$10\times3=30 \qquad 10\times 8=80$$
$$10\times4=40 \qquad 10\times 9=90$$
$$10\times5=50 \qquad 10\times10=100$$

Education, therefore, is the gradually acquired ability to see an object (or an idea) as a whole through an understanding of the relationship of its parts.

THE RELATION BETWEEN THOUGHTS AND WORDS

The difference between the mental processes of animals and of men is largely a matter of words. For words, whether spoken or written, are tools that enable us to translate our images into ideas, and to associate these ideas into a pattern known as the expression of human reason. It is by means of words that we are able to obtain, and to communicate, a fairly definite picture of the world we live in. And it is because of the inadequacy of our words—both as to their number and their meaning—that our picture of the world is only *fairly* definite. The larger a man's vocabulary and the clearer his definitions, the greater his understanding of life.

The acquisition of words has served our human thinking in another way. It has enabled us not only to *formulate* our thoughts but to *store them away* for future use. And thus we can develop a chain of associations as we go through life, linking our past with our present experiences, and turning our fragmentary snapshots of the world into a consecutive and composite picture.

It is this faculty of thought association through word association that makes it possible for us to expand the simple impulse of the eating of an apple into a variety of memories and ideas as complex as the universe itself. This faculty belongs to man alone, because he alone has been able to develop his linguistic tools for the classification of his ideas.

But these ideas differ, from country to country and from age to age, because of the differences in our human languages. Thus it is impossible through any translation to convey to a Frenchman the idea of our English word *home*. For this English word has no exact equivalent in the French language. A great deal of international misunderstanding has resulted from the impassable linguistic gap between the various countries. Treaties have been broken, and wars declared, because of different interpretations given to important key phrases as set down in different languages. Hence the occasional attempt, on the part of internationally minded scientists, to create a universal language. For the inability of two countries (or of two individuals) to get together may be due merely to a misunderstanding of one another's words.

THE MEASURE OF OUR INTELLIGENCE

If we select a large group of children (or of adults) at random from the general population and try to classify them in the order of their intelligence, we shall get, roughly, the following results:

1. A handful—perhaps only one or two—at the top who are geniuses.

2. A somewhat larger number who are brilliant but not geniuses.

3. A still larger number who are able but not brilliant.

4. The largest number, in the middle, who are just average, or normal.

5. A fairly large number who are dull.

6. A somewhat smaller number who are morons.

7. A very small number, at the bottom, who are imbeciles or idiots.

A person's intelligence is not the *amount of his knowledge* but his *capacity for knowing*. Our intelligence reaches its full development at about sixteen years of age. But our education may go on till the last day of our life.

The test of a man's (or a child's) intelligence, therefore, is a measure not of what he has learned but of how he is able to learn. This test takes, as an average standard, the learning capacity—or aptitude—of an average child of twelve. Thus, if a child of ten has the learning ability of a twelve-year-old, we say that he has a mental age of twelve; if he has the learning ability of an eight-year-old, we say that he has a mental age of eight.

In testing the relative intelligence of a group of persons, it is important that all these persons should be similarly adjusted to the *conditions* of the test. That is, all the contestants must come from the same racial, economic, and social background if the test is to be an accurate measure of their adaptability to learning. An intelligence test that is applied to individuals who come from different backgrounds must be carefully analyzed and correlated before the final results can be tabulated.

But, with these general precautions in mind, a carefully prepared intelligence test—and the psychologists have devised a number of them—is a good measure of a person's capacity for various kinds of education or work.

One of the most common of these tests is the so-called "measurement of the intelligence quotient"—or I.Q. This measurement is obtained as follows: divide the mental age of the person tested by his chronological age, and multiply the product by a hundred. Thus, a normal child of ten with a mental age of ten will have an I.Q. of 100: $10 \div 10 = 1$; $1 \times 100 = 100$. A child of ten with a mental age of five will have an I.Q. of 50: $(5 \div 10) \times 100 = 50$. And so on. The intelligence quotients of various grades of mentality have been found to be, approximately, as follows:

Near genius	I.Q. of 150 or over
Brilliant minds	I.Q. of 130–150
Able minds	I.Q. of 115–130
Average minds	I.Q. of 85–115
Dull minds	I.Q. of 70–85
Morons	I.Q. of 50–70
Imbeciles	I.Q. of 20–50
Idiots	I.Q. below 20

It is interesting to note that the average intelligence of most adult persons is about equal to that of a fourteen-year-old. Grownups, as a rule, have acquired a greater store of learning than their children. But their equipment for learning—that is, their ability to perceive relationships—remains no greater than it was in the days of their childhood. Indeed, as old age advances, a person's intelligence begins to recede, and he falls back—mentally as well as physically—into a stage of second childhood.

Yet there is a wide variety of useful work to be done within every grade of human intelligence. Some people are endowed with stronger bodies; others with more powerful minds. But the hope of a fulfilled life—as psychologists have repeatedly demonstrated through the application of their intelligence tests—can be held out to the weaker as well as to the stronger members of the human race. The I.Q. and similar devices have frequently saved society from putting the wrong person into the wrong job. But they have often helped the individual by finding the right job for the right person.

INTROVERTS AND EXTROVERTS

The famous Swiss psychologist, Dr. C. G. Jung, divided all individuals into two mental types: those whose minds are *turned in* upon themselves, or *introverts;* and those whose minds are *turned out* toward the world, or *extroverts.*

The introvert is the subjective, solitary, bashful type living largely in his fancies and his thoughts. The extrovert is the objective, sociable, aggressive type devoted mainly to a life of action. The introvert is a dreamer; the extrovert an adventurer. To the introvert the business of the world is a means toward the formulation of ideas. To the extrovert the ideas of the world are a means toward the stimulation of business. The introvert, afraid of the present, projects himself longingly into the past and the future. The extrovert, disinterested in the past and the future, throws himself heartily into the present. The introverts are the hermits of the world—the poets, the philosophers, the painters, the sculptors, and the *composers* of music. The extroverts are the showmen of the world—the fighters, the statesmen, the merchants, the actors, and the *performers* of music.

And the two types react differently to abnormal as well as to normal stimuli. During the two World Wars the psychiatrists made an interesting observation to that effect. When the soldiers broke down under the stress of fighting, the breakdown—as a rule —took the form of neurasthenia, or passive nervous prostration, in the introverts, and of hysteria, or the development of physical symptoms without a physical cause, in the extroverts.

The above, in brief, is the general distinction between the two different types of mind. Actually, however, every human mind belongs partly to the one and partly to the other type. Or, to be more exact, every human mind keeps constantly shifting between the moods of introversion on the one hand and of extroversion on the other. The individual mind may show a general *tendency* toward an inward-looking or outward-looking pattern. But this pattern is never sharply defined. There are poets, for example, who are very shrewd businessmen. Shakespeare was such an all-around type. And there are statesmen who are very competent philosophers. Thomas Jefferson was a man of this intricate type. Moreover, a glass of alcohol may turn a reticent mouse into a roaring lion. And, on the other hand, a sedative powder may tame a swaggering fighter into a quiet and reflective mood.

No individual, in other words, is always and entirely an absolute introvert or extrovert. Yet most individuals can be typed as belonging to either the one or the other class in accordance with the *customary drift of their minds.*

And every person's mind, we must remember, is closely related to the structure of his body. We cannot (ordinarily) expect a "tough" mind in a "tender" body—the fighting spirit of a Napoleon, let us say, in the delicate physique of a Shelley.

For the body and the mind grow up together, and their gradual development and ultimate organization are mutually interdependent. A study of insane people has shown that generally those who suffer from dementia—a quiet (or introvert) type of madness—are generally small-muscled, narrow-chested, and thin, while those who suffer from mania—a violent (or extrovert) type of madness—are more likely to be thickset, big-boned, and sturdy. And this relationship between the body and the mind holds true in the sane as well as in the insane type of person. The sane introvert—the prophet, the idealist, the weaver of images—is generally a man with "a lean and hungry look." And the sane extrovert—the politician, the materialist, the man of affairs—is ordinarily stocky, well built, and well fed.

The Germans have an old proverb—"*Man ist was Man isst* [we are what we eat]." This proverb contains a great measure of psychological truth. A man's food determines the nature of his physical growth, and the nature of his physical growth determines the configuration of his mind. The "starved" individual is the introvert —the inward-looking manufacturer of fancies and dreams. But the "sated" individual is the extrovert—the outward-looking trader in experiences and goods.

OUR EMOTIONS, AND HOW TO CONTROL THEM

A thought is a *conception* of the mind. An emotion is an *agitation* of the mind, or an excitement of the feelings.

Our emotions are difficult to analyze, whether we examine them subjectively or objectively.

For if we try to study them subjectively—or introspectively— we can merely observe our feelings. But we cannot observe the accompanying secretions of the adrenal glands—the little "chemical whips" that lie near our kidneys and whose function it is to lash the various organs of the body into action as a result of their stimulation. Moreover, our observation of our own emotions is likely to be inaccurate. For any scientific observation, if it is to be trustworthy, must be made coldly and judiciously, and without any emotional bias. But how can we *coldly* study our emotions in the very *heat* of these emotions?

On the other hand, if we try to study our emotions objectively, we cannot be certain about the accuracy of the results. For we have no instruments to probe into the internal reactions of a physical organism at the moment of its emotional manifestations. And if we dissect the object in order to study its emotions, the dissection will have killed the emotions of the object together with the body.

Yet, in spite of these limitations, the psychologists have been able to discover a great deal about our emotions, or the responsive internal adjustments of our body-minds to the irritations of the world.

These responses of our body-minds to the irritations of our stimuli are brought about through the impulses of the nervous system—the telephone exchanges of the human organism. Thus an excessively *emotional* person is popularly—and rightly—called a *nervous* person.

Our nervous impulses are always in operation. All human activity—even in the least emotional among us—is colored by human feeling. However *intellectual* we may consider our actions, they are always at bottom *emotional*.

And many of our emotions are related to one another. Thus fear and anger are but different aspects of the same internal response to external stimuli. We are said to be afraid if our responses induce us to *withdraw* from the stimulus; and we are said to be angry if our responses command us to *defy* the stimulus. But in every emotion of fear there is an element of anger; and vice versa, in every emotion of anger there is an element of fear. The angry aggressiveness of a Hitler was largely the expression of a defensive terror. He was so bent upon domination because he was so fearful of enslavement. He wanted to conquer the world because he felt convinced that the world wanted to conquer Germany. William James made a great contribution to psychology when he observed that we do not run away because we fear, but we fear because we run away. The precise order of a developing emotion, he said, is contrary to our general belief. We see a bear, we run, and we become afraid. Or else we see a bear, we advance, and we become angry. Professor Wallace T. Wait, in his *Science of Human Behavior*, has made an interesting observation bearing on this point. "Whether the soldier on the battlefield is a hero or a coward," he writes, "will often depend upon whether he gets started forward or to the rear." This explains the psychological necessity for the proper training of soldiers—the conditioning of a man's fear reactions into the reactions of courage.

And thus emotion is a *conditioned* physicomental reaction to stimuli, a reaction conditioned by experience. Since no two persons have had exactly the same experience, it follows that no two persons will react exactly alike to the same stimuli. One of them may have been conditioned to *run timidly away* at the approach of danger; another, to *run angrily forward* to meet it; and still another, to *turn contemptuously* from his personal danger to the pursuit of more important matters—such as the nursing of the sick in the midst of a plague.

This brings us to the subject of controlling our emotions. How is this possible? *By the training of our physical responses to produce the desired states of emotion.* For example, we can nurse our anger by slamming the door, stamping our feet, and indulging in such other physical reactions as will continue to add fuel to the flame of our wrath. But, on the other hand, we can allay our fear by "whistling in the dark," and we can mitigate our sadness by humming a cheerful tune.

This training of an undesirable emotion into something more desirable may be a long and tedious process, and many temporary setbacks may retard the final result. But patience—a judicious striving for victory in the face of defeat—has brought about the desired transformation in many an emotional response. The eminent behaviorist, John B. Watson, has been exceptionally successful in his efforts to control the emotions of children—to train their unreasonable tantrums and fears and hatreds out of their minds.

As for our less flexible adult minds, they too can be trained into more reasonable emotions. This can be done through a rigid discipline of our physical reactions under the determined control of the will.

But "the willing," as Professor A. A. Roback observes in his *Popular Psychology*, "must be done in between . . . the outbursts" of emotion. And furthermore, this mental willing must be accompanied by physical action. *Act* cheerfully, and you will in time learn to *feel* cheerful. Do the friendly deed, and you will acquire the warmth of friendship. The Judaeo-Christian religion is psychologically, as well as spiritually, sound. If you actually and habitually return good for evil, you will transform your *destructive passion* into *constructive compassion*. If you channel the reactions of your anger into acts of forgiveness, you will ultimately convert not only your own, but your enemy's, disquietude into tranquillity and hatred into love.

WHAT IS PERSONALITY?

Your personality, or character, is that which makes you a distinct person—an individual different from all other individuals. It is the sum total of your appearance, your thoughts, your emotions, and your will—a continuous moving picture, so to speak, of your entire life.

This psychological picture, in order to be an accurate representation of your total self, can never stand still. For your personality never stands still. It keeps changing all the time—with the changes of your anatomy, your environment, your stimuli, and the state of your physical, mental, social, and spiritual growth. And for this reason it is extremely difficult to define the personality of any individual. The best we can do is to note a person's total behavior, over a considerable period of time, in order that we may *approximate* the picture of his character. And we must always be frank to acknowledge that our personality pictures of one another are *mere approximations at best.*

When we look upon one another's personalities from this objective point of view, we find ourselves involved in another difficulty. We have a human habit of posing for our mental and moral as well as for our physical pictures. Whether deliberately or otherwise, we rarely present our real selves to our neighbors. We like to *primp up* our persons for our social visits. We want to *appear* better than we *are.*

For every one of us has a *double* personality: the *inner* self for the home, and the *outer* self for society. The inner self is something of which we may be ashamed; we may even try to hide it from our own consciousness as well as from the contemplation of society. And the outer, or *better,* self may be even more than a pose; it may be an ideal. "This is what I like to *appear* to be, because at bottom it is what I like to *be.*"

But, whatever the motive, the outer personality is the mask. And it is this mask, rather than the face behind it, that we are generally able to see when we try to analyze one another's characters.

This mask is not only a concealment but an *inflated* concealment. A man's *estimate of himself,* as seen in his actions, is *an exaggeration of his real self.* This exaggeration may have either bad or good results. It may align the individual on the side of the sinners or of the saints. For the inflated ego represents an effort on our part to escape from the reality of frustration to the fantasy of achievement. And the fancied achievement may be in the direction either of malice or of charity. Not every man who poses as a saint is a hypocrite. In his blunderings—and even in his deceptions—an individual may be expressing his subconscious desire to be something better than he is.

Bearing all this in mind, let us see what sort of picture we can get from the objective study of an individual's personality. There are any number of approaches to this sort of objective study. I shall mention six of them.

1. We can distinguish a person by his physical traits—his size, his features, the proportions of the various parts of his body, the coloration of his skin, and the like. This point is so obvious that it needs no further comment. We shall therefore go on to the second approach.

2. We can recognize a person by his gestures—the manner of his sitting, standing, and walking, the play of the lights and shadows in his eyes, the smile about his lips, the warmth or the coldness of his speech, the mobility or the apathy of his face, and the general manner of his reactions to the multitudinous contacts of his daily existence.

3. We can classify a person by the expression of his thoughts—his readiness or his reluctance to accept new situations, new ideas, new friends, the acuteness or the dullness of his understanding, the speed or the slowness of his responses to his mental stimuli, his propensity to "swallow whole" whatever he reads or to "read between the lines" in order that he may arrive at his own conclusions, his tendency to look at an emergency "straight in the face" or to "dream his way around it" in order that he may avoid the unpleasantness of a fight, and his general proclivity toward a closed or an open mind, a habit of thinking along a single track or of branching off into any road that may promise a wider point of view.

4. We can observe a man's personality through his emotional responses—the coloring that he gives to the expression of his thoughts—his ability or inability to control himself, the ardor or the frigidity of his temperament, the optimism or the pessimism of his general approach to life, the firmness or the fickleness of his devotion, the pride or the humility of his spirit, the pity or the cruelty of his heart.

5. We can often get a key to a man's character through the general state of his health. We have already seen the close relationship that exists between the body and the mind. A person's physical condition, therefore, can materially influence his habits, emotions, and thoughts—in short, his entire personality.

6. The final approach to a man's personality is through his social relationships. Is the man aggressive or submissive, openmouthed or closemouthed, illiberal or tolerant, conniving or honest, irresponsible or reliable, slovenly or neat, dependent or helpful, arrogant or modest, cynical or civil, excitable or calm? These opposite types of personality—and all the gradations in between—may be multiplied indefinitely. But they can all be summarized in a single observation. The social approach to personality determines whether a person is socially desirable, undesirable, or just merely tolerable. And the social is perhaps the most important of all the approaches to the study of personality, for man is a gregarious animal. He is meant to live with his fellow men.

Thus the best way to develop our own personalities—that is, to make ourselves into socially desirable persons—is to look into the mirror of our own character, to see ourselves as others see us, and to train our responses toward the gradual elimination of our unattractive and the gradual cultivation of our attractive traits.

SICK PERSONALITIES

When the personality—whether good or bad—acts as a unit, it is said to be *integrated* or *whole*. When it is split into disunited reactions—that is, reactions that are incompatible with one another—the personality is said to be *disintegrated*, or *divided into parts*.

A disintegrated personality is a *sick* personality. Sometimes it results in the development of a *double* or a *multiple* personality. Dr. Morton Prince, who has conducted extensive researches in this field, tells us some interesting stories about unfortunates who had two antagonistic individuals within a single body. For example, he cites the case of a young woman who, as the result of a number of emotional shocks, turned—like Dr. Jekyll and Mr. Hyde—into two entirely different characters. These two characters alternated with each other in taking temporary possession of her body. One of the characters was gentle, studious, modest, self-sacrificing, religious, sensitive, and very fond of children. The other was vain, cantankerous, selfish, scornful of learning and religion, uncontrollable in temper, and definitely averse to children.

And, strangely enough, the two characters, though they belonged to the same body, seemed to experience two different states of health. The first or gentle personality was frail and incapable of extended exertion; and the second or aggressive personality was active and strong.

Furthermore—and here was another strange phenomenon—the two personalities knew little, and cared even less, about each other. The only way in which they communicated with each other was by means of notes. But each of the selves would resent the unwanted advice from the other self.

And thus the young woman led, alternately, a double life, acquired two sets of friends, and conducted an incessant mental warfare between her two conflicting personalities.

And then there came a still more amazing development. A third personality emerged out of the twisted character complex of the young woman. This third personality was a preadolescent, mischievous, irresponsible, and irrepressible imp who heartily despised her other two selves and in return was heartily despised by them.

But this triple personality, Dr. Prince informs us, was finally "hypnotized" into one, and the patient was cured. And this was done *through the process of integration*—the reconciliation of the conflicting tendencies into a state of rational compatibility, or mental sanity.

The above is an extreme example of what happens to many of us at one time or another. Certain types of nervous temperaments are susceptible to repeated dissociations between different groups of tendencies within the personality. In most cases, however, such dissociations are only temporary; and the personality can be reintegrated—or restored to a unified contact with reality—without medical aid.

But when the dissociation becomes permanent, the mind loses completely its hold upon the reality of the world and turns back upon itself. This disease is known as *schizophrenia*, or the splitting away of the inward-looking from the outward-looking self. It represents the final divorce of the mind from the world. The personality becomes, in a literal sense, cloistered within the body, unaware of what is going on beyond, and concerned only with the shadows of its own delusions and dreams.

And, as the disease progresses, the mind becomes more and more atrophied through its inability to exercise itself in the daily activities of the world. And the various shadows of its delusions and dreams become smaller and fewer and less and less distinct, so that finally the mind may give out altogether or confine itself to a single repeated reaction or fixed idea. A visit to the playground of a mental hospital is a most poignant experience. Here are a number of patients—you cannot call them a group—who are living in a number of worlds entirely different from one another. There is no conversation, no communication, almost no recognition among them. Each of them is concerned exclusively with his own thought, his own action. One of them goes around and around in a circle. Another makes a speech, repeating the same words and the same gestures over and over again. Still another picks up a bit of gravel from the walk, replaces it upon the grass, returns it to the walk, replaces it upon the grass, and so on and on and on. Each of them has become a living automaton preoccupied with the simple operation of an ingrowing urge.

Yet these victims of the fixed idea that has become *ingrown* are not so very different from the enthusiasts of the fixed idea that grows *outward*. The prophet, the inventor, the martyr, the revolutionist, the saint—these, too, are seized with a sort of madness. But there is this important distinction between the madman and the saint: the madman's mind is *completely out of touch with reality*, but the mind of the saint is *founded upon reality*. Indeed, it is often difficult for society to distinguish between the two. For the meaning of *reality* is often misinterpreted as being synonymous with *the popular prejudice of the day*. And this is why we have imprisoned and killed so many of our saviors and saints.

And thus, psychologically, there is some sort of resemblance

—though, at the same time, a great measure of difference—between insanity and exaltation. There are eminent psychologists who regard all exaltation—even genius—as a precious disease of the human mind, just as the pearl is a precious disease of the oyster's body. "Perhaps," observes Balzac in his novel, *Louis Lambert*, "those whom we call insane are the only people in the world who are truly sane. Perhaps they alone can penetrate most deeply into the reality of things."

All the above types of mental abnormality have to do with dissociations in the mind of the individual. But there is another kind of abnormality, or mental illness, which is caused by the fact that dissociation is impossible. There are some minds so closely interwoven that they cannot separate one group of ideas from another. And when two such inseparable groups of ideas come into conflict—like two incompatible members of a family compelled to live in a single room—there is likely to be a period of depression bordering on despair.

The nature of this trouble is psychologically known as an anxiety neurosis, a disease based on the patient's inability to decide between two sets of antagonistic drives—let us say, a man's love toward his mother and his conflicting love toward his wife. Unable to make a definite choice, he drifts helplessly upon the crosscurrents of his emotions, wastes his time in unnecessary anxiety, and retards his own recovery by reproaching himself for his weakness instead of trying to recruit his strength. He becomes irritable and unamenable to reason. While not entirely divorced from the world, as the schizophrenic is, he becomes rather indifferent to it—and despises himself for his indifference.

The conflicts of an anxiety neurosis can generally be adjusted when the patient is directed, either through medical aid or through a turn of events, to a decisive duel between two sets of ideas that may seem to pull him in opposite directions.

There is another type of mental maladjustment that is somewhat similar to neurosis. This type of illness is hysteria. The conflicts that lead to hysteria are generally the same as those that lead to neurosis. But the personality of the patient is different. The hysterical patient, as a rule, is the overactive person, while the neurotic patient is the overcontemplative person.

Hysteria is a boiling over of the emotions, generally accompanied by an irrational activity of the body. It is due to an excessive suppression of the emotions by the controlling centers of the brain. It is the effort of the unconscious to break loose when the lid of our conventional behavior has been clamped down too tightly. By hysteria the psychologist does not mean what we popularly term hysteria—the sudden tantrums into which our companions, and even we ourselves, may fly at any moment without reason or rhyme—but rather those disorders which are characterized by a physical symptom which has no apparent physical cause, like the following:

1. A person whose eyes are physically intact grows suddenly blind. The immediate cause of the blindness may be an attack of conjunctivitis, a temporary but curable inflammation of the mucous membrane of the eyes. But the ultimate cause is a suppressed conflict within the "cellar" of the patient's mind. The patient has been overburdened with an undue sense of remorse over some major—or even minor—sin. He has been ashamed to face the world. And he has tucked away into the recesses of his subconscious the conflict between his sense of shame and his inability either to remove the shame by improving his conduct or to condone his conduct by lowering his standard of ethics. This conflict has been simmering for some time, has finally come to a boil, and has broken out into an explosion of *hysterical blindness* when the shock of his conjunctivitis blew off the lid of his emotions.

2. A soldier who has distinguished himself in battle is found wandering after the battle, a victim of amnesia. He doesn't know who he is, where he comes from, or what he has done in the past. Examination into the identity of the victim and the causes of his illness discloses the following facts: he is a man of superior culture and sensitivity; he comes from a refined and peaceful background; he has always abhorred war and feared violence. But he has been trained to hate and kill and to show—if necessary, to pretend—that he is unafraid. And thus there was a conflict between his distaste for war and his fear of personal injury on the one hand, and his desire on the other hand to *appear*—and if possible to *be*—heroic. And this conflict came to a head when a

shell burst near him and knocked him unconscious. When he recovered consciousness, his memory was gone. He is a victim of *hysterical amnesia*.

3. A man has entertained a great animosity toward his in-laws, but he has stifled this emotion out of regard for his wife. His wife dies, leaving him with an only child. The in-laws insist upon the possession of the child. This results in a violent quarrel. The impact of the quarrel, the hatred against his in-laws, the anxiety about his child, and his inability to help himself out of this complication of emotions—all these factors culminate in a mental and physical blowout. Not only does his mind go flat, with an entire loss of memory, but his body becomes paralyzed, and he is compelled to stay in bed. But—and here is the strangest part of his illness—he is able to run about in his sleep, hugging his pillow to his breast and shouting that this is his child whom wicked people are trying to take away from him. This man's suffering has brought about a case of *hysterical paralysis*.

4. And here is the case of a man whose suppressed emotional conflict against the world has finally exploded into a total abandonment of his adult personality, together with his sense of social obligation and his capacity for self-control. He loses his grown-up identity, the memory of his mature life, and reverts to the recollections and reactions of his childhood. He crawls on all fours, fusses and cries and utters inarticulate grunts, refuses all food unless it is put into his mouth, and displays all the other characteristics of the careless, conscienceless, and helpless infant. He has gone back from the difficulties and the dignities of his adult life to the indignity and the safety of his cradle days. This man suffers from *hysterical regression*.

The above are but a few of the mental maladjustments that afflict the human personality. And in this turbulent generation of ours nearly all of us are exposed to the shocks that may at any moment result in a milder or a severer form of one of these maladjustments. Though not mentally sick, many of us are teetering dangerously close to the border line. Life in this century is too rapid, our economic and social problems are becoming too numerous and too complicated, our machinery has traveled too far ahead of our morality, our inventiveness for destruction has outstripped our capacity for co-operation, our wounds of the last war are becoming irritated with the premonitions of the next war, and thus our minds have been caught up in a whirlpool of fears and compulsions and passions that seriously threaten the sanity of the human race. Hence the popularity of, and the need for, the various recent developments in psychotherapy—that branch of psychology which deals with the reintegration of disintegrated personalities, or the mending of broken minds.

We shall briefly consider one of the most interesting of these latest scientific attempts at the healing of the stricken soul.

PSYCHOANALYSIS

Psychoanalysis is a method of exploring the innermost depths of the human mind, in order to bring into the open and thus to "air out" the ideas, impulses, and desires which may lie suppressed in the unconscious and which may thus be the cause of various emotional disturbances.

For it is the belief of the psychoanalysts that the "mental demons" of the unconscious can be "exorcised"—or that at least they can be robbed of much of their morbidity—if the patient is enabled to meet them face to face.

The method of psychoanalysis arose out of the study of hysteria and of similar neuroses—diseases in which no structural change is apparent—such as obsessions, compulsions, anxieties, phobias (or morbid fears), and the like. In the latter part of the nineteenth century a young Viennese physician, Sigmund Freud, studied the symptoms and the treatment of hysteria under Charcot and Breuer —two of the leading European neurologists of the time. Partly as a result of their teaching, but largely through his own observation, he came to the conclusion that the "best approach to the treatment of a neurosis is to probe into the patient's mind through continued questioning."

For the subconscious part of the mind, he declared, is the repository of all the fundamental instincts of the race. "Especially the sex instinct, or *libido*." This impulse toward sexual lust, he said, is the one important motivation in all human activity. Perhaps his exaggeration of the sex instinct as the cause of all trouble was accounted for by his own childhood environment. He was the son of an old father and a young mother, and his early memories were full of the jealousies and quarrels that resulted from the unequal union of his parents. But, whatever the early coloration of his mind, he maintained that every emotional distress is caused by the suppression of a sex desire. The conventions of our puritanical society, he declared, have developed a censor within our consciousness. This censor is generally on the watch against the emergence of our subconscious libido, and the subconscious is always on the alert to outwit the censor and to give the libido full sway.

And sometimes when the consciousness is weak—when we are asleep, for example—"the libido rises to the top." But even then the censor will not allow our lustful thoughts to pass undisguised beyond the gate. And hence, declared Freud, the subconscious is compelled to clothe them in conventional symbols, so that our dreams are mere paraphrases of our desires. Thus a dream may reveal the object of a subconscious lust and disguise the act, or it may reveal the act and disguise the person. Most frequently, however, the dream will disguise both the person and the act.

And thus, declared Freud, there is an incessant struggle between the desires of the unconscious and the censorship of the conscious. And this struggle results in the various neuroses of the human mind. These neuroses, according to Freud, exist not only in diseased minds but in all mental behavior. Psychoanalysis, therefore, offers a new approach to the entire field of psychology.

And a somewhat pessimistic approach. For it reveals us to ourselves as creatures of subterranean desires, hypocritical suppressions, and neurotic complexes. Thus every boy, according to the Freudian view, is at some time or other moved by a physical desire for his mother and a consequent jealousy of his father. This is known as the Oedipus complex. (Oedipus was the ancient Greek king who—unintentionally—killed his own father and married his own mother.) And every girl, declares Freud, is subjected to a similar complex—a physical longing for her father and a consequent rivalry against her mother.

But the later advocates of the psychoanalytic method have

departed from Freud's extreme views about the "lustful desires of our subconscious." Thus Adler, for example, maintains that the underlying impulse of our behavior is not physical lust but the will to power. And Jung advances the still broader view that the subconscious is "not a cesspool but a well-spring"—a source not only of evil passion but of sublime aspiration.

Which brings us to the more constructive—and, therefore, the more optimistic—side of psychoanalysis. For, as generally understood today, this branch of psychology deals with the possible transformation of our unworthy desires into worthy actions. This process is called *sublimation*.

Sublimation is the direction of a lower urge into a higher form of activity—an activity that is socially beneficial. Thus an urge to selfish lust can be sublimated into an act of unselfish love, an urge to ruthless power can be translated into a generous power for service, and so on.

A sublimation, according to modern psychoanalysis, is the healing of a neurosis through the judicious guiding of the subconscious into a wholesome channel of consciousness. And thus, maintain the advocates of this school, our evil impulses need not be suppressed. They need merely to be liberated, through intelligent control, into noble aims. Our complexes generally tie up our minds into knots. The method of sublimation, declare the psychoanalysts, is to untie these knots and to weave the strands of our emotions into useful patterns.

Our subconscious, therefore, is a repository of "anti-social impulses, frustrated desires, and libidinous dreams." And these impulses, desires, and dreams may take one of three directions: unhindered expression, resulting in beastliness, sensuality, and filth; excessive repression, leading to perversions, compulsions, and fears; or disciplined redirection into religious devotion, social service, scientific discovery, cultural achievement, and creative art.

The psychoanalyst thus regards himself as a teacher with an expert understanding of the human mind.

REVIEW QUESTIONS IN PSYCHOLOGY

1. What is psychology?

2. Are there any mental processes without physical action?

3. Define the process of *making up your mind*.

4. What is the psychological meaning of behavior?

5. What two groups of facts must be known in order to determine a person's behavior at any moment?

6. What are the factors that determine a person's reaction to his stimuli?

7. What are the two parts that constitute the "central office" of the brain?

8. What is the general distinction between the human brain and that of the lower animals?

9. Has the human brain any elements not included in the brains of the lower animals?

10. What is a reflex?

11. Does the removal of the cerebral hemispheres of the brain affect the reflexes of the nervous system?

12. Does it remove the mentality of the brain?

13. What is an instinct?

14. Can a reflex be modified through learning?

15. Can an instinct be modified through learning?

16. What is a conditioned reflex?

17. What is thought?

18. Are any of the lower animals capable of reasoning?

19. What three kinds of images go into the formation of your "apple thoughts" when you eat an apple?

20. What is education?

21. What, briefly, is the method of education advocated by the Gestalt psychologists?

22. What is the chief difference between the mental processes of animals and of men?

23. Why have some scientists tried to create a universal language?

24. What is the test of a person's intelligence?

25. What is the average standard for such a test?

26. What do the initials I.Q. stand for?

27. What is the I.Q. for genius? For able minds? For average minds?

28. What is the average intelligence of most adult people?

29. In what way have the I.Q. tests helped society as well as the individual?

30. What famous psychologist divided all individuals into two mental types?

31. What is an introvert?

32. What is an extrovert?

33. According to this classification, what type of man was Shakespeare?

34. What is an emotion?

35. Why is an emotional person called a nervous person?

36. What is the relation between fear and anger?

37. Do we run away from danger because we fear it?

38. What is the psychological value of military training?

39. How can we control our emotions?

40. Why is it difficult to get an exact picture of an individual's personality?

41. What is the meaning of an *inflated ego?*

42. What are the six approaches to the objective study of an individual's personality?

43. Why is the social approach perhaps the most important?

44. What is an integrated personality? A disintegrated personality?

45. What is schizophrenia?

46. What is an anxiety neurosis?

47. What is hysteria?

48. What is psychoanalysis?

49. What, according to Freud, is the underlying impulse of our behavior? According to Adler? According to Jung?

50. What is sublimation?

ANSWERS TO THE QUESTIONS IN PSYCHOLOGY

1. The study of the mind in action.

2. No.

3. The process of arriving at a unified personal response to a certain situation.

4. Action, whether good or bad.

5. The composite nature of the stimuli, and the physicomental structure of the person.

6. His heredity, state of maturity, past experience, and state of his health and of his physical, mental, and spiritual hunger.

7. The cerebellum and the cerebrum.

8. The human brain, though similar in structure to that of the lower animals, contains a greater complexity of folds.

9. No.

10. A simple response to a simple stimulus.

11. No.

12. Yes.

13. A "developed" response to stimuli, involving the entire body.

14. No.

15. Yes.

16. A physical reaction acquired through mental experience.

17. A judgment of the mind.

18. No.

19. Images of recognition, of education, and of association.

20. The process of readjustment—through repeated experience—between the individual and his environment.

21. The act of "putting together" the parts of an object or an idea by "visualizing" the relationship of these parts.

22. Our human ability to use words.

23. To bring the world together through a mutual understanding of one another's words.

24. Not the amount of his knowledge, but his capacity for learning.

25. The learning capacity of a child of twelve.

26. The measurement of the intelligence quotient.

27. 150 or over. 115–130. 85–115.

28. About equal to that of a child of fourteen.

29. They have saved society from putting the wrong person into the wrong job, and served the individual by finding the right job for the right person.

30. Dr. C. G. Jung.

31. A person whose mind is "turned in" upon himself.

32. A person whose mind is "turned out" toward the world.

33. A combination of both types.

34. An agitation of the mind.

35. Because our responses to our stimuli are produced through the impulses of our nervous system.

36. They are different aspects of the same emotional response to our stimuli.

37. No. We fear it because we run away.

38. It conditions a man's fear reactions into the reactions of courage.

39. By the training of our physical responses to produce the desired states of emotion.

40. Because it never stands still. It keeps changing all the time.

41. A person who exaggerates his own dimensions.

42. An observation of his physical traits, his gestures, the expression of his thoughts, his emotional responses, the state of his health, his social relationships.

43. Because man is a gregarious animal. He is meant to live with his fellow men.

44. One that acts as a consistent unit. One that is split into disunited reactions.

45. A disease in which the disunion of the personality has become permanent.

46. Depression due to the inability of the mind to decide between two sets of antagonistic ideas.

47. A boiling over of the emotions, accompanied by an irrational activity of the mind.

48. The method of exploring the innermost depths of the mind, in order to bring into the open the suppressed ideas and desires that may cause emotional disturbances.

49. The sex instinct, or libido. The will to power. Either the will to selfish achievement, or the aspiration for social improvement.

50. The transformation of a selfish urge into a social activity.

BIOGRAPHICAL SKETCHES OF GREAT PSYCHOLOGISTS

Locke, John (1632–1704). British philosopher. Born at Wrington, Somerset, he was educated at Oxford, from which he received his degree in 1658. He commenced the study of medicine, but he never received his medical degree. Exiled on political grounds for seven years, he prepared the material for his classic volume, *Essay Concerning Human Understanding*, which he published upon his return to England. In the book he controverts the theory of innate ideas and substitutes for it the doctrine that the mind at birth is a *tabula rasa* (blank tablet) upon which is subsequently written the experience of sensations. In many respects Locke is regarded as the father of modern psychology.

Hartley, David (1705–57). British philosopher. Educated at Cambridge University, he practiced medicine throughout his lifetime. He is celebrated for being the founder of the Associationist school of psychologists. A follower of Locke, believing that the mind originates as a *tabula rasa,* he declared that consciousness develops according to the law of growth. He explained mind according to the concept of association and the doctrine of vibrations (an offshoot of Newtonian physics).

Bain, Alexander (1818–1903). Scotch philosopher. Born in Aberdeen, he entered Marischal College at the age of eighteen for training in the arts. He became a close friend of John Stuart Mill's, and assisted him in his philosophical writings. He himself achieved recognition for writings on logic, grammar, and rhetoric.

He occupied the chair of logic and English in the University of Aberdeen. His chief contributions, however, were made in the field of psychology. He was one of the first to insist that the methods of science be applied to psychology. He performed intensive research in the physical origin of feeling, the nerves, and the brain.

Wundt, Wilhelm Max (1832–1920). German psychologist. Born at Neckarau, near Baden, he studied medicine at the universities of Tübingen, Heidelberg, and Berlin. At thirty-two he was appointed assistant professor of physiology at Heidelberg, and he taught on the faculty for ten years. Wundt pioneered in experimental psychology. In 1879 he opened the first psychological laboratory. He engaged in an intensive study of religion, custom, and language from the standpoint of psychology.

James, William (1842–1910). Born at the Astor House in New York City, he studied in various European schools—at Geneva, Bonn, London, Paris, Boulogne—and finally decided to devote his life to natural history. He joined the Brazilian expedition of Louis Agassiz; and upon his return he was appointed instructor of physiology at Harvard. From physiology he moved to psychology; and from psychology to philosophy. His most important scientific book—his many philosophical works are omitted here—was his *Principles of Psychology,* "a study of living persons rather than of lifeless facts."

Freud, Sigmund (1856–1939). The father of psychoanalysis. Born at Freiberg, Moravia, he studied medicine at the University of Vienna, where he was appointed lecturer on nervous diseases. For a time he studied in Paris under Charcot, and in 1902 returned to the University of Vienna as associate professor of neuropathology. In 1938, when Germany annexed Austria, he found himself compelled to leave Vienna. He went to London, where he died the following year.

Binet, Alfred (1857–1911). French psychologist. Born in Nice, he was educated at Paris. He was appointed to the staff of the laboratory of psychology and physiology at the Sorbonne, and he eventually became the director. His chief contributions were in the field of human intelligence, particularly his tests devised to measure individual intelligence. In addition he published papers on hypnotism and edited a celebrated journal of psychology, *L'Année psychologique.*

Adler, Alfred (1870–1937). Austrian psychologist and psychoanalyst. Born in Vienna, he entered the profession of medicine. He specialized in psychiatry. For a while he was associated with the school of Freud, but, believing that Freud overstressed the influence of sex in human behavior, he founded his own school. He developed his own doctrine in which he enunciated the concept of the "inferiority complex" and emphasized the individual's striving for power.

Jung, Carl G. (1875–   ). Swiss psychologist and psychoanalyst. Born at Basel, he followed the teachings of Freud until 1911, when he established a new school of psychology at Zurich. He abandoned the term psychoanalysis. Instead he called his teaching "analytic psychology." He classified the four primary functions of mind as thinking, feeling, sensation, and intuition. Rejecting Freud's doctrine of the sexual etiology of the psychoneurosis, he based his doctrine on the creative impulse in man. He divided men into introverts and extroverts. He stressed the tremendous potentiality of the unconscious, terming it underdeveloped rather than repressed. He believed in the possibilities of co-operation between the conscious and the unconscious, declaring that the unconscious contained within it, in addition to the Self, the collective characteristics inherited from ancestors.

Watson, John Broadus (1878–   ). American psychologist. Born at Greenville, South Carolina, he took his bachelor's degree at Furman University and received his Ph.D. at the University of Chicago. For five years he taught as an assistant and instructor in psychology and then he joined the faculty of Johns Hopkins University as professor of experimental and comparative psychology and director of the psychological laboratory. He became celebrated as the chief formulator of behaviorism.

CAREERS IN PSYCHOLOGY

The field of psychology offers a wide variety of careers. All jobs requiring contact with people, as a matter of fact, utilize psychology. Psychiatry is an ever-expanding profession. More and more people are suffering from mental ills caused by the complexity of our society. The dynamic profession of psychoanalysis is still in its pioneering stage. The government offers positions to psychologists working in the field of juvenile delinquency. The opportunities for social workers who advise families suffering from personality maladjustments or economic distress are on the increase. Moreover, there is a demand for medical social workers who assist doctors, therapists, and nurses in dealing with community problems. Child welfare societies, juvenile courts, probation services, and the Red Cross offer jobs for social workers trained in psychology.

A preparation in psychology is useful also for those who desire to become children's librarians, who desire to guide the reading habits of the young. Training in psychology is a prerequisite for various types of personnel work. There is a growing demand for employee counselors in industry, specialists who help to promote a smoother relationship between the workers and management, and for vocational guidance counselors to assist people in finding the correct jobs. The United States Employment Service, the Veterans Administration, the Vocational Rehabilitation Service, private bureaus, and schools are all on the lookout for specialists in vocational guidance. In addition public health agencies, public welfare departments, playgrounds, community centers, boys' clubs, and church agencies are increasingly in need of students trained in social service.

There is almost no limit to the opportunities afforded to students in psychology, whether they utilize their training broadly or within a specialty. The study of the human personality is a prerequisite for all social activities.

children's librarian

EXPERIENCE REQUIRED: Graduation from accredited library school. Training in adolescent psychology desirable. Comprehensive reading background.

DESCRIPTION OF JOB: Guides reading tastes of children. Keeps up with current books, extensive reading.

OPPORTUNITIES FOR ADVANCEMENT: Department head, administrative.

WHERE TO APPLY FOR JOBS: Placement services of library school.

clinical psychologist

EXPERIENCE REQUIRED: College education and graduate study in psychology. Apprenticeship in psychological laboratory or similar organization.

DESCRIPTION OF JOB: Administers and interprets psychological tests.

OPPORTUNITIES FOR ADVANCEMENT: Administrative, own practice.

WHERE TO APPLY FOR JOBS: School systems, psychological testing bureaus, social service organizations, government.

community organizer

EXPERIENCE REQUIRED: Training in accredited school of social work and experience in field.

DESCRIPTION OF JOB: Deals with social welfare planning and co-operation of all the social agencies for welfare of community.

OPPORTUNITIES FOR ADVANCEMENT: Teaching, administration.

WHERE TO APPLY FOR JOBS: Public health agencies, community chests, councils of social agencies, public welfare departments.

employee counselor

EXPERIENCE REQUIRED: Training in personnel techniques. Experience as a worker with some shop practice.

DESCRIPTION OF JOB: Orientates new employees. Helps them to make adjustment. Helps to facilitate better understanding between workers and management.

OPPORTUNITIES FOR ADVANCEMENT: Personnel management, various kinds of executive positions.

WHERE TO APPLY FOR JOBS: All large industries.

family social worker

EXPERIENCE REQUIRED: Training in accredited school of social work.

DESCRIPTION OF JOB: Advises, assists in economic distress, illness, personality maladjustments, broken homes. Determines client's eligibility for financial assistance, etc. Refers clients to other community agencies for specialized services.

OPPORTUNITIES FOR ADVANCEMENT: Teaching research, administration.

WHERE TO APPLY FOR JOBS: Social service agencies, county or state public welfare departments.

medical social worker

EXPERIENCE REQUIRED: Special training in accredited school of social work.

DESCRIPTION OF JOB: Collaborates with doctors, nurses, and therapists in investigating and treating emotional problems related to illness. Often aids patient in difficulties that obstruct successful medical treatment.

OPPORTUNITIES FOR ADVANCEMENT: Teaching, research, administration.

WHERE TO APPLY FOR JOBS: Public and private hospitals, social service agencies, state public welfare departments.

personnel director

EXPERIENCE REQUIRED: College degree and graduate work in personnel administration recommended.

DESCRIPTION OF JOB: Supervises and directs personnel department. Formulates plans for selection, training, compensation, welfare of employees.

OPPORTUNITIES FOR ADVANCEMENT: Industrial relations manager, vice-president.

WHERE TO APPLY FOR JOBS: Industry, department stores, government.

personnel technician

EXPERIENCE REQUIRED: College degree, major in psychology. Graduate study desirable. For advanced work, experience in personnel research.

DESCRIPTION OF JOB: Supervises, assists, devises tests and various other personnel measurement techniques.

OPPORTUNITIES FOR ADVANCEMENT: Civil service upgrading.
WHERE TO APPLY FOR JOBS: Government.

psychiatric social worker

EXPERIENCE REQUIRED: Specialized preparation in accredited school
of social work.
DESCRIPTION OF JOB: Helps people with mental or emotional disorders. Supplements work of psychiatrist who diagnoses and
directs individual treatment.
OPPORTUNITIES FOR ADVANCEMENT: Teaching, research, administrative positions.
WHERE TO APPLY FOR JOBS: Public and private hospitals and clinics
for the mentally ill. Child guidance clinics, juvenile protective
societies, institutions for delinquents, Veterans Administration,
American Red Cross.

psychiatrist

EXPERIENCE REQUIRED: Medical degree. Training in psychiatry.
DESCRIPTION OF JOB: Practices psychiatry in the field of mental ail-
ments.
OPPORTUNITIES FOR ADVANCEMENT: Professional advancement.
WHERE TO APPLY FOR JOBS: Government, hospitals, mental institu-
tions, own profession.

psychologist (government)

EXPERIENCE REQUIRED: College degree, major in psychology. Graduate study or teaching. Experience in clinical research for advanced work.
DESCRIPTION OF JOB: Applies techniques of psychology to the prevention and cure of juvenile delinquency, etc.
OPPORTUNITIES FOR ADVANCEMENT: Civil service upgrading.
WHERE TO APPLY FOR JOBS: Government.

recreation leader

EXPERIENCE REQUIRED: College degree with specialization in psychology, sociology, education. Experience as play leader, social worker, teacher, or assistant director of education.

DESCRIPTION OF JOB: Deals with recreational guidance. Plans and directs programs of music, drama, arts and crafts. Active in directing social gatherings, nature study groups, etc.

OPPORTUNITIES FOR ADVANCEMENT: Supervisor of special activities, supervisor of playground or community center.

WHERE TO APPLY FOR JOBS: Boards of education, park systems, Y.M.C.A., boys' clubs, church agencies, commercial recreation agencies.

BIBLIOGRAPHY: BOOKS ON PSYCHOLOGY FOR FURTHER READING AND STUDY

Adler, Alfred: *Understanding Human Nature,* tr. by Walter Béran Wolfe. New York, 1946.
Averill, Lawrence Augustus: *Introductory Psychology.* New York, 1943.
Bernhardt, Karl Schofield: *Practical Psychology.* New York, 1945.
Boring, Edwin Garrigues: *Introduction to Psychology.* New York, 1939.
Cole, Lawrence Edwin: *General Psychology.* New York, 1939.
Dockeray, Floyd Carlton: *Psychology.* New York, 1942.
Freeman, Ellis: *Principles of General Psychology.* New York, 1939.
Freud, Sigmund: *The Basic Writings of Sigmund Freud,* tr. and edited by Dr. A. A. Brill. New York, 1938.
Gates, Arthur Irving: *Educational Psychology.* New York, 1942.
Goodenough, Florence Laura: *Developmental Psychology.* New York, 1945.
Higginson, Glenn De Vere: *Psychology.* New York, 1936.
James, William: *Psychology: Briefer Course.* New York, 1920.
——: *The Principles of Psychology: Advanced Course.* New York, 1918.
Jastrow, Joseph: *Getting More out of Life.* New York, 1940.
Jung, Carl Gustav: *The Integration of the Personality,* tr. by Stanley M. Dell. New York, 1939.
Koffka, Kurt: *Principles of Gestalt Psychology.* New York, 1935.
McDougall, William: *Body and Mind.* London, 1938.
Menninger, Karl Augustus: *The Human Mind.* New York, 1945.
Morgan, John Jacob Brooke: *Psychology.* New York, 1941.
Munn, Norman Leslie: *Psychology.* Boston, 1946.
Overstreet, Harry Allen: *About Ourselves.* New York, 1928.
Roback, A. A.: *Popular Psychology.* Cambridge.

Roberts, William Henry: *Psychology You Can Use.* New York, 1943.

Robinson, Edward Stevens, and Virginia Kirk: *Introduction to Psychology.* New York, 1935.

Ruch, Floyd Leon: *Psychology and Life.* Chicago, 1941.

Sargent, Stephen Stansfeld: *Basic Teachings of the Great Psychologists.* New York, 1944.

Schoen, Max: *Human Nature in the Making.* New York, 1945.

Sherman, Mandel: *Basic Problems of Behavior.* New York, 1941.

Sperling, Abraham Paul: *Psychology for the Millions.* New York, 1946.

Strecker, Edward Adam, and Kenneth E. Appel: *Discovering Ourselves.* New York, 1943.

Symonds, Percival Mallon: *The Dynamics of Human Adjustment.* New York, 1946.

Varnum, Walter Clark: *Psychology in Everyday Life.* New York, 1942.

Wait, Wallace Theodore: *The Science of Human Behavior.* New York, 1938.

Watson, John Broadus: *Psychology from the Standpoint of a Behaviorist.* Philadelphia, 1929.

Index

index